WINE FACT

&

WINE FACT & FICTION

FACTS, LEGENDS

AND ADVICE

FOR WINE LOVERS

ANDREW JONES

The Flying Wine Man

A Wine on the Web Ltd publication

www.wineontheweb.com

First published by Wine on the Web Ltd
4 Moorfield Road, Orpington,
Kent BR6 0HQ England

The moral right of the author has been asserted.

A catalogue record for this book is
available from the British Library.

ISBN 0-9544517-0-8

Edited by Helen Austyn
© Illustrations by Rowan Barnes-Murphy

Set in Verdana
Production by Tom Moore / Jo Saxton /
Amerjoth Singh Taak
Printed and bound in Singapore by Craftprint

Contents

Preface

My chief hope is that anyone who enjoys a bottle of wine may get some real pleasure from this book. My aim is to entertain and inform. Wine should be fun and no-one should take the subject too seriously – apart from the wine producers. Wherever I have travelled around the wine world during the last 20 years I have searched for both curious and helpful information, and I am only too glad to share some of it with the readers of WINE FACT & FICTION.

Whilst every endeavour has been made to check and re-check the content, inevitably the occasional item may be superseded by the time the book reaches the shelves. Please be assured that the facts are true and correct to the best of my knowledge at the time of publication. However I cannot guarantee the validity of every item in the chapter titled *Unsubstantiated Stories*.

Important Wine Dates

7000 BC Earliest-known cultivation of vineyards in Republic of Georgia.

1200 BC First datable Biblical reference to wine, *Melchizedek, King of Salem brought food and wine*.

1000 BC Homer wrote about the wines of Thrace, now Southern Bulgaria.

800 BC Greek sailors settle on Mediterranean coast from Sicily to Spain, planting their bush vines, which many sources claim were Muscat.

55 BC The Roman leader Julius Caesar exhorted his legionnaires to consume $1^1/_2$ litres of wine a day to protect them against disease.

33 AD Jesus Christ used wine at the Last Supper inspiring the spread of vineyards amongst future Christian countries.

350 AD Only proven Roman vineyard in England, near Northampton.

596 AD Earliest proven date for continuous vineyard ownership – Josephshöfer, part of the estate of Reichsgraf von Kesselstatt, in Germany's Mosel Valley.

1300 AD Château Pape Clement, the first wine chateau, was founded in Pessac in the Graves region of Bordeaux by Archbishop Bernard de Got, later Pope Clement V.

1493 AD Christopher Columbus planted vineyards in the Lesser Antilles in the Caribbean Sea; unfortunately they failed.

1524 AD In Mexico, the explorer Cortez ordered all landowners to plant 10 vines for every dead Indian.

1531 AD First bottle-fermented sparkling wine in the world was produced at the Benedictine Abbey at Limoux in South-Western France.

1548 AD First successful vineyard in the Americas planted in Copiapo, Chile by the Spanish conquistador Francisco de Aguirre.

1629 AD Probable date of first successful cultivation of vines on today's US mainland. It was a Franciscan vineyard at Senecu in what was then the Spanish colony of New Mexico, now part of the USA.

1661 AD Jan Van Reebeck pressed the first vines in Western Cape (South Africa). He recorded in his diary, *Today, praise be to God, wine was pressed for the first time from Cape grapes*.

1756 AD The Port wine vineyards in the Douro Valley of Portugal become the first officially regulated wine region in the world.

1788 AD Governor Philip planted first vineyard in Australia in Sydney Cove.

1819 AD The Anglican missionary Rev. Samuel Marsden cultivated the first vineyard on the North Island of New Zealand at kerikeri.

1828 AD Australia's oldest surviving winery was founded by English settler George Wyndham.

1847 AD Johann Gramp planted 4 acres of vines on his Jacob's Creek vineyard, the first commercial vineyard in the Barossa Valley.

1854 AD Date of origin of Mirassou Vineyards, California, America's oldest continuous winery.

1863 AD The first phylloxera was found in a vineyard near Montpellier, France. The aphid, which causes the roots of vines to shrivel, threatened to eliminate the entire French wine industry, but the discovery that some native American species of vines were resistant to the aphid saved the situation. Thomas (Volnay) Munson, a Denison, Texas based horticulturist was largely responsible for saving the vineyards of Burgundy by grafting wild Texas vines with the French stocks. In gratitude the Burgundian village of Volnay gave him his middle name.

1875 AD The 3rd Marquess of Bute tried to revive wine production in Great Britain. Unfortunately he planted mostly red grapes in the cold damp climate at Castell Coch.

1920 AD The Baron Leroy registered Chateauneuf-du-Pape as the first appellation contrôlée vineyard region in France. Its regulations permitted the use of 13 different grape varieties.

1921 AD The first vintage of Blue Nun, which was a fine sweet Auslese sold in small volume. The label later marketed as Blue Nun Liebfraumilch introduced many millions of consumers to the wine drinking habit.

1920-33 AD The Volstead Act was enforced in the USA resulting in the Prohibition of wine and drink production. Consequently America lost several generations of wine drinkers, for the 1933 repeal of the act was followed by the Economic Slump and World War II. In California, the once busy Napa Valley did not really begin to revive until the mid-sixties with the construction of The Robert Mondavi winery and the development of Sterling Vineyards.

1951 AD The first experimental vintage of *Grange Hermitage* was made by the late Max Schubert.

Wine Facts

Champagne but not Champagne The inhabitants of the small Swiss town of Champagne have been supporting a group of their local winemakers who, at the time of writing, are appealing to the European Courts of Justice against the European Union ban on the use of the word *Champagne* on the labels of their still wines. Since France, the home of the King of Wines, is a senior member of the European Union and Switzerland has not yet joined, there seems little doubt which way the decision will go. Unconfirmed reports, which suggest that some of the Swiss villagers have stored bottles of French Champagne to celebrate should there be an unexpected victory, might just be propaganda.

Earliest known wine barrels The Greek historian Herodotus (480-425 BC) wrote of the Assyrians making barrels from palmwood for the transportation of wine. It is unlikely that they were used for any deliberate aging purpose.

Highest priced vineyards Transactions involving outstanding vineyards are often conducted in great secrecy, but the acquisition in late 2002 of a Napa Valley property by Hollywood director Francis Ford Coppola was assuredly the highest price paid for a vineyard to date. The film mogul and wine producer is believed to have paid US$350,000 (£225,000) an acre for 24 hectares (60 acres) of the Cohn vineyard in Rutherford, California. The total cost was around US$21 million (£13.2m). The Cohn vineyard borders his existing Niebaum-Coppola estate.

Longest stone cellar The longest stone cellar is the Terreirinho Vault belonging to Croft Port in Vila Nova de Gaia, Portugal. It is 140 metres (455 feet) long and contains 5,928 pipes of Port, the equivalent of 4,347,199 bottles.

Owners of the greatest number of oak barrels The California wine giant Kendall-Jackson owns over 275,000 oak barrels and Jess Jackson even controls the quality by owning a stave mill in France, as well as sharing in a joint venture with a cooperage.

Most northerly vineyard Hallingstad Vineyard near Horten on the banks of Oslofjord in Norway at 60°N. It was planted in 1992 by Sveier Hansen with Pinot Noir, Chardonnay, Riesling, Viognier and several other minor varieties. 1995 saw the first vintage produced.

Most southerly vineyard Black Ridge Winery, at Alexandra in the Central Otago region of New Zealand lies fractionally below 45°S.

Only vineyard on the Equator The Valley Vineyard at Bushenyi, in western Uganda, owned by retired schoolteacher William Mukaira, covers one hectare (two and a half acres), on a hillside at around 1,394 metres(4,600 feet) * See **Wine Countries**

Shiraz Known to the French as Syrah, the varietal is believed to have been introduced to Australia by the French wine producer Paul Jaboulet Aîné. Australians resorted to its original name, derived from its home around the ancient Iranian city of Shiraz, on the eastern side of the Persian Gulf. Due to Iran's fundamentalist Moslem policy, vines are no longer cultivated there. In recent years the varietal has become largely associated with Australia which produces many outstanding examples. Serious collectors should head for the tiny Zema Estate in Coonawarra to discover classic hand-crafted Shiraz that needs 10 years bottle-aging to reach perfection. In the meantime larger volumes are available from Penfold's Grange.

Sobering thoughts Before the wine producing country of Persia became the abstaining nation of Iran, wine played an important role in decision making, a state of affairs that developed over many centuries. Persian leaders and heads of local communities would take great pride in getting drunk before making decisions. They would never act on those decisions until they had re-considered them when sober. Curiously the reverse also applied.

Wine in the Bible Wine plays a prominent role in The Bible from Noah planting the first vineyard in Genesis to Jesus performing his first miracle at Cana in Galilee and St. Paul urging St. Timothy to *take a little wine for the sake of your digestion*. The actual word wine is found 161 times, vineyards are mentioned 72 times and there are 57 references to *vines*.

Did You Know?

Belly Button bottle Just before Christmas 2002 the long-established Italian wine producer Tosti launched an eminently quaffable sparkling Pinot Grigio onto the UK market. There was a surprise in store when the bottles were placed on retail shelves, because each one displayed a small, belly button-like indentation. Apparently somebody of a sexist nature at Tosti had suggested that the first drop of fizz from each bottle should be consumed from the navel. The suggestion didn't seem to imply a hairy male navel and so the word spread and the previously unseen Tosti bottles were soon out of stock. A later theory that putting one's thumb in the belly button makes it easier to open the bottle has not been taken too seriously.

Blue Ridge winery is not in the Blue Ridge Mountains of Virginia, as in the famous song, but is a state-of-the-art winery in Bulgaria, at the edge of the *Sinite Skali* (Blue Ridge) mountains. A leading Australian cellar construction company purpose-built the winery to suit the local climate and conditions, resulting in excellent value Chardonnay and Merlot and a surprising Black Rosé, which is a full-bodied 100% Cabernet Sauvignon that falls halfway between rosé and red.

James Bond had a much wider taste in Champagne than is generally acknowledged. A careful search through all the Bond books will show his appreciation of Taittinger, Dom Pérignon, Bollinger, Veuve Clicquot, Pommery, Krug and Pol Roger.

Champagne tap Champagne taps became popular in the late 19th century and the odd example can still be found in use in Europe. They are made of stainless metal and inserted in place of a cork into the neck of the bottles, which are then inverted. As the tap is opened the

Champagne remaining in the bottle descends by gravity without too much interference from the bubbles. Rumours have existed that some members of the English aristocracy still position them alongside their baths.

Change of use In early 2002 the prestigious French Rhône wine house Paul Jaboulet Aîné announced the opening of what is believed to be the world's largest tasting room. Situated in Chateauneuf-sur-Isère, an area of nearly 3 hectares (approximately 7 acres) of underground caves has been transformed into a wine store and tasting centre. Perhaps what is more noteworthy is that the previous occupants of the property were prehistoric men. The great Hermitage wines of Paul Jaboulet Aîné have an excellent reputation for aging but not for that length of time.

Coolest bottles on Earth? Ambitious producers, quite understandably, often dream of their finest wines being served in the most stylish and highly reputed restaurants and hotels. So imagine the rush from the makers of Canada's glorious late-picked icewine when they learned of the opening of the Quebec Ice Hotel at Sainte-Catherine-de-la-Jacques Cartier in 2001. Its construction used over 11,000 tons of snow and 350 tons of ice. The lucky winner of the in-house order was the Inniskillin winery from Niagara, whose supporters can now sign in at an ice reception desk, view ice statues and architecture and stay in ice bedrooms where they can open fridges and sip icewine. There are two minor qualifications – reservations may be weather dependent and, as yet, prices have not been frozen.

Dangerous use of a wine bottle Kinkead Ridge, near Ripley, Ohio is in many ways typical of small boutique wineries across the USA, in that it depends on a number of occasional, volunteer staff, who are not always aware of the winemaker's habits. In December 2002 a bottling run was underway for its 2001 Riesling when someone noticed that the winemaker's *checking bottle* was missing. This item was a regular, 750ml bottle filled with the precise volume of water, to check and confirm that the level of all the other bottles of wine was correct. Suddenly the awful realisation dawned that the bottle of water had somehow been accidentally labelled as wine and packed into a case. Hours later, amidst the debris of many torn cartons it was found, with one winemaker vowing never, ever, to fill a wine bottle with water again.

Doctor, Doctor The owner of the Hunter Valley, New South Wales brand called *The Wine Doctor* is both a doctor medicine and of philosophy, as well as being an eminent wine historian. Dr Philip Norrie, a man of dry humour and keen wit, has been a general practitioner in the Sydney suburb of Elenora Heights for many years. He has also written various wine-related papers, including *The Art of Sensible Drinking*. Just to keep himself busy and in good health he owns the Pendarves Estate winery in the Hunter Valley.

Furthermore, he might research and write the Australian equivalent to *Wine is the Best Medicine* by the late French author, wine expert and medical specialist, Dr. Maury. In his work the French medicine man analysed the soils of all the leading French wine regions, tasted copious volumes of the local wines and concluded which diseases could be prevented by consuming which wines. Just imagine recommending Barossa Shiraz for one's pancreas or spleen.

Eventful ski trips Neighbouring Sonoma winemakers Randy Ullom of Kendall-Jackson and Nick Goldschmitt of Simi have different skiing tales to tell. In 1972 Randy, then a young mining engineering student in the University of Utah, travelled to Chile on a winter sports vacation and liked the country so much that he stayed a while and began seeing a young Chilean lady. But it seems he was more impressed with her father than with the girl. The man claimed to be Chile's leading gourmet and the nation's sole subscriber to the renowned *Food & Wine* magazine. During the 18 month relationship Randy learned more about wine and food than he could have imagined. His potential father-in-law taught him perfection in both haute cuisine and wine. Meanwhile Randy also learned how to prune vines from a French neighbour. Gradually he found himself turning into a man of wine and food.

Eventually having decided that the romance would not be permanent, the quickly maturing Randy considered his future prospects. *Mining engineering didn't look so attractive, so I thought to myself, what other career would allow me to eat and drink so well?* The only obvious answer was wine and so a fresh period of study was undertaken, before he took the first step of his career as a winemaker at the humble Grand River winery in Madison, Ohio. It was the first step on a ladder which now finds him thriving as Winemaster for the Kendall-Jackson group overseeing wine production in Italy, California, Australia, Argentina and Chile. Surprisingly, 3 decades after his Chilean adventure, Randy retains a remarkably slim figure and wears a broad smile on his face, qualities which he insists are due to *haute cuisine*.

Nick Goldschmitt's reputation as a skier is well known amongst fellow winemakers, most of whom fear to challenge him on the giant slalom. But Nick's major skiing claim to fame occurred in Vail, Colorado one Saturday in November 2000. He spent the morning burning up the slopes and then a couple of hours in the afternoon as a lively guest on The Gabby Gourmet show of KHOW Radio, in a broadcast from the Marriott Mountain Resort. Nick was so exhilarated that he lit up the airwaves with his wine and ski enthusiasm. After the show he kindly gave host Pat Miller a couple of sample bottles, which sadly were never drunk, for the hotel burned to the ground that night.

First New Zealand Sauvignon Blanc The first example of Sauvignon Blanc being cultivated in New Zealand – an act that transformed the country's wine industry – is correctly credited to Matua Valley Wines. Ross Spence, one of the founders and still a partner in the winery, attended Fresno State University in California, where he became fascinated by the characteristics of the varietal. A first attempt by Ross to plant it in his native country as early as 1965 failed, because of plant viruses. But in 1974, from a rented tin shed at Henderson, the humble Matua Valley Winery made its first commercial production of Sauvignon Blanc. The results swiftly aroused the interest of other winemakers. One famous overseas visitor, Robert Mondavi, persuaded the Spence family that they should re-name the varietal Fumé Blanc, as he had done in California, thinking it would attract more attention. So for its early years in New Zealand the varietal was known by that name. Later, as others followed the Matua example, they preferred to retain the Sauvignon Blanc name and Matua reverted to that description shortly afterwards.

In 1980 Ross took one of the early Matua Sauvignon Blancs to a conference for winemakers in Western Australia, a flight of some seven hours. It was tasted there by David Hohnen of Cape Mentelle who was overwhelmed. A week later David flew to New Zealand and began searching for the perfect location for the varietal, which he found in the little-known Marlborough region, in the north of the South Island. He purchased land near the coast at Cloudy Bay and took the name for his new winery. The rest is history, as Cloudy Bay has since, on many occasions, been heralded as the finest example of Sauvignon Blanc on Earth.

First Californian tasting room In July and August 1904 both Giuseppe and Pietro Simi died in Healdsburg, Sonoma County, California, leaving Giuseppe's teenage daughter Isabelle in charge of the Simi family wine business. Months later she instructed her cellar workers to move a giant redwood vat from the cellar to the roadside in front of their Montepulciano winery alongside the old Redwood Highway. They carved sections out of it and converted it into what was claimed to be *California's first winery public tasting room*.

Dr Konstantin Frank For generations New York was the biggest wine producing state in the USA but once California unleashed container loads of noble varietals like Chardonnay and Cabernet Sauvignon onto the Eastern Seaboard, its position was doomed. For New York State was simply growing the wrong grapes and selling the wrong wine.

Few non-Americans understand that the main New York vineyards lie around the beautiful Finger Lakes some 400 miles northwest of New York City, close to the Canadian border. Unfortunately the location caused the eventual downfall of the state's major markets because growers believed that French noble varieties couldn't tolerate the climate. The region was simply so cold in winter and experienced such heavy snowfall that it was thought only French-American hybrids and native Labrusca grapes could survive. Thus the situation remained until one dedicated man demonstrated that vitis vinifera vines could not just survive but actually thrive there. Vitis vinifera is responsible for all the world's finest grape varieties.

The individual concerned was Dr Konstantin Frank who was born in the Ukraine in 1898 and graduated in viticulture in the University of Kiev in the early 1920s, when he completed a doctorate with a thesis on *growing vitis vinifera vines in a cold climate*. Then as communism gradually swept westwards from Russia he decided to leave and emigrated to New York. He was so poor when he arrived, that to survive he washed dishes in a Manhattan restaurant. His English was virtually non-existent at that stage but in due course he was promoted to waiter. This gave him the opportunity to taste some of the unfinished glasses of wine he had to clear away. He was horrified at the foxy taste of the New York State wines and vowed to improve the situation personally. So, as soon as he could afford it, he took a bus to the Finger Lakes and called at various wineries until he found a job.

His next problem was that he was a very humble newcomer who couldn't make himself understood when trying to explain to his bosses the errors of their ways in planting the wrong species. As a result he was regarded as a contro-versial figure and it took many years for him to really prove his point. Eventually in 1953, aged 55, on a beautiful hillside above Keuka Lake he purchased what became known as Dr Frank's Vinifera Wine Cellars and started a vine nursery nearby. One relatively simple task that he taught growers changed the working lives of many throughout the state of New York and the whole northeast of the USA. It was to raise the soil high up the vine trunks to protect the stocks during excessively cold weather. Growers soon found that this practice worked and began to listen more attentively. Today the vineyards of up state New York are well on the way to recovery, thanks to Dr Frank who died in 1985 and who is remembered by his family who still run the winery and the nursery.

Grapes and silkworms During the Second World War transport restrictions and the lack of fuel caused enormous problems for wine producers in occupied countries. Desperate to supplement their meagre incomes they sometimes returned to practices which had long since been abandoned in their localities. One example occurred in the Valpolicella region of Northern Italy where the 200-year-old silkworm industry was revived. The producers placed the silkworms on the reed trays normally used for drying grapes in attic spaces for Recioto wines and fed them on their favourite food of mulberry leaves.

MD confusion In the Central Otago region of New Zealand, visitors have to be careful in one leading winery not to refer to the letters MD. They represent the winery's name Mt Difficulty, the name of the winemaker Matt Dicey and the name of the MD (Managing Director), Matt Douglas. Hopefully they have never succumbed to drinking the inexpensive American fortified wine called MD 20/20. Incidentally the New Zealand MD has an increasingly good reputation for Pinot Noir. (No jokes about a Dicey winemaker please.)

Meursault The production of this celebrated Burgundy is not entirely white, just a small proportion is made as red. The name Meursault comes from *murasalt* meaning a walled fort on high terrain. Surprisingly the village does not appear to justify the name, for while it has a relatively small slope it certainly cannot claim any *high terrain*. It does however produce some of the most elegant dry white wines.

Longest New Zealand wine tradition Frank Nobilo, the New Zealand golfer, has been successful on the international circuit for many years. He is a cousin of the Nobilo wine family from New Zealand and no doubt related to the same family *back home*. Wine lovers in many countries will know the Nobilo labels, but not many will be acquainted with the fact that when members of the New Zealand Nobilo family talk about *back home* they are referring not to the country where they currently reside but to the village of Lumbarda. The village is actually on the Croatian Island of Korcula where they have been growers for many generations. When Nikola Nobilo planted his first vineyard at Huapai near Auckland in 1943 he was simply continuing a family tradition that began over 300 years ago and still continues to this day.

Oldest active winemaker This title could be claimed for the greatly revered Russian-born California-based winemaker André Tchelistcheff, who died in 1994 Aged 91, when he was still employed as a consultant winemaker by Beaulieu Vineyards and Inglenook Estate. However Lou Foppiano of Foppiano Vineyards in Sonoma, California worked the 2001 vintage aged 92, and at the time of going to print is looking forward to the next.

Not just oak Woods other than oak have been and, in some instances, still are used for barrels and vats. These include chestnut which can occasionally be found in the Loire Valley of France, mahogany which is the material for some large vats in Portugal and California redwood, which is now virtually unseen but was used extensively for storage in the Golden State as late as the early 1980s. In Greece pine has been used for centuries, but in recent times it has been replaced. In parts of Italy both cherry wood and walnut have been used but few traces are found any longer. A timber called Raule is still occasionally seen in South America particularly in Argentina.

Probably the most adaptable country has been Australia, which has used Huon pine and stringy bark for barrels, red gum for vats and beech and jarrah for both barrels and vats. Today, of course, it uses mainly American and French oak.

Part-Aboriginal winemaker Robert Paul, now a much-respected Australian wine consultant, was formerly head winemaker at the Montrose winery in Mudgee, New South Wales. When the writer first met him in 1993 Robert revealed that he believed that he was the first part-Aboriginal winemaker. It may only be a 32nd part but it mattered greatly and *you never know, he said I might be able to make a land claim*.

Pink lemonade A September 1998 visit to California brought the opportunity to attend *The Crush* at Fetzer Vineyards in Hopland, Mendocino and better still be invited to eat under the stars with the winemaking team. Having dined *al fresco* with winemakers at harvest time in various countries I looked forward to plenty of tasty food and an enjoyable glass or two of wine. In fact, I have frequently found that even at such a busy time the head winemaker has tucked away a couple of interesting bottles to sample. The tasty food arrived but strangely there was no sign of the wine. Instead a young winemaker appeared with a jug and poured out foaming pink lemonade. It was quickly explained that at Fetzer regulations insisted that alcohol was forbidden when machinery was operating. However if I fancied a beer, then in an hour's time, when the evening shift finished we could call on the nearby Hopland Brewery, but as for a glass of wine – forget it.

Red wine made by solera system
Mavrodaphne from Patras in the northwest Peloponnese of Greece is a unique, lightly fortified, red wine which is made using the solera system, rather like Sherry. It is red and sweet and, in this time of dry tastebuds, it is increasingly popular. Mavrodaphne means *black laurel* and is the name of one of the two grape varieties used. The other is Korinthiaki. Mavrodaphne has a reputation for matching well with chocolate.

Local legend insists that the original wine was created by a heartbroken young winemaker, when he lost his black haired lover just before their wedding day. The young woman died suddenly with little warning, leaving him in great distress. He then decided to create a memorial by making a new wine and naming it after her. *Mavro* refers to her long black tresses and *Daphne*, meaning Laurel, was her name.

Cecil Rhodes was the remarkable adventurer and developer who crowded so much into a relatively short life. His activities number the grubbing out of the vineyards of the Boschendal winery in the Paarl region of South Africa. In 1896 having witnessed the vines being ravaged by phylloxera, he purchased the estate and some other surrounding properties at a very humble price. He then ordered the vines to be torn up and had new fruit trees planted on what became known as Rhodes Fruit Farms. Fortunately, a little later, his successors replanted grafted vines and began once more to build up the reputation that had been developed since 1685, when this picturesque farm was settled in the Drakenstein Valley by Jean de Long, one of the very earliest French Huguenots. Oddly he didn't give it a French name but preferred *Bossendaal*, which has become Boschendal meaning *wood and dale*.

Sangiovese Nowadays this fruity red variety is grown in relatively small quantities in many New World countries, but in its homeland of Tuscany it reigns supreme. In particular it has brought fame to Chianti, where it is even blended occasionally with white grapes like Trebbiano to produce a blood red colour. Not surprising for a variety which translates as *The Blood of Jupiter*.

Shakespeare's vinous error Many references have been made to Shakespeare's colourful execution when the Duke of Clarence *drowns* in a butt of Malmsey. An impossible feat. A butt then would have been between 500-600 litres (110-132 gallons) in size, and normally laid on its side with the only access to its contents being through a small hole sealed by a hardwood bung. However much the executioners of the Duke of Clarence had tried they simply could not have forced his body, let alone his head, into a butt.

There is no real evidence that Shakespeare had any serious wine knowledge but he lived in England during an era when wine flowed quite freely and was normally transported in barrels. He certainly would have enjoyed it in the homes and inns he visited across the land, yet it never really plays a prominent role in his work.

Doktor and Sonnenuhr German wine labels can be difficult both to pronounce and understand, but certain words like *Doktor* and *Sonnenuhr* can help. Doktor suggests health benefits and Sonnenuhr, meaning *Sundial*, excellent exposure to the sun. Bernkasteler Doktor earned its name in the 14th century, with the miraculous recovery of the dying Archbishop Bohemund II when he drank a glass. Wehlener Sonnenuhr is so called because it surrounds a small sundial where vineyard workers take their noon lunch in the sunniest part of the vineyard.

Most prolific taster The English wine journalist Malcolm Gluck could make a well-grounded claim to this title. He is the weekly wine contributor for *The Guardian* newspaper but is probably better known as the author of the annual publication *Superplonk*, which is a lively and comprehensive guide to sensibly priced wines in the popular market place. Between April and August, *during* the season, he tastes up to 250 wines a day and across the average year tastes and spits between 8-10,000 samples. For a change he is believed to enjoy a glass of wine.

NB Challenges to this title are expected from frustrated wine journalists and winemakers.

Nebbiolo or not? The magnificent and highly complex wines of Barolo and Barbaresco, in the rolling hills of Piedmont in Northern Italy, are cultivated amidst some of the finest red wine regions worldwide and both are made from the same grape variety *Nebbiolo*. The grape is named after the Italian word *nebbia* meaning fog, which swirls across the vineyards in the autumn challenging the fruit to reach its ripening potential. It is a particularly tight-skinned variety and often gives formidable tannins which can, in some wines, take a decade or more to dissolve. The results from the best producers are often glorious. A Barolo must be called *Nebbiolo* until its wine is 3 years old. Then it officially becomes Barolo. Nebbiolo is also the main grape variety for Ghemme, Gattinara and Carema, also from Piedmont. It sometimes seems as if it is not getting the credit it deserves.

Interestingly, of all the great red grape varieties from Europe that have been re-planted around the various countries and regions of the New World, very little has been seen of *Nebbiolo*.

Passito di Pantelleria The island of Pantelleria which produces this delicious curiosity of a dessert wine lies nearer to the coast of Tunisia on the North African mainland than to its official homeland of Italy. It is a fortified naturally sweet wine, pressed from Muscat of Alexandria grapes which have been grown on short, stubby vines called *albarello*, before being picked and left to dry out-of-doors on straw mats for approximately two weeks. The results are some of the finest examples of this varietal.

Sunny side of Prohibition Merryvale Vineyards in California's Napa Valley has the most unlikely address – for a winery – of 1000 Main Street, St Helena. The description would be more fitting for a downtown shop or office rather than the wine cellars and vineyards that actually do exist there.

Apart from its urban setting, the property, known as the Sunny St Helena winery, has a claim in the annals of history as the first US winery to be constructed following American

Prohibition (1920-33). Its name appears to be a comment on the dark era from which the USA had just emerged. Work on the site began in December 1933, shortly after the official repeal.

It is a favourite stopping place for Napa visitors, many of whom take great trouble to reserve the unique barrel room for lunch, which is a single giant Redwood cask, containing a dining table and chairs.

Vintage Bin AD 2015 Barossa wine producer Peter Lehmann always dates his favourite fortified wine 21 years in advance. He keeps matters within legal limits by publishing the true vintage as well as the future date on the label. For example in January 2003 his web-site was offering the Peter Lehmann Vintage Bin AD 2015, with 1994 at the top of the label. His explanation is that his *fortified wine is made for patient people, as it is at its optimum after 21 years*. In a process reminiscent of Port production in Portugal, ripe Shiraz grapes are picked from old vines and part-fermented before being aged in old oak hogsheads for 12 months and then bottled with their sediment.

World's oldest barrel? The Saint Catherine cask owned by the Hugel winery at Riquewihr in Alsace, France was built in 1715 but was never used by the first generation of the family wine business, because they did not begin trading until 1639.

World's largest wooden barrel in use This claim has a touch of circus fever about it. Indeed it seems that at one time early in the 20th century there were at least four claimants to the title. The most famous of these was the Dubonnet cask that still stands in its original setting and is used continually, at Thuir, in the French Pyrenees. It was commissioned by Joseph Dubonnet, late in the 19th century. Apparently he planned it as a gimmick to attract visitors to his rather isolated cellars and he succeeded, as the fast developing French railways brought tourists from hundreds of miles away and the Dubonnet Vermouth became extremely popular. His barrel, which is reputed to have a volume of 100,000 litres (22,000 gallons), could easily be swallowed up by the Heidelberg Tun in Germany, with its capacity of 220,000 litres (48,400 gallons). It was built in 1751 and has only ever been filled on 3 occasions, as it has continually leaked.

Which vintage (1) In some years, climatic conditions are so advanced around Tulbagh in the Western Cape of South Africa that grapes which are usually picked in January or February need picking as early as December 26th or 27th of the previous year. But by law they can only be made into wine that carries the vintage date of the following year.

Which vintage (2) Donald Ziraldo and Karl Kaiser, joint owners of the Inniskillin winery in the beautiful Niagara Valley in Ontario, Canada admit to having some complications with their icewine harvest in 2002. The problem was that under normal conditions, the grapes would have been picked late in 2001, but instead they were not gathered until March 2002. The next crop was picked in December 2002; therefore Inniskillin had two harvests within 8 months of the same year.

Red grapes always pressed in the year following their harvest The grapes for 3 wines in northern Italy; Amarone, Recioto and Sfurzat are picked in September or October, then dried on trays before being pressed 120 days later in January or February. The drying process takes place in large attics and causes the grape juice to become more concentrated, as the water content reduces by around 40 per cent. This adds complexity and flavour to the wines. Amarone and Recioto are both made in the Valpolicella region and Sfurzat in Val Tellina in Lombardy, near the Swiss border.

Voting for two hour lunch breaks In 1983, when a British film crew were shooting sequences 110 feet underground in the chalk cellars of Champagne Veuve Clicquot in Reims, they were taken aback to be told that they must quit the caves each day between noon and 2.00pm because of the cellar workers' lunch break. Gentle words from the Public Relations Director of the house indicated that it was a delicate subject. He went on to explain that Veuve Clicquot had wished to change the system and negotiations with the relevant trade union led to a vote on whether or not to abandon the centuries-old two hour lunch break in favour of one hour, thus allowing the workers to finish earlier in the evening. To the great surprise of the management the result was a resounding *Non!* The reason given was perfectly understandable. Virtually all the cavistes used the two hours to return home, have lunch and undertake minor domestic tasks or shopping before returning to work. If they took only one hour they would probably have to bring packed lunches to the cellars and not have the opportunity to enjoy their little routine. Neither would they have seen daylight for many months.

Jack the spy Jack Croft (1778-1862), the 4th partner of the famous Port house to be baptised John, was known to his close friends and family as Jack. Yet some of them may never have heard how he had risked his life as an important spy for the British Army under the Duke of Wellington during the Peninsular Wars. In 1810 he organised a network of agents in northern Portugal, north-western Spain and southwestern France. These brought regular intelligence reports on the movement of French troops, when the combined Portuguese and British armies were attempting to rebuff the challenge of Napoleon's forces.

Jack Croft was born in Portugal and educated there by a bi-lingual tutor. He became fluent in English and Portuguese and quite accustomed to the lifestyle of both nationalities. Eventually he travelled to England to study sciences in Oxford and London, later taking up the post of assistant to two renowned scientists, Sir Joseph Banks and Sir Humphrey Davy. Through their influence he was invited to become a fellow of The Royal Society.

Early in 1810 he was told by Charles Stuart, the British Minister in Lisbon, that the Duke of Wellington was experiencing great difficulty in acquiring intelligence reports on the movements of the French forces. Despite having no experience of such operations Jack Croft immediately volunteered to organise the necessary espionage network. He put into effect, with amazing alacrity, a network of agents stretching northwards from Oporto to La Coruna, eastwards along the Spanish Atlantic coast to San Sebastien and across the French border to Bayonne. During this work he covered hundreds of miles on horseback, was attacked at least twice and twice escaped unharmed. Had he been arrested he would have faced execution. His system was simple but effective. Under cover of darkness the British Navy would send small boats to shore and their crews would collect documents written by the agents describing French troop activity. These *paquets* of information were taken to Jack Croft in Oporto who, in due course, would pass them to the British Minister in Lisbon. He, in turn, would provide the relevant material to Wellington.

In 1811, following the defeat of the French, Jack Croft was appointed joint chief of a British charitable fund to support thousands of starving and desperately impoverished Portuguese from the battle-scarred areas. In total he and his team brought food, grain, livestock, iron and cash funds to over 70,000 people in 10 months. His work rate was prolific as he deeply affected by the suffering and poverty he witnessed. However he was not easily fooled by dishonest claimants, and if he suspected anyone of making a false claim, he would arrive in a towns or village a day early, disguised as a poor traveller. He would visit local inns and encourage fellow drinkers to talk about the conditions they had experienced. He became so loved by his second nation that its Regent awarded him its highest honour of Baron da Serra da Estrella and the British awarded him a baronetcy as Sir John Croft Bart.

Aboriginal Names

Aboriginal names have added dignity and a historical perspective to Australian wineries, as well as providing individuality. The names have been drawn from a variety of Australian Aboriginal Languages.

Alkoomi The name of the high-flying Frankland River winery in Western Australia, it means *the place we chose*.

Arakoon This tiny McLaren Vale, South Australia winery is named after a forest area and means *a place without water*.

Cambewarra Estate *Misty mountain* or *mountain of fire* are the two translations for this small New South Wales winery which is actually situated at Cambewarra.

Coolangatta Estate This historic location is *the site of the first European settlement on the south coast of New South Wales*. In 1822 Alexander Berry and Edward Wollstonecraft received a 4,000-hectare (10,000-acre) land grant and an allocation of 100 convicts to work the land. The winery was founded as late as 1988. The word Coolangatta means *view*.

Coonawarra This important wine region was initially created as a unique project by Scottish landowner and philanthropist, John Riddoch in 1890. He owned over 12,000 hectares (30,000 acres) and having decided which areas had the most suitable local red soil, he offered humble folk, (whom he called *blockers*), the opportunity to buy land on 100 per cent mortgages at 5 per cent interest, with a guarantee that he would purchase all their grapes. Following his death in 1901 the plan collapsed but just one grower, called Bill Redman, continued to produce red wine for 50 years until a new generation of growers took up the challenge. During the last 10 years Coonawarra, which means *wild honeysuckle*, has developed an international reputation for its minty red wines.

Doonkuna Estate Winery and Vineyard *Rising ground* is the apt translation of Doonkuna, the vineyard at Murrumbateman near the Australian capitol of Canberra. The winery is located at one of the higher altitude sites in the country, peaking at 620 metres (2,015 feet). Doonkuna also produces a second more moderately priced wine actually called Rising Ground.

Eurunderee Flats The location of this small Mudgee winery is named after the favourite walk of legendary Australian poet Henry Lawson. It is rumoured that he would sit under the Eurunderee, or *lone tree* and write his poetry. This story also influenced the naming of the Poet's Corner brand.

Goona Warra Apparently this name, which bears a close resemblance to *Coonawarra* has an entirely different meaning, as it is from a different Aboriginal language. It means *Resting place of the black swan*. Goona Warra Vineyard is found only a few kilometres from Melbourne Airport in Victoria.

Jindalee The title of this progressive winery in Victoria translates as *a bare hill*. The name originally came from a dirt track between two properties. Of course the area is no longer bare as it is planted with vines.

Kangarilla Road sounds a little like the Australian equivalent of *King Kong*, but the humble folks at the emerging McLaren Vale winery have another, simpler explanation; it means *birthplace*. It certainly is the birthplace of a promising Shiraz, which Kangarilla Road markets in a black bottle with a monochrome label showing a single vine leaf.

Kulkunbulla This Hunter Valley, New South Wales winery is aptly named, for it refers to the story of a hunter called Nirunja. He is featured in an Aboriginal legend which has uncanny similarities to a Greek myth. Nirunja descended from the skies to chase after seven sisters called the Kungkarangkalpa, who had decided to visit the Earth. He seems to have gone round and round in circles, because in due course the sisters escaped and returned to their starry origins where they became known as the constellation of the Pleiades. Nirunja continued his chase into the night and became Orion who still pursues them across the sky.

The Kulkunbulla are a group of Nirunja's warriors, dancing a corroboree. They form the bit and scabbard in the constellation of Orion. The Kulkunbulla winery logo displays the 3 bright stars in Orion's belt, called Alnilam, Alnitak and Mintaka.

Little Boomey In actual fact this particular *Boomey* is not so little. For Little Boomey, near Orange, New South Wales is one of the largest single vineyards in Australia at 513 hectares (1,282 acres). The word means *where the waters run deep* which must be a relief to the person in charge of irrigation.

Lirralirra is the charming name of a Yarra Valley, Victoria winery and means *small bird*. It refers to a tiny blue wren that is seen in the locality.

Moorooroo A legendary Barossa, South Australia estate, with a small vineyard dating from around 1850. It lay at the confluence of Moorooroo Creek and the North Para River. The word simply means the *meeting of two waters*. It was the home of William Jacob, the assistant land surveyor for the South Australia Company, the man who gave the land grant at Jacob's Creek to Johann Gramp. William Jacob settled on the property with his sister Ann in 1840, but unusually for that decade, only planted cereals and root crops.

Narkojee This thriving winery near Glengarry in the Gippsland region of Victoria, was first planted in 1980. It specialises in Chardonnay, Cabernet and Shiraz. Its name means *Place of Flowers*.

Pirramimma When Alexander Johnston bought 48 hectares (120 acres) of land in McLaren Vale in 1881 he called it Pirramimma meaning *the* *moon and the stars*. Today the winery is still in the hands of the same family but its holdings have increased to 240 contiguous hectares (600 acres), of which (180) 450 are now vineyards.

Porongurups These granite hills are said to be amongst the oldest in the world, and are the location of a number of wineries in Western Australia. During his first expedition Captain Wakefield recorded the name *Puringorup* after hearing his Aboriginal guides Mokare and Nakina identify them. It means *Spirit Home of Spirits*. Surprisingly none of the wineries in the region knew the translation.

Tatachilla *Red Earth Place* is the translation of this successful McLaren Vale, South Australia winery. The region is a prolific source of Aboriginal winery names.

Turramurra The label with its picture of a *high hill* provides the translation for this emerging winery on the Mornington Peninsula in Victoria.

Wirra Wirra Another of the Aboriginal names favoured in McLaren Vale. It translates as *amongst the gums*. This neither refers to dentists nor to swilling wine in your mouth, but to the local gum trees.

Yalumba Australia's oldest family-owned winery was founded by Englishman Samuel Smith in 1849. In 1852 he went to the Bendigo gold strike and returned with £300 profit which was sufficient to purchase *all the country around here*.

Maori Names

These are native to New Zealand.

Ata Rangi This international award winning winery pioneered Pinot Noir in Martinborough, and by so doing brought a new era to the wine region. Its name *Ata Rangi* appropriately translates as *Dawn Sky – New Beginning*. In reality the origin of the name is much more prosaic. It was the idea of a local Maori chief, who chose it at the request of founding partner Clive Paton. Clive, a dairy farmer turned grape grower, realised with glee that he wouldn't have to be up at dawn to tend the vines – unlike cows, which require early milking.

Kaikoura Wine Company Kai means *food* and Koura is *crayfish*. The area is abundant with them, which helps boosts the sales of local dry white wines.

Kaimira Estate Winery is a property in Nelson, named after a flourmill in the village of Brightwater and Kaimira means *mill* in Maori. The mill, which no longer exists, was once the centre of local activity, and is commemorated not just by the winery name, but also by the local school, which adopted the mill wheel as its logo. Two partners own the winery: June Hamilton and the appropriately named Ian Miller.

Kaituna Valley *Kai* normally means *food* or is connected with food and *tuna* means *eels*. So ask for smoked kaituna and wash it down with Sauvignon Blanc or Pinot Gris.

Kanuka Forest Wines *Kanuka* is a tree known for its healing properties. Suggestions that it is added to Kanuka Forest wine are completely without foundation. The wine is apparently excellent medicine in its own right.

Koura Bay Wines *Koura* is Maori for *crayfish* (rock lobster) and the wine from Koura Bay matches perfectly.

Mahurangi Estate Hamish MacDonald, possibly of Scots origin, advises that *Mahurangi* translates as *rock pointing to the sky*. Mahurangi Estate has 2 quite separate vineyards. One near Warkworth, about an hour's drive north of Auckland and the other on the famed Gimblett Road in Hawke's Bay, both on New Zealand's North Island. Presumably the rock is pointing to the giddy heights achieved by its Syrah (Shiraz).

Matariki Wines *Matariki* is the Maori name for the mother of the small cluster of stars in the constellation called Taurus (The Pleiades). The 6 prominent stars around her are believed to be her beautiful daughters. Matariki appears in the night sky in late June, around the time of the shortest day in the Southern Hemisphere. It brings light to the bare vines as they rest in the chill of winter. Maori folklore taught that if Matiriki and her daughters shone brightly the next harvest would be bountiful.

Matua Valley There appear to be a few different translations for *Matua* but I am inclined towards *the head of a family*. Interestingly when the winery was founded in 1974 it was constructed in the Waikoukou Valley. *Imagine having that as your brand name*, explained a winery spokesperson. So with reference to nearby Matua, which doesn't have a valley, one was invented.

Ngaruroro River The dried-up bed of this river is the major influence on the Gimblett Gravels sub-region of Hawke's Bay. Its name derives from a story about a Maori chief, who was walking his dog alongside the river when it startled a shoal of whitebait. *Ngaruroro* was the word he used to describe the sudden rippling and sparkling of the surface of the water.

Te Koko Cloudy Bay had to get in this list somehow, bearing in mind the reputation that it has earned for New Zealand Sauvignon Blanc. *Te Koko* is the Maori translation of Cloudy Bay and is the name used on the *full-bodied alternative style of Sauvignon Blanc, fermented in barrel and aged on yeast lees for 18 months*, which the winery produces.

Tohu Wines was the first Maori-owned wine to be exported. There are other small Maori wineries but Tohu is the brainchild of 3 Maori investors; the Wakatu Incorporation, which is a major force in farming and fishing, Ngati Rarua Atiawa Iwi Trust and Wi Pere Trust. *Tohu* means the *marque* or *signature* of the Maori.

Waipara There are 3 different wineries in Waipara, North Canterbury using this name: Waipara Downs, Waipara Springs and Waipara West. The second winery in particular seems to have made a curious choice because *Waipara* means *muddy waters*.

Wairau River Wines The Wairau River is an important factor influencing the cool climate of the Marlborough region, which is arguably the best source of Sauvignon Blanc in the world and Wairau River Wines produces a fine example. *Wairau* means *long river*.

Waitiri Creek Wines Waitiri is in the Gibbston Valley near Queenstown. It means *rumbling water* and is taken from the Nevis Rapids on the Kawarau River.

Unsubstantiated Stories

Cost of the candle The saying *one man's pain is another man's gain* was certainly true in France during the economic depression of the early 1930s. Many enforced sales of properties and businesses brought devastation to the original owners and joy to the new buyers, who often paid very little for their new acquisitions. One extreme example was the sale of the Burgundy Grand Cru vineyard and estate of Clos de Tart.

On a freezing December day in 1932 the Mommesin family, who owned a flourishing wine business in the Beaujolais region, apparently had some difficulty in persuading its head, Joanny, to travel to the Burgundy village of Morey Saint-Denis to bid for this unusual *monopole*, or small individual appellation. When Joanny arrived at the mayor's office where the sale was being held, he wondered why he had bothered, for no-one other than the auctioneer was present. Then he recalled that under ancient French law the sale must proceed and involved the burning of a candle. The auctioneer was obliged to ask him to name his bid, then light a regulation size candle and they both sat and waited. The law decreed that the highest bid when the candle burnt out would gain the property and the auctioneer himself was not permitted to bid. Seconds must have seemed like minutes and minutes like hours but eventually the candle spluttered and died and Clos de Tart became the possession of Mommesin. Neither the family nor the auctioneer ever revealed the price, but rumour suggested that it was merely the cost of the candle.

Harem lady In the mid-18th century a young Frenchwoman from a good but humble background, whom we shall call Odalisque, fell on hard times and in desperation took to the streets of Bordeaux as a prostitute. She chose to work along the ancient Quai des Chartrons, where many of the great Bordeaux wine merchants of the day had their cellars and where the bars and taverns sold a fascinating variety of wines by the glass or jug. Her particular favourite was a sweet white Graves, little seen today.

She anxiously sought a better life and by some means or other was hired as a lady's maid on a voyage to North Africa. As the small ship approached its destination it capsized in a storm off the Moroccan coast. She was rescued by local sailors who promptly sold her at the nearest slave market, where she was purchased by the slave buyer for Sultan Suliman of Turkey. She was taken to his harem where, no doubt, she used her Bordeaux experience to charm her master, for she quickly became his favourite and was known as the White Sultana.

During her dalliances with the Sultan she often told him about the delicious sweet white wines of Bordeaux and one she had grown to love called Chateau Carbonnieux from the Graves region. Eventually, to please her, arrangements were made to import the wine by a method which would circumvent the strict Moslem temperance laws, but it took a little planning by the Benedictine monks who then owned the chateau. They labelled the consignment *Eau Minérale de Carbonnieux* meaning carbonated mineral water. The wine found its way to the White Sultana and one account suggests that Sultan Suliman tasted the liquid treasure by accident and then remarked *How can these Christians drink wine when they have such delicious mineral water?*

The current owners of Chateau Carbonnieux have suggested that the story may not be entirely accurate, which may be true. But by strange coincidence, for several generations afterwards, the chateau produced a sweet white wine called Vin Odalisque.

Lost forever? The late Public Relations Director of Champagne Pommery, Patrick Bertrand, was an extremely charming and amusing man. He was generally a gentleman of some discretion, but even he could find his tongue loosened by a few glasses of the finest fizz. His routine included a daily round trip of 180 kms (112 miles), from his Paris home to Reims and back by AutoRoute, so he was meticulous about his consumption. On the odd occasion he stayed overnight in Reims and then he would allow himself a little relaxation. The writer was present on one such evening when Patrick revealed a most remarkable tale. He recalled how the Pommery cellars were in fact old Roman chalk pits, which Madame Pommery had excavated into *galeries* or sections of tunnel. Each of these *galeries* had been *baptised by her with the name of a new city she had conquested*. In fact plaques to identify the cities had been erected on the walls, rather like street signs, with names like Edinburgh, Madrid and Rio de Janeiro but the longest of all the *galeries* was Montreal at around 1 km (0.625 of a mile) and it concealed a secret.

At the very beginning of the World War I, in 1914, it was clear that the city of Reims would be a prime target for occupation. The front line did come perilously near the Pommery cellars but never actually reached them. No doubt efforts were made in many of the great Champagne houses to hide as much stock as possible, though in reality this posed quite a problem. Patrick related the action that had been taken at Pommery and the outcome, or lack of outcome.

A team of 7 trusted cellar workers built a false wall, creating an extra lining to a section of one of the main walls of the Montreal Galarie. Between the 2 walls they hid 100,000 bottles of Pommery Champagne. Then they took great care to plaster over the surface and disguise any trace of the work. A little later, one by one, the 7 men received their call-up papers and left to fight for their country. The war dragged on for 4 years with horrendous loss of life and when the official

armistice was signed in Reims in 1918, one might have presumed that daily life would gradually return to normal. At Champagne Pommery et Greno, as it was then called, the occasional caviste returned to resume work, but tragically none of the 7 cellar workers survived and throughout the rest of the century no-one had ever been able to find the hidden 100,000 bottles. By the time Patrick related this story to me in 1982, it was probably uneconomical to search, so the liquid treasure will remain hidden for many more generations, until one day in the distant future, when some construction workers may have quite a surprise.

Mysterious beast of Cantemerle The beautiful Chateau Cantemerle, the chateau of the song thrush, is one of the first wine properties to be seen when leaving the city of Bordeaux and many a visitor has been impressed by the estate. It includes densely wooded parkland, which for many generations was said to be the home of a terrifying beast that lived on the blood of young virgins. Unfortunately it hasn't been seen since the 1960s.

Nelson's Marsala vineyard At the end of the 18th century, in gratitude for protecting the ancient kingdom of The Two Sicilies from the forces of Napoleon, history relates that Admiral Horatio Nelson was rewarded with the gift of a vineyard by King Ferdinand and Queen Carolina. It was allegedly situated in the Marsala region on the West Coast of the island of Sicily and a picture of it was displayed in a City of London inn. In fact Nelson began to trade in the wine on some scale, and he persuaded King George III of England that he should supply the British Navy with a generous allocation of his Marsala wine. It comprised 500 pipes (550 litre barrels, around 282,000 bottles), a volume which suggests a rather extensive estate.

Curiously, despite making enquiries amongst a number of Nelson historians, no trace of any Marsala vineyard belonging to the Admiral can be found. He was also given a substantial property called Brontë, further east on the island of Sicily, and some Nelson followers have suggested that the wine could have been made there. But that is unlikely since there is no record of a sweet dessert wine of the same style being made in the vicinity.

Ironically, amongst the drinks used in 1805 to celebrate the British naval success at the Battle of Trafalgar, one was called *Marsala Victory Wine*, which it is presumed came from Nelson's secret source. Unfortunately, whilst it did toast a triumph, Nelson couldn't enjoy the moment for he lay dying on the deck of his flagship HMS Victory.

Royal Swan and Coonawarra In the United Kingdom that magnificent but rather haughty bird, the swan, has been protected by law as the sole property of the Crown for several centuries. In fact anyone who accidentally kills one is required to offer it to Her Majesty the Queen. Surprisingly few such birds are offered and even when they are, no-one ever appears to receive an official acknowledgement from the Monarch.

Perhaps the most enlightening tale concerning the illegal consumption of a swan comes from an old pub somewhere in the South of England, appropriately named after the bird in question. In the 1990s a small gourmet circle met there once a month, to enjoy tasting the wines of the world with matching dishes. For years the choice of food had been a little conservative until one night the landlord, who was also a member, suggested being somewhat more adventurous. This brought a lively debate, with the inevitable outcome; those who ate and drank at the Swan should, it was decided, consume the royal bird. The landlord declared that whosoever could provide a swan would be guaranteed anonymity and no questions asked.

A few weeks later 3 of the members returned from an expedition, very near to a certain Royal castle on the Thames, with 3 black bin bags, entered the pub by the back door and handed over their prize to the safe custody of the landlord. Hasty telephone calls quickly spread the word that the menu for the next session had been changed and everyone guessed the implication. Subsequently there was not a spare place to be found at the table. The President for the year, a successful lawyer, selected 6 wines from 6 different countries to be tried with their prize. There was a dry white Trimbach Alsace Riesling from France, Chateau Xanadu Margaret River Semillon from Western Australia, a Charles Heidsieck 1982 Vintage Champagne, a Barolo from Pio Cesare, an Amador Foothill Zinfandel from California and a rich red 1990 Saint Hugo Coonawarra from South Australia.

As usual they took a vote, by show of hands, to signify their preference. It was quite clear which wine had found favour with the majority. The chairman for the evening, who happened to be the local Police Superintendent and a long-standing member of the circle, gave the final verdict. *The swan was flaming tough as old boots but it went beautifully with that Saint Hugo Coonawarra.*

That's funny, said the Vicar sitting beside him, *if I remember correctly, Saint Hugo, not of Coonawarra but of Chinon in France, is the patron saint of wild birds*. Much laughter ensued, before the President tapped his corkscrew on the table and called for a toast to The Queen and all tough old birds!

Two for one The Champagne cellars of Louis Roederer and GH Mumm in the city of Reims are contiguous, a circumstance which was put to good use during World War I. A secret entrance was knocked through between the 2 cellars to facilitate the movement of workers in the event of bombardment causing any roof collapse. When peace returned it was some while before the wall was re-sealed. However it was sealed rapidly when it came to light that some cellar workers had been operating an illicit trade. They had been exchanging bottles from one house to the other for their private consumption, and the established exchange rate was 2 bottles of Mumm for one of Roederer.

Rarest Wine

Ceja Vineyards In the 1960's Pablo Ceja was a transient Mexican grape picker who worked the harvest seasons in the Napa Valley. In 1967, with his wife Juanita and 6 children, he emigrated to California and settled in Saint Helena. Soon 4 more children had arrived, but despite the family's size both parents worked for different wineries and saved assiduously. In 1983 the Ceja family became the first Mexican grape pickers to buy their own vineyard in the valley. Since then they have increased their initial 6 hectares (15 acres) to 45.2 hectares (113 acres).

Constantia/Earl Spencer In 1989 at Althorp in England, the late Earl Spencer, father of Princess Diana, told the writer about the oldest bottle in his ancient cellars. It was a priceless 1787 Constantia, correctly known as Vin de Constance, from the original Cape Town, South Africa vineyard of that name, planted by Simon Van der Stel, the first Dutch Governor of the settlement. The rich, complex, style of aged dessert wine, which has a reputation for exceptional longevity, is believed to have been pressed from red Muscatel and white Frontignac grapes and has not been made for generations, though it was once sought by Royal families throughout the world. The last known sale was at Christie's in London on April 6th 2000 when 2 bottles of Constantia 1791, from the private cellar of The Duke of Northumberland, sold for US$1,350 (£900) + 10 per cent buyer's premium per bottle. Christie's considered it possible that not more than a couple of dozen bottles from that era survive.

Nowadays there are modern vineyards in this small wine region, producing some successful table wines but nothing to equal or even challenge the reputation and character of the great Constantia of old. However in 1986 Duggie Jooste, the owner of the Klein Constantia estate, began a project to replicate the original wine using Muscat de Frontignan grapes. The production of this *Vin de Constance* involves leaving the bunches on the vines to shrivel, and maturing the wine for 2 years in French oak *barriques*. It will take some generations to see if his plan succeeds.

Apparently following the death of the late Earl Spencer large stocks of old and fine wines were removed from the Althorp cellars and sold. Matters were a little disorganised on the estate at the time and some interesting old bottles have subsequently been found, hidden in secret places. So any impatient millionaire wine lovers might be well advised to carefully observe the building renovation schedule at Althorp. Maybe one day some major fund raising will prove necessary to restore the East Wing. For it is believed that the bottle of 1787 Constantia may have survived intact and still lie in its place beneath the mansion, now owned by the late Earl's son, the current Earl Spencer and former broadcast journalist Charles Althorp, who arranged my visit with his father.

A strange coincidence arose in the 1990s, when Charles Althorp made a (what later proved to be temporary) decision to emigrate to South Africa, where he bought a house in Constantia.

Champagne Salon Arguably the most exclusive of all Champagnes is the magnificent Salon le Mesnil. Founded by Eugene Aimé Salon in 1911, he attracted friends as investors and vowed to them that Salon would only make its Champagne in the finest of vintages. His promise continues to be upheld by his successors, for since 1911 only 35 Vintages have been made. In all the other years Salon has sold its young wine to other Champagne houses, preferring to maintain its founder's principle.

Denali, Alaska Impossible to make wine in Alaska many readers will think. But of course you can. What you cannot do is make it from grapes grown in that state. The Denali winery, in urban Anchorage, offers wine consumers the opportunity to ferment their own wine at home. The firm apparently ships hundreds of 18.9 litre (5 gallon) bladders of grape juice from certain Canadian companies, which are then used in kits sold to customers, who can make their own wines with labels such as *Merlot Product of Alaska*.

   * Please no e-mails about the original source of the bladders.

Inkameep 2000 Inkameep Cellars vintage 2000 of Chardonnay, Merlot and Pinot Noir were the first wines ever produced and marketed by North American Indians. Inkameep is situated in the Okanagan Valley of British Columbia, about 15 miles north of the US border. The vines are planted on reserve land belonging to Osoyoos Indians. Vines were first planted there in the 1970s but unfortunately these were hybrids. Also the grapes were always sold to other producers until Osoyoos Chief, Sam Baptiste, replaced them with vitis vinifera varietals in 1989. Since then their Cabernet Sauvignon grapes have become highly sought by other producers but the finest of them are now used for their Inkameep label.

January Folly is the translation of *Folie de Janvier*, an icewine produced within 2 hours drive of the Mediterranean Sea by Domain Cauhapé in Jurançon. The wine was specifically named for a 1999 vintage, picked during unusually cold weather in January 2000. Unfortunately the Petit Manseng grapes were picked too late in the day, by which time they had thawed. Contact domain-cauhape@wanadoo.fr.

Pompeii wine The Roman city of Pompeii was once famed for its wines but like everything else in the region its vineyards were entombed by the molten lava of Mount Vesuvius in AD 79. It wasn't until 2 millennia later that new vines were planted. In 1996, an experimental vineyard just a single hectare (2.5 acres) in size and comprising a mere 3,000 vines, owned by the Mastroberardino family, was planted amidst the ruins. The project is an attempt to replicate a Roman vineyard and the grape varieties selected are amongst those believed to date from that era. They are Greco, Fiano, Aglianico, Piedirosso, Olivella, Code di Volpe and Falanghina.

Rasteau Rancio For about a century the French wine authorities have policed their wine regions under the appellation contrôlée system and have wondered why the rest of the wine world has not rushed to implement the same regulations. In many ways much can be learned from the French system which gives specific names to wines from particular regions, which use approved grape varieties and display local characteristics.

So far so good, thought the technocrats of the European Community, we'll cope with this pattern. That was until one day in the 1980's when the EC authorities stumbled across the small cellar of Monsieur Emile Bressy at Rasteau in the Côtes du Rhône region. Monsieur Bressy, a law-abiding pillar of the community had quite a widespread reputation for his Rhône wines, but not for the lone barrel he made from time to time of a *vin doux naturel* (sweet natural fortified wine). This, after seven years or so he bottled and labelled as *Rasteau Rancio* indicating its lengthy period of breathing through the pores of the oak.

There was consternation; nowhere could any official find authorisation for such a title. *Rasteau Vin Doux Naturel* was acceptable but there was nothing to permit the use of the word *Rancio*. Eventually it was discovered that Emile Bressy was the only winemaker who continued to make this old fashioned style of wine, one which other families had forgotten a century earlier. In other words one man had his own appellation for a wine which in some years is never made.

Rot Eiswein (Red Icewine) As the cultivation of icewine spreads, one traditional winemaker in Austria called Willi Opitz, produces in some vintages a few hundred bottles of red eiswein, from his minute 2 hectares (5 acres) vineyard on the edge of the Neusiedlersee in Burgenland. Find a bottle and you will have something very rare indeed. Neusiedlersee is a shallow lake on Austria's border with Hungary and it creates one of the most humid atmospheres in Europe, which consistently encourages noble rot. It was also the place where the first refugees began to walk through the *Iron Curtain* in 1989.

St Paul's Presbyterian Church, Mudgee In 1978 this small non-conformist Church in the quaint old wine town of Mudgee in New South Wales, Australia hit upon an unusual idea to publicise its centenary. To the surprise and pleasure of the local community it decided to produce its own wine. So a unique batch of 1,000 cases of both red and white wines were made and sold.

Presbyterian rogue There are not many wineries that can claim an ordained clergyman as head winemaker, but it is true of Weisinger's Winery. The winery is located in Ashland in the Rogue Valley of Oregon, near the Pacific coast of the United States and was founded by the Rev. John Weisinger and his wife Shenita in 1988, following his retirement from the Presbyterian ministry. It remains a very small concern producing around 4,000 cases per annum, few of which are ever seen outside their homeland.

Seldom Seen Viognier, Mudgee This wine gains the attractive New South Wales wine town of Mudgee its second place in this section, simply by a clever choice of name. It is in fact seldom seen in any other country, unless purchased by an astute wine enthusiast when holidaying in Australia. The Chardonnay and Shiraz have good local reputations.

Which Vintage A bottle of the popular Pepper Wood Grove California Chardonnay seen in Tunbridge Wells, Kent, England in October 2001 appeared a little confused about its vintage. The front label clearly said 1999 while the back label pronounced 1998.

Wine Graces

Most readers will have said Grace before meals at some time but how many have ever said Grace before enjoying wine on its own? Here are a few examples, some of which might just raise a laugh.

- Pull the cork and pour the wine. Thank You Lord for the gift of the vine.

- Lord, may we remember the feet that trod this Port. May the taste be fine and the palate not offended by the thought.

- Fruit of the vine, work of human hands, blessed gift to mankind for sharing and joy. May we remember those who made this wine and the soil where it was born.

- Colour, bouquet, flavour, character and aftertaste, we hope to find them Lord in these wines – and when we do – let us remember the soil that gave them, the climate that nurtured them and the people that made them.

- Let us remember Cana in Galilee and drink the worst first.

- Red, White, Rosé or Blush, Lord teach us to savour and never to rush.

- From California's golden coast to Chile's narrow valleys, watered by mountain peaks, through Coonawarra's rich red soil and Marlborough's cooling land come grapes and wine. May we share them Lord and praise you for your bounty.

- Raise your glass, salute the wine, thank the Lord for this gift divine.

- Picked by hand, pressed with gentle care, fermented in steel and aged in wood; after so much effort, Lord, let the wine be good.

- Sparkling wine clear and cool, bubbles rushing from stem to rim: thank the Lord and praise Him.

- Thank you Lord for this gift of the vine. May it be smooth and may it be fine.
- Noah planted the first vines, Jesus turned water into wine, monks around the world spread early vineyards and the inhabitants of the Earth imbibe for fun and pleasure, appreciation and enjoyment, – and some for more important reasons.
- Vines produce too many shoots, so they are pruned; vine leaves produce too much foliage, so they are thinned; too many grapes dilute the flavour, so for better wines, fewer are selected. Thank you Lord for allowing us to assess the fruit of this work. *
- Merely a sample, simply a taste; please dear Lord may it not add to my waist.
- Lord, may we remember that some talk of wine that has a purple robe and the rest of us can only see it. Let it always remind us of you – to the very last drop.
- Let us taste, Good Lord, the fruit of the Vine and may we be the healthy branches that bear the rich, ripe grapes of man's best endeavours.
- A little white, a little pink, perhaps a little red – but not all mixed within us, before we go to bed.
- The gentle mousse of fine Champagne, the glinting green lights of Marlborough's Sauvignon Blanc, the great rich colour of Brunello bring our first notes of appreciation before we even examine the bouquet, or taste the wine. Thank you, Lord, for the privilege.*

* For Wine Appreciation/Tasting Societies.

What's in a Name

Bodega Norton The charmingly named English gentleman, Sir Edmund James Palmer Norton founded this outstanding winery in the Mendoza region of Argentina in 1895. Later, out of respect for his new homeland, Sir Edmund translated his first name into Spanish and became *Sir Edmondo*. He was a pioneer railway engineer, who worked for the Buenos Aires Railway Company to open up a route from the Atlantic Ocean through the Andes Mountains to the Pacific. Whilst occupied with this challenging project, he fell in love with the beautiful Mendoza region and needed a worthwhile reason for staying. The answer was to become a wine producer, so he imported vines from France and developed the winery which still bears his name. Today Bodega Norton is noted for its *Privada* wine and is owned by another foreigner, the Austrian businessman, Gernot Langes-Swarovski. It is managed by his stepson Michael Halstrick.

Bonny Doon This winery, founded in 1981, is situated in Bonny Doon Road, Santa Cruz, California and is owned by a middle-aged former philosophy lecturer and eccentric humourist called Randall Grahm. The only problem in understanding some of his jests is that consumers need to be extremely knowledgeable to get the point.

In the 1980s he launched a Rhône-style red called *Le Cigare Volant* or *The Flying Cigar*. This poked fun at a 1950s French proclamation banning UFOs from landing within the Chateauneuf-du-Pape region. In a further tongue-in-cheek attack of Chateauneuf-du-Pape he introduced *Old Telegram*, a direct translation of the highly rated *Vieux Telegraphe* from that region.

Later to simplify matters he greeted Italian wine lovers with his own Italian-style offering called *Ca del Solo* with a label showing a cat sitting alone up a tree. The reason was that the original wine, in what has now become a series of styles carrying the name, was 100% Muscat which he was bottling on its own for the first time.

Curiously, few ever ask why the winery is called Bonny Doon. Initially the title comes from the road in Santa Cruz which was named by 19th century Scottish immigrant John Burns, who took it from his national poet Robbie Burns (no relation). The poet wrote a song, set in western Scotland, called *The Banks O'Doon* which recalled *O bonie Doon* referring to the river that runs from Loch Doon to the Firth of Clyde.

Canary During the 18th and 19th centuries the word *canary* described 2 popular items shipped from the archipelago, known as the Canary Islands, off the West Coast of North Africa. The first was the little yellow songbirds and the second, a golden brown wine with a light sweetish flavour. The wine graced the cellars of the wealthy on both sides of the Atlantic, from the mansions of Virginia to the country estates of England. It had excellent properties for long aging and it was not unusual to find bottles, many of them generations old, at auctions as late as the mid-20th century. Apparently its shipment faded away because the Canary Islands were not a manufacturing force and had little otherwise to export, and trading ships wished to have full cargoes when arriving or departing.

Canepa Wine consumers in several countries are enthusiastic purchasers of the Canepa brand from Chile. Yet another Chilean winery called Terramater (Mother Earth) is a partnership between 3 Canepa sisters who decided to run their own operation. They produce what is claimed to be the world's first Zinfandel-Shiraz blend. In contrast the tiny Canepa Vineyard in Sonoma, California produces a small volume of its own Chardonnay, usually not more than 400 cases, and sells most of its grapes.

Chablis Over the last 150 years no wine name has probably suffered from more conflicting images than Chablis. On the one hand the greatest French examples of authentic Chablis can be such elegant, discreet, firm dry white wines of style and finesse. Yet, by contrast, in the past the word has been used to describe a cheap, low quality, bulk wine that did nothing for the reputation of the American wine industry for generations.

As with many famous names there are a number of possible derivations but the writer prefers an explanation that harks back some 2,000 years. Even then the actual French site was known to Celtic migrants as a crossing point on the River Serein, which was usually small and peaceful. The Celts were heading west to the sea, either to Brittany or the British Isles. They originated in the Carpathian Basin in today's Hungary. Leaving the mountains of central Europe they sought the most straightforward journey to their destinations. When they reached the Serein, crossings were made on a flat-bottomed boat that would be pulled by a rope or cable and the Celtic word for this was shable. This argument is supported by the Roman name for the town, *Cableia*, and as the Romans were the first to plant vines there, it is highly likely that some of their wines were transported using the same river crossing.

Many do not realise that all Chablis is 100% Chardonnay and has been committed to that varietal long before the first such vine was planted in the New World.

Chateau Smith-Haut-Lafitte There is no dispute that Smith, in its various forms, is the most common European name. Yet many are surprised that the English form is included in the French name of a highly esteemed Grand Cru Classé Graves from Bordeaux, France. Since the foundation of the property by Scotsman George Smith in 1720, its name has been spelt 3 different ways. It began, as it is now, as *Chateau Smith-Haut-Lafitte* but in 1756 his George's son and successor Christopher Smith was sympathetic to France's alliance with Austria and changed Smith to *Smidt*. In 1860 the property was inherited by Martin Sadi Duffour-Dubergier, who even changed its name to simple *Chateau Schmith*. This was a little unpopular during the 1870 Franco-Prussian war but it remained intact. In 1905 the chateau was purchased by a German company, from whom it was confiscated after World War I. Immediately following the 1919 Treaty of Versailles orders were given to restore its original title and its name returned to Chateau Smith-Haut-Lafitte.

Chauffe-Eau Cellars Chauffe-Eau means a geyser (water-heater) and this Sonoma property lies in a region that is renowned for these. Apparently the founders felt that a *French sounding name* might improve their fortune. Their choice might also have caused them problems, as they might have finished up in hot water.

Clonakilla Many wine enthusiasts are fooled by the name of this small winery in the Canberra District of Australia, imagining it to be an Aboriginal word. In fact it was chosen by the founder Dr John Kirk because it was the name of his grandparents' farm in County Clare in the Republic of Ireland.

Duck Muck Shiraz When Baltimore wine guru Robert Parker gave the 1997 Duck Muck Shiraz a 100 points rating, many of the great taster's followers must have said *Duck What*? Only 200 cases were produced at the humble winery at Heathcote in the Razorback Hills of Victoria, Australia and few bottles travelled far. Many were amazed to learn that David *Duck* Anderson, winemaker and owner of Wild Duck Creek Estate, had never taken a single lesson in winemaking in his life. Not surprisingly the wine is rumoured to be the ideal with wild duck but is a little more difficult to find than that tasty bird, and nowadays much more expensive.

Duxoup This is a rather small Sonoma, California winery, founded in 1981, which is usually called Duxoup Wine Works. It is named after the Marx Brothers' classic comedy film *Duck Soup* and is pronounced the same. The winery should not be confused with Duckhorn Vineyards which is one of the leading producers of Sauvignon Blanc and Merlot in the nearby Napa Valley. The name there has no Hollywood connection but comes from senior partners Dan and Margaret Duckhorn. But they do invite potshots with their second wine called *Decoy*, which features a sitting duck on the label.

Francisco de Aguirre This relatively young winery in the Limari Valley of Chile has been producing some stunning Shiraz. It comes from one of the most northerly vineyards in that country, where the vines are planted on steep terraces in the foothills of the Andes to the south of the Atacama Desert, claimed to be the driest region in the world. The winery is named after the monk Francisco de Aguirre, who planted the first vines in Chile near Copiapo in 1548. No doubt he must have found irrigation a little more difficult than the modern eponymous winery.

Gimblett Gravels Gimblett Gravels is a unique growing district within the Hawke's Bay wine region, on the east coast of the North Island of New Zealand. The district is also a voluntary association with its own disciplinary code. In some ways it is a New World equivalent of the Chianti Classico Consorzio. It covers 800 hectares (2,000 acres) of gravelly soils which were formed by the continual flooding of the Ngaruroro River, which finally changed course in 1867 revealing extensive gravel beds. The district has various micro-climates with temperatures averaging 3° Celsius above the norm in Hawke's Bay. This is a key element in ripening grapes – red varieties in particular – and much interest is being taken in the quality of the main Bordeaux varietals and Syrah (Shiraz).

Goats do Roam The South African Fairview Estate at Paarl is not just the home to a major winery but also is *South Africa's largest producer of speciality cheeses* and markets goats' milk. This means that *goats do roam* around the vineyards and any other building they can enter. Subsequently their own *goat tower* has been built to keep them out of harm's way. Their inquisitive nature inspired this popular label after one occasion when they escaped into a new vineyard of succulent young Rhône varietal vines. However few can ever have imagined that the name would develop into a successful international brand. Its red style is usually a blend of 5 or 6 varieties and there is also a rosé and of course its name is a play on the French wine Côtes du Rhône.

Heidsieck Champagne There are 3 prominent Champagne houses bearing the name Heidsieck: Charles Heidsieck, Piper-Heidsieck and Heidsieck Monopole. They are all entitled to carry the family name. The last is the eldest, being directly descended from the original Champagne Heidsieck et Cie which was founded by Florenz-

Louis Heidsieck in 1785. The word *Monopole* was adopted from one of their original styles.

Next in seniority comes Champagne Piper-Heidsieck, which came about in a rather unusual manner. In 1834 Christian Heidsieck, a nephew of founder Florenz-Louis, formed a breakaway house using his own name. Just one year later he died prematurely and two years after that his widow married one of the young assistants called Henri Piper, who then became the principal partner and changed the infant house's name to Champagne Piper. This did not please their New York agent, J-C Kunkleman, who complained bitterly that he had spent a lot of time building up the reputation of Champagne Heidsieck. He insisted on re-labelling the bottles for the American market as Piper's Heidsieck and later this was modified to Piper Heidsieck.

Champagne Charles Heidsieck was a slightly later addition, founded in 1851 by Charles-Camille Heidsieck, a great nephew of Florenz-Louis Heidsieck. Charles was a particularly flamboyant character, immortalised in the song *Champagne Charlie*. He seized the opportunity to trade with the French-Canadian settlers in Louisiana and developed an annual trade of over 300,000 bottles, which was tantamount to putting *all his eggs in one basket* as he had relatively few sales in France, or elsewhere. The 1864 US Civil War very nearly put him out of business as well as costing him his life.

Charles found himself in a position where he couldn't receive any payments from Louisiana and so set off from France to collect them. Despite many attempts, he found his route blocked by the battlefront, or other troop movements. Ultimately he arrived in the port of Mobile in Alabama, which was then in Confederate hands, and discovered that the only way to get to New Orleans about 320 kms (200 miles) distant, was by working as a barman on a ferry. At this point he made a major mistake, for he agreed to take a package to deliver to the French vice-consul in New Orleans. Unfortunately the ferry was stopped by Yankee forces and everyone searched. The package was opened and found to contain negotiations for French military support for the Confederates. Charles was arrested on suspicion of being a spy and thrown into a rat-infested fort in the Mississippi Delta. It took the French authorities 6 months to obtain his release and Charles needed another 6 months to collect all the funds owed him before returning to France. In due course Champagne Charles Heidsieck spread its business much more widely.

Huia Vineyards This leading Marlborough, New Zealand vineyard is named after a native bird that was last sighted officially in 1907. The winery says *it was the only bird in the world in which the bills of the male and female birds were different in shape*. Its luminescent tail plumage were adornments which apparently denoted great dignity and wisdom. Hopefully the same two characteristics are attributable to Claire and Mike Allan who own and operate the winery.

Jacob's Creek The internationally successful wine had the humblest of beginnings. It was founded by a Bavarian immigrant called Johann Gramp in 1847 and was the first commercial vineyard in the Barossa Valley of South Australia.

In 1837, when aged 17, Johann left his tiny village of Eichig in Bavaria intending to go to sea. He arrived in the great port of Hamburg and being a strict Lutheran simply went to the nearest church of that denomination. To his surprise he was invited to become one of a group of 54 members of the congregation, who intended to emigrate the following month to the new colony of South Australia.

When they arrived after a $4^{1}/_{2}$ month journey, the men in the group were committed to work for 3 years on building the city of Adelaide. Ten years later, in 1847, Johann left his friends and travelled inland with his wife and child, to join a Lutheran settlement at Bethany in the then unknown Barossa Valley. There, he was apparently inspired by the luscious ripeness of the grapes on a couple of rows of vines, which would have been planted for sacramental use. So he decided to start his own vineyard. To do this he travelled $1^1/_2$ miles to the south where William Jacob, the assistant land surveyor of the South Australia Company, gave him a 40-acre land grant alongside a tiny stream. On the map, William Jacob ensured that he personally would be remembered for posterity, by calling the stream Jacob's Creek. There in 1847 Johann Gramp planted 4 acres of his historic vineyard and in 1850 constructed an ironstone cellar which survives to this day.

John Hancock John Hancock is literally the signature label from Trinity Hill in Hawke's Bay, New Zealand. The label shows the very bold signature of senior partner John Hancock. He was clearly taking advantage of an American tradition. People being asked to sign bills or agreements in the USA are often asked for their *John Hancock*. This refers to the President of the Congress who was the first person to sign the 1776 Declaration of Independence and who was said by some to have pressed so hard that his signature could never be removed.

Kanonkop Many have suggested that this winery in Stellenbosch is the ideal benchmark for South African Pinotage, a fullish red wine that at its best can have the most appealing characteristics. The property is a section of the original Uitkyk farm, which was a land grant to Jan Oberholster in 1712. Few, who have not visited the property, will realise the origin of its name. Quite refreshingly it comes from a gun of peace, which is prominently displayed on its label. In the 17th century the farm's *kopje*, or hilltop location, on the slopes of the Simonsberg Mountain, was the base for a rather noisy cannon. This was fired to advise local farmers that sailing ships were entering Table Bay and was the signal for rushing their fresh produce to the harbour to trade with welcome strangers.

Leapfrogmilk Amiable and zany Napa Valley winemaker-owner John Williams was poking fun at German Liebfraumilch when he launched this wine. He was also influenced by the fact that his Frog's Leap winery used to be a commercial frog farm, which provided the delicacies required by French immigrants in San Francisco in the late 19th century. John is also a talented former athlete and is known to leap to great heights when performing on his private basketball court within the main cellar, a demonstration he loves to give to visiting journalists.

Oregonese A recent tasting of some superb Oregon Pinot Noir examples would have needed an assortment of dictionaries to translate the names. The first wine was *Torii Mor*, which was named by Donald Olson when he founded the winery in 1993. He chose the Japanese word *Torii* meaning ornate gates and the ancient Norse word *Mor* for earth. The winery states *By integrating these two distinctive languages, the romantic image of a gate to an earthspace or passageway to beautiful things is formed*. It is respectfully suggested that they focus on producing delicious wines and leave the literary works to others.

The second wine was *Cristom*. Suspecting some Christian background, enquiries were made only to learn that the name was quite simply a modern amalgamation. Owners Paul and Eileen Gerrie merged Christine and Tom, the names of their children.

Third came Chehalem (pronounced *Chuh-hay-lum*) which, according to the winery, is a native American Indian word meaning *gentle land or valley of flowers*.

Or how about *Champoeg* from Butteville in the north of the Willamette Valley? The winery stands on the site of one of Oregon's oldest vineyards, believed to date from around 1840, when it was cultivated by French-Canadians who worked for the Hudson's Bay Company before the days of the Oregon Trail. They found Kalapuyan Indians gathering the bulbs of the Camas flower and eating them as winter crops. *Champ* is the French word for field and *Poeg* was the word the Indians used for the bulbs.

Abacela Vineyards and Winery is another example of how so many cultures and languages coalesce in Oregonese. The property is the realisation of a dream for Earl and Hilda Jones, who love all things Spanish – especially the wines. They searched for a vineyard site in a suitable climate in Oregon to *abacela* or *plant grapevines* and found one, in the Umpqua Valley, at the delightful address of Lookingglass Road, Roseburg. They planted Tempranillo, Grenache, Graciano, Bastardo and Tinta Roriz, believed to be the first Iberian varietals grown in the Pacific North-West. Incidentally the word *Umpqua* is truly Oregon coming from tribes of Indians that were native to the state.

Sainte Chapelle Winery Wine enthusiasts around the world might be surprised to learn that there is a major winery in the sparsely populated American State of Idaho, in the northwest of the USA. Superbly set above the Snake River, it was founded in 1976 and named Ste Chapelle after the magnificent la Sainte Chapelle in Paris. The historic edifice was constructed by Louis IX, known as the Saint King, in the 13th century. The name was chosen by founder Bill Broich who had been greatly impressed by the original building during a visit to France. When 2 years later he sold the winery to the Symms family, they continued the theme by building the Visitor Centre, Tasting Room and Retail Shop in the same Gothic architecture with high vaulted ceilings and 2 storey windows. Today it is owned by the Canandaigua Wine Company and produces a wide range of wines from Gewürztraminer to Cabernet Sauvignon, with its Chardonnay highly recommended. Interestingly the first Idaho vineyards were planted by French and German settlers in 1872.

Spier This exciting South African winery dates from 1692 but its name derives from its second owner Hans Heinrich Hattingh, a native of Speyer in the German Rhineland. He travelled inland from Cape Town and found a property for sale alongside the bulrushes, that still can be found on the banks of the little River Erste. Hans must have decided the coincidence was too great, because the Afrikaans word for bulrush is *Spier*. Today the Spier Estate is an inspiring 3,000 acre park with a remarkable assortment of leisure facilities including its *Cheetah Outreach* and *Eagle Endeavours* and the Spier winery produces impressive Sauvignon Blanc and Cabernet Sauvignon.

Suckfizzle Augusta This alarmingly named winery from the stunning Margaret River region in Western Australia is named after a character created by the French novelist Rabelais called *Lord Suckfizzle*. The winery is a close neighbour to the celebrated Leeuwin Estate and has earned a good reputation for its estate-bottled Cabernet Sauvignon which neither sucks nor fizzles.

Valpolicella This attractive fruity *denomination of origin* red wine from near Verona in northern Italy is enjoying a renaissance after some years in the doldrums. Curiously the name comes from ancient Greek and means *the valley of many cellars*. The earliest written evidence of the name spells it as *Val Polesela* in a legal document of 1177 AD.

Whalesback The name of this delightful New Zealand Sauvignon Blanc from the Koura winery has its origin in a Maori legend. It tells of two wives of a paramount chief who ran away from home while the chief and his warriors were on a raiding party. The angry chief sent a group of his princely warriors to find them but they were unsuccessful. Despite this the chief was sufficiently pleased with the efforts of his princes to allow each of them to choose some land as their own. So Prince Tapuae o uenuku (footsteps of the rainbow god) paddled along the coast in a canoe until he saw the Awatere (swift flowing) river valley near today's town of Kaikoura. He decided to swim to the shore but found himself struggling, only to be rescued by a whale which carried him to the land.

On a happy note, this area was settled in the 19th century by European whalers but today is a tourist centre for watching these magnificent animals.

Wyndham Estate George Wyndham, an adventurous Englishman with a sense of wanderlust, founded Australia's oldest surviving winery in 1828. George was born at Dinton, near Salisbury in the west of England, where his father was a wealthy landowner. George enjoyed the privilege of attending England's prestigious Harrow public school and actually played in its famous cricket team in 1818. He then attended Cambridge University before, in 1824, departing for Canada with the explorer and novelist John Galt.

He returned the following year and decided to undertake the Grand Tour of Europe that was fashionable for many of the young gentry of his generation. On Christmas Day 1825 he found himself in Rome, feeling rather dejected after a fever and reminiscing nostalgically on the festivities in his family home. To shake off his melancholy and for exercise, he took a stroll to the Pincian Hill, where by incalculable coincidence he happened upon his good friend and neighbour John Still. John invited him to join his party of family and friends, which included a young lady from Brussels called Margaret Jay. The pair soon fell in love and George followed Margaret home across Europe to ask her father for her hand in marriage. The wedding promptly took place but for some unaccountable reason George appears to have omitted to tell his parents until after the event. Understandably he was not too popular on his return to England.

A decision was made to emigrate to New South Wales and the young married couple left Plymouth for Sydney, on the 440 ton SS George Horn, on August 17th 1827. On board George shipped an entire flock of Southdown sheep, which couldn't have made conditions too pleasant for the passengers or crew. The boat arrived on Christmas Eve and George headed for Sydney to try and purchase some land, which he did without seeing it. He travelled overland with some drovers and reached the Hunter Valley a few weeks later, having sent his wife by ship to Newcastle to shorten her journey. He had bought a 2,000 acre estate called Annandale but quickly changed its name to Dalwood after a portion of his father's English estate.

As was the custom then he was allocated a number of convicts to work on his land. He soon developed a good reputation with them as a fair master. On one occasion when there was a revolt in the area by some *bush rangers*, as escaped prisoners were called, George feared for the safety of his family and the property. He need not have worried for one morning he awoke to find a barely legible note nailed to his gate. It stated that he had been a kind master and they would not hurt a hair on his head.

Legend suggests that the derivation of the Bin numbers on modern Wyndham Estate wine labels comes from this era. Most of the convicts were illiterate and found it difficult to identify the various wines in the Dalwood cellars, so George Wyndham devised a scheme where he numbered the brick cellar bins with 111 and 222 and so on. The story is impossible to prove but the unique system which only avoids an obvious 666 must have started somewhere.

He developed 2 main vineyards; the first at Dalwood and the second 300 miles further inland called Bukkulla, on the McIntyre River near the borders of Queensland. The latter was described in advertising as having *soil and climate very similar to that of Spain*.

George specialised in Shiraz and other red wines and some of his original Shiraz vines, planted in 1828 were still contributing to wine until the mid 1950s. No doubt he would have loved the current Wyndham Estate Bin 555 Shiraz with its delicious style.

Xanadu In recent times this exciting winery has been waving the flag energetically in several countries for Margaret River and Western Australia. Xanadu was originally founded by medical practitioner Dr John Lagan in 1977. This loquacious Irishman, now partly retired, is a real culture vulture, with a great love of Literature and Art, who announced on arrival in Margaret River that he had found his *Xanadu*. He was referring to the summer palace and pleasure dome described by Samuel Taylor Coleridge in his poem, *Kubla Kahn*.

Wartime Wine

Acinatico Wine experts attending a Christie's wine auction in New York in February 2001 would have been incredulous to see 4 bottles of the virtually unknown Bertani *Acinatico* 1928 sell for US$2,500 each. Indeed few readers will have heard of this almost forgotten dessert wine from the Valpolicella region of Italy, for it hasn't been made for generations. One of its finest producers was the classic Veronese house of Bertani; their 1928 vintage was considered outstanding and had been given almost perfect cellar aging.

The *almost* refers to the time when the Bertani family took prompt action to move the remaining stock of the wine, to avoid the thirsty palates of the German army as it swept south into Italy in 1940.

The family also owned a small farm called Sacole where they took great trouble to hide their liquid treasure. The wisdom of the move was soon confirmed, for the Nazis set up their headquarters in a building immediately opposite the Bertani winery at Arbizzano, where they established an evening routine that reflected the highest German discipline. At 5pm they would have gas mask drill whilst they sang *Lily Marlene*, at 7pm they would dine in a hurry and at 7.30pm they would cross the road to the winery and drink their fill, overlooking to pay the bill as they left.

The consignment of *Acinatico* was not returned from *Sacole* to the Bertani cellars until 1961 and today the family still possess 7,400 bottles of the 1928 vintage. After the recent results there are rumours that production of the wine may start again one day.

Clos du Maréchal is an example of a wine name that sounds authentic but anyone who attempts to find it on a map, or in any literature prior to 1942 or after 1944, will be disappointed. Before 1942 and after 1944 the vineyard land concerned belonged to the world famous wine charity, the Hospices de Beaune. But in May 1942 it was given by the Hospices to Marshall Petain, the octogenarian leader of the Vichy government and First World War hero, in honour of his services to France. At a time when many French people believed that Petain was still serving France well, the charity selected one of their oldest vineyards, enclosed it with a stone wall, named it Clos du Maréchal (*The Marshall's Enclosed Vineyard*) and presented the title deeds to Petain. Two years later, as the Germans retreated and the Vichy Government lost its authority, the Burgundians realised the folly of their act, rescinded the legal action that had given him the property, demolished its walls and took it back.

My name is Von Mumm In 1919, at the end of World War I, The Treaty of Versailles was published. One of its major undertakings was to confiscate all German assets in France. This meant that the Champagne house of G. H. Mumm, famous for its Cordon Rouge (*Red Ribbon Label*), was offered for public sale. It was removed from the ownership of the aristocratic German, Von Mumm family and acquired at auction, in 1920, by a new company controlled by various businessmen from Northern France. This action was bitterly resented by the Von Mumm family who vowed to win their company back. They even began trading, in that same year, as G. H. Mumm in Bern, Switzerland. Prolonged and exceptionally complicated litigation ensued and it wasn't until 1933 that the French house could prevent the German family from using its name on bottles of sparkling wine.

However revenge was taken just 8 years later in 1940, when the Germany Army returned to occupy Northern France. Amongst its senior officers was Godefroy Hermann Von Mumm who, on October 27th that year, marched into G. H. Mumm's Paris office, announced his name, told the directors they were no longer needed and restored the ownership of the large Champagne house to his German family. For nearly 4 years it remained under its control until the Allies approached the limits of the city of Reims. Then Godefroy Hermann Von Mumm said his brief farewell and G. H. Mumm returned to French hands.

Never Monsieur! Around 1979 the writer visited Chateau de la Guimonière, in the Chaume-Coteaux du Layon appellation in the heart of France's Anjou region, and met the elderly and charming Madame Doucet. During the course of conversation I asked her which vintage of their long-aging dessert wine she considered the greatest. She immediately responded with the most moving story.

She explained that in 1940 her family were given just 24 hours to flee south from the advancing *Bosch*. Her husband ordered them to pack their car as full as possible with clothing and essential items and said there was only room for one case of wine. *We just looked at each other and declared unanimously, the 1921*. Quite clearly it was the finest vintage she had drunk. She then related what had happened to each of the bottles.

The first was consumed 2 years later when her son was born. Then one was enjoyed following his baptism. The third and fourth honoured the birth and baptism of her daughter. The restoration of peace in 1945 saw another consumed. Years later when Madame Doucet's son married they opened one more, and similarly when the first grandchild was born and so on, until today only one bottle of that 1921 survives. *When will you drink that, Madame?* I enquired. *Never Monsieur, it will be buried with me when I die, because it is deserving of a higher place.*

The Secret of San Vittorio is an amusing film set during World War II and starred Anthony Quinn, Anna Magnani, Virna Lisi and Hardy Kruger. It told the story of how the humble inhabitants of an Italian village frantically hid their wine from the advancing Germany army. Quinn played the bungling mayor, who despite being scorned by his wife as an incompetent buffoon, rose to become the hero of the day. The film was based on a true account of around one million bottles being hidden by the villagers of San Vittorio in the famous Cinzano family cellars, where they were stacked behind false walls.

Champagne Führer When Germany occupied France with awesome speed in 1940, the German leaders realised that French wine was a particularly valuable asset, both in terms of money and morale. So they appointed special officers to control the trade and movement of goods in each of the major French wine regions. The individuals chosen had previously been the heads of German wine importing companies and so had many connections and knowledge in the relevant areas. These officers quickly became known as the weinführers.

Under the circumstances it appeared quite a sensible move, for everyone knew that the war wouldn't last for ever and that normal import trading would resume one day, so it would be wise to keep matters as cordial as possible. This attitude was fine in theory, until the Nazis started making ridiculous demands on the weinführers themselves.

As the German army rolled into the Champagne region the Wehrmacht had appointed one Otto Klaebisch to take full control of the entire Champagne production. Prior to World War II he had been the general manager of Matteus-Müller, a German wine company that specialised in producing inexpensive sparkling wine known as sekt. The firm had also imported various Champagnes from France.

His task as *Champagne Führer* was to ensure that not a single bottle moved out of any Champagne house without his approval. Initially progress was fair but gradually the demands from Berlin became more and more extortionate. At one stage Klaebisch was expected to find 2 million bottles a month. With horses and tractors requisitioned and agricultural supplies virtually non-existent, plus appalling weather, production had dropped drastically. This meant many of the Champagne houses had to supply inferior wines, and complaints from the *Fatherland* pushed Klaebisch into taking punitive action against the heads of some of the most famous houses.

It was later reported that, at one stage, Klaebisch thought he had a brainwave to overcome the supply and demand problem. He decided upon his own classification of the Champagne houses in order to help him meet the demands of the German forces. He gave instructions that Louis Roederer should be supplied to the most senior officers, and so on with the other houses, finishing with Moët for the most junior officers, and sparkling Saumur from the Loire Valley for the ranks.

In fairness to Moët et Chandon the demands placed upon them were absurd, as the house was required to supply about 10 per cent of all the Champagne needs of the Nazis. It is a matter of historical fact that the directors of the house acted with great courage and tenacity; several of them were imprisoned and even threatened with execution.

Otto Klaebisch was not a fanatical Nazi and most of the Champagne community realised that they were safer in his hands than in those of someone who didn't understand Champagne and held more extreme opinions. After the war he returned to his original role as a director of Matteus Müller and over the years welcomed many French wine producers to his home.

Chateau Palmer The illustrious Grand Cru Classé from Margaux in the Bordeaux region was named after a British general who served in the Napoleonic wars. Over a century later, during World War II, it was requisitioned as a German administration centre and anyone who searches through its unoccupied attic rooms can still find writing on the doors and walls in the German language. It is almost unbelievable to learn that from 1940-42, two Italian Jewish families comprising 4 adults and 3 children were hidden in a sealed section of some out-buildings, a mere 20 metres (65 ft) from the main headquarters of the German officers. Led by a Signor Montuori, who had been a successful wine broker in Trieste, they had fled westwards when Mussolini had implemented an anti-Semitic policy.

They had literally knocked on the door at Chateau Siran, one of several major Bordeaux chateaux owned by the Miaihle family, whom Signor Montuori had known for some years. War had still not been declared and as some vacant rooms were available in Chateau Palmer, which they also owned, the Miaihle family allowed the Montuori party to stay there. Quite a surreal situation developed as the summer of 1939 drifted into autumn and everyone waited for the official declaration of war. At Chateau Siran the Miaihles hosted regular musical soirées as Signor Montuori was a talented violinist, who had been a member of the Trieste Orchestra, and he would regularly play classical pieces accompanied by Madame Miaihle at the piano.

The inevitable happened and war was declared but for a long while it was called *the phoney war* because little or no action occurred. Eventually the German forces moved south through France and in summer 1940 the German army arrived in Bordeaux and began requisitioning chateaux to provide accommodation for their troops. The Miaihles, with the help of the Lardon family, quickly sealed off a section of outbuilding as a small secret apartment for the Italians and then camouflaged it by stacking wine bottles around it. Monsieur Lardon was the *regisseur*, or estate manager, at Chateau Palmer and his wife Madame Lardon was the *châtelaine*. During the next two years the Miaihles and Lardons were to risk their lives supplying food to the families through a small trap door.

As time elapsed, so fear for the safety of the Montuori party grew, as hundreds of Jews were being interned in a camp at Mérignac near the site of today's Bordeaux airport. In 1942 it was decided that an attempt must be made to smuggle them to another country where their safety would be guaranteed. Because of some Italian connections Signor Montuori nominated Argentina. After some weeks of preparation, the Miaihle family managed to obtain some forged German travel documents and the plan was finalised. Everything was timed for the end of the vintage in early October, when increased activity would not appear out of the ordinary. Edouard and Louis Miaihle drove two Renault cars, which had been converted to operating on charcoal due to the fuel shortage, and arrived at nightfall to collect the families and their meagre belongings, including the violin. First they drove them to Chateau Siran and then 200 kms (125 miles) to Bayonne near the Spanish border, where arrangements had been made to take them on board the very last ship to leave for South America until the resumption of peace. Quite how it all succeeded no-one will ever know but the bravery of the Miailhe and Lardon families was remarkable.

Joseph Camo was a mysterious American citizen of Turkish heritage, and is believed to have been an employee of the Taylor Fladgate Port house before being made a partner in 1808, at the time of Napoleon's invasion of Portugal. The English partners were unable to remain in the city of Porto because the French were expected at any moment and they feared imprisonment or worse. They surmised that because of an existing treaty between France and the United States, all Americans would be safe. They fled leaving Joseph Camo in charge.

Joseph put into effect a careful plan, devised by the London-based senior partner Francis Grey. He overcame many obstacles to hire 3 British trading ships, with the idea of placing the entire stocks of Taylor's Port on them, comprising over 700 pipes (barrels). The intention was to ship them to an assortment of harbours scattered around the British Isles, where they could be stored in the warehouses of local merchants. Everything was ready to proceed when freak weather conditions brought a heavy snowfall upstream on the River Douro. This following thaw was accompanied by torrential rain, causing the river to flood and subsequently the loading of the ships was delayed. In due course the water level fell and Camo had the cellarworkers roll the pipes down the cobbled roads on the Vila Nova de Gaia hillside to the quay, where they were hauled onto the ships. Unfortunately by then the infamous sand bar at the river entrance had become totally choked with debris. The plan seemed doomed, as the French Army under Marshall Soult was rapidly heading for Oporto and Camo decided the time had come for him to flee to Lisbon.

The arrival of the French saw the massacre of thousands of Portuguese. When the military occupied the city they must have viewed the prospect of capturing some 700 pipes of Port as an unexpected bonus. Then Lady Luck played her hand for Taylor Fladgate, for Soult's army was a land force and had no ships. The French officers, who no doubt included many gourmets and connoisseurs, could only gaze longingly across the Douro estuary at the 3 ships loaded with Port anchored just inside the sand bar, and know they were powerless to unload them. Several visits were made by individual officers, who hired Portuguese boatmen to row them across in little skiffs and no doubt they drank to their heart's content, but any attempt to return with a full pipe of Port would have sent the tiny vessels straight to the bottom.

Weeks later Porto was relieved by a British force under Sir Arthur Wellesly, (later the Duke of Wellington) and in due course Camo and the English partners returned, and normal trading resumed.

Wine for the French Army Since Napoleon Bonaparte insisted that French wine was essential for the good morale of his soldiers, it has been the order of the day – with one exception. In 1930 The French were governing The Lebanon under a mandate from The League of Nations (forerunner to the United Nations) during a time of economic hardship. This affected the shipment of French wine for the consumption of soldiers, with the result that supplies were minimal and of poor quality. It became such an issue that senior officers reported back to their French headquarters that there was likely to be a breakdown in discipline.

Consequently the French Government advertised a sizeable grant for any suitable person who would plant vineyards in The Lebanon and make wine to satisfy the palates of the French forces there. After many complications, a man called Gaston Hochar was chosen and with advice from the late Ronald Barton of Chateau Leoville Barton fame, he planted vineyards in the Bekaa Valley, which in due course produced the internationally acclaimed Chateau Musar. Ironically The French Army didn't encounter war in The Lebanon but long after it had gone, during the 1980s, the winery did lose 2 vintages because of fighting in the vicinity.

Grown at around 3,000 feet its unusual red blend of Cabernet Sauvignon, Syrah (Shiraz) and Cinsault has attracted friends in many lands and praise from many wine journalists.

Wynford Vaughan Thomas The late Welsh broadcaster first rose to international fame for his live World War II radio report, the first-ever in action, from an RAF bomber flying over Berlin on September 4th 1943. What is not so well-known is that he later held a less risky position as a Communications Officer for the Allied forces as they headed up the Rhône Saône Corridor bringing freedom to previously occupied towns and villages. Quite how he aspired to undertake this work when he was still serving as a BBC War Correspondent is not known. He told the writer about his experience in some detail during a long weekend's wine tasting at the BBC Entertainment Centre in Cardiff, Wales in 1981.

He related that the role involved dedicated work, returning some of the best-known wine communes in the world to their rightful owners. He even mentioned that arrangements had been made by the senior officers on both sides to avoid fighting in the finest Grand Cru vineyards of Burgundy. He specifically explained his preference amongst all dry whites, for Meursault, the famous White Burgundy. He recalled how some of the citizens of that town were so grateful to hear the official words of liberation from his lips, that he and his little group were immediately invited down into their cellars to celebrate. *We didn't see daylight for 3 days*, he claimed. It clearly was a marvellous party and perhaps it was understandable that he couldn't remember the names of the others present. *But that was nothing, after all we had stood on the balconies of the mairies of Châteauneuf-du-Pape, Hermitage and Ampuis (Côte Rotie) while I announced the official liberation of the vineyard towns*. What was extraordinary was that he remembered anything!

Monks, Popes & Wine

Following the crucifixion of Jesus Christ, the need for sacramental wine for celebrating the Eucharist grew steadily, as Christianity spread across the known world. Demand increased when The Roman Emperor Constantine adopted Christianity as the official religion of the Roman Empire in the 4th Century AD.

Over a thousand years later, when monks undertook sea voyages with explorers, the monastic orders began to ship their vine cuttings to the New World. Meanwhile, in Europe, monasteries amassed great wealth and extensive estates, on which they developed some of the finest vineyards.

MONKS

Benedictines The Benedictines are best remembered by the eponymous liqueur, despite the fact that they never actually produced Benedictine commercially. The drink was a blend, created in 1863 by Alexandre LeGrand, who came across an ancient recipe believed to have been formulated by the monk Dom Bernardo Vincelli in 1510.

However the order did play a major part in the development of sparkling wine. In 1531, the Benedictine monastery of Saint-Hilaire at Limoux produced the first bottle-fermented sparkling wine. It is highly likely that the methods used for its production were available to another Benedictine monk, the illustrious Dom Pérignon, who was born 108 years later. This in no way undermines the stature of the cellar master of the Abbey of Hautvillers, and the significance of the work he undertook in the late 17th century. Dom

Pérignon used new, reinforced glass bottles from London and new corks from Spain and Portugal, and tied the corks onto the bottles of wine to hold in the bubbles, and by so doing became the first person to control the bottling of Champagne. More importantly, he was an excellent taster and blender and much has been written of his selection of grapes, a procedure which has developed into an art in this current generation. He would walk through the vineyards collecting grapes from certain sections and leave them to ripen on a windowsill. Then he would re-taste them periodically. In this way his knowledge of the vineyards deepened and he could judge the overall progress of ripening more easily.

Carthusians The Carthusians, who founded la Grande Chartreuse near Grenoble in the French Alps in 1087 AD, have been best known for their Chartreuse liqueurs but they also have been active wine producers. They had a second main priory in Tarragona in north-east Spain where it is believed they first produced the now fashionable Priorato in the 12th century. Additionally the Carthusians invested in vineyards in the Bordeaux region, especially in Graves where the most reputable property was Chateau Carbonnieux.

In 1983, with the support of the Carthusians, the writer carried out some research at la Grande Chartreuse and was a little surprised to discover the wine drinking habits of the choir monks. These men lived in basic cells where they spent much of their time praying, often apparently for the rest of the world. They were served by other brothers, who brought them their meals, including their wine allowance of $1^{1}/_{2}$ litres a day!

Christian Brothers The Christian Brothers made a significant contribution to the development of California wine from 1882 until 1989. They were originally based in Martinez but moved to the Napa Valley during Prohibition in the 1920s when it was still permissible to make sacramental wines. Their cellar master Brother Timothy, who was a former Chemistry teacher, was an inspirational figure. Under his guidance their Mont La

Salle winery became a major player on the inter-national wine scene, and circa 1980 they owned or farmed around 2,500 acres, including many prime sites in the Napa Valley, making them the largest monastic wine producer the world has ever known.

It was with much sadness that in 1989 Napa residents and California wine lovers learned that they had sold their large winery to a British company and ceased all winemaking operations.

Cistercians The Cistercians once owned one of the most valuable vineyards on Earth – Clos de Vougeot in Burgundy, which is also the largest enclosed vineyard in France. Some claim that the order was the first to plant Chardonnay vines in the Chablis region, and it is true that at one time the whole Yonne region, surrounding and including Chablis, was predominantly a red wine area before Chardonnay suddenly appeared there in profusion.

The Cistercians were possibly at their strongest in Germany where the celebrated Kloster Erbach was the jewel in the crown of their holdings.

Franciscans The Franciscan order had consider-able influence on the early cultivation of vines in the Americas. They planted many of the first vineyards in South America in the middle of the 16th century and more specifically they were responsible for the first successful vineyard on the mainland of today's United States, at Senecu, New Mexico in 1629.

Their most memorable achievement was the planting of vineyards to accompany the 22 missions they settled from San Diego to Sonoma between 1777 and 1823. There were 3 principle reasons for their activity: first they wanted to make sacramental wine for the Eucharist, second they could not always trust the quality of local water supplies and so consumed wine instead, and finally if they produced any surplus they could sell it locally to help support their monastic community. They usually planted grape seeds rather than vine cuttings and taught native American Indians how to cultivate the new vines as they grew.

Kerikeri New Zealand The Rev Samuel Marsden planted the first experimental vineyard, with many different varietals, at Kerikeri on the North Island of New Zealand in 1819. He had been sent there as an Anglican missionary to a scattering of Europeans and Maoris. Previously he had served as a padre to the convict population at Botany Bay in New South Wales where wine was less available.

Jesuits The Jesuits seem to have been less prominent than some orders in the development of wine, their influence being largely confined to South America. In Argentina the Jesuit Father Cedron planted the first vineyard at Coyo in 1556. The order also pioneered vineyard plantings in Peru in the 17th century.

The most historic wine venture of the Jesuits was probably The Novitiate at Los Gatos, situated on the hills above the Santa Clara Valley of California. It produced sacramental and other wines for around 100 years. It was founded in 1886 when The Jesuit Order constructed a training college there for novices. They purchased 40 acres of existing vineyards and built a traditional 3-storey winery, which operated by gravity. The winery was built into the hillside, allowing grapes for pressing to be delivered on the top floor from the rear of the building. The new wine was fermented on the second floor and put into barrels and bottles on the third floor, which had ground access from the front elevation. The Novitiate is probably best remembered for Angelica, a fortified wine, and for the sacramental wine it sold to churches in San Francisco and elsewhere. The winery also produced some table wines from Pinot Blanc, Cabernet Sauvignon, Mataro and Grenache.

Married millionaire One of the most beloved Napa Valley winemaking characters was Justin Meyer, who died in August 2002 aged 63. Famed for his development of Silver Oak Cellars, Justin was born Raymond Meyer, the son of a Bakersfield railroad worker. He became a Christian Brother, taking the name Brother Justin and beginning his service as a schoolteacher in the California State capitol of Sacramento. In 1964 he was sent to the order's Napa valley winery to assist Brother Timothy. Doubtful that he was suitable for the role, he found himself inspired by the cellar master. Subsequently he attended the University of California, Davis where he mastered in viticulture before returning to the Christian Brothers winery.

The Sacramento Bee in its obituary wrote *in 1972, he left the order. He married Bonny, whom he had met at UCD, and teamed with Raymond Duncan, a businessman, to launch Silver Oak*. At the time he was penniless but he met the ideal partner in Duncan who was a Denver oil multi-millionaire with a dream of making great wine.

In 2000 Justin Meyer sold his share to his partner for $120 million and began a new project to make Port-style wines under the Meyer Family name. The same newspaper reported that prior to that sale *he was already a very wealthy man, thanks to investments in oil, a ski resort and a buffalo ranch*. He was remembered with many fond tributes.

Saint Martin of Tours This colourful individual lived from 316–397 AD, at the time when the Roman Empire was adopting Christianity. He played a major role in spreading the cultivation of church-owned vineyards. It is difficult to prove but it seems likely that he was responsible for much of the development of viticulture from the Loire Valley to the River Mosel.

A 596 AD document, housed in the museum of Trier in the Mosel Valley, confirms the ownership of The Josephshofer vineyard by the order of Martinshofer. This is possibly the earliest-known evidence of the winemaking activities of a monastic order.

Zarephath This is one of the very rare instances of a relatively new monastic vineyard, founded in 1994, at East Porongurup, in the Great Southern region of Western Australia. It is owned by a Benedictine community known as the Brothers and Sisters of the Christ Circle and its wines are available for sale. The name derives from a town mentioned twice in The Bible. Its most important role was as a marker for the northern limits of Israel in the time of Obadiah the prophet. The First Book of Kings also describes it as being a place in Sidon, one of the Phoenician ports.

POPES

John Paul II Unlike many of his predecessors Pope John Paul has always shown himself to be a man of simple tastes. When in Rome he regularly enjoys a glass or two of basic dry white wine, but much prefers to slake his thirst on a well-chilled Polish beer.

Leo IX Leo IX was elected Pope in 1048. He was raised in the Alsace wine village of Eguisheim and was probably responsible for the introduction of the first dry white French wines to the Vatican. His dedication in bringing their local wine to fame was so appreciated by the villagers that to this day the name Leo is extremely popular there.

Whilst accurate records on the subject are difficult to find, it is believed that almost always it had been the practice of the Papacy to use red wine for the Communion chalice, unless only white was available.

Papal supermarket For those minions of the Vatican who are on the actual payroll but don't aspire to the Papacy or role of Cardinal, a wide selection of Italian wine is available in the Holy See's supermarket within the bounds of the Vatican City. Better still, Papal discounts are given for slower moving wines. Unfortunately being a mere Catholic doesn't entitle one to shop there; proof of Vatican residency is required.

Pincerna From roughly the 13th-18th centuries the *pincerna* held a unique job in the Vatican. He was the official taster, both at masses conducted by the Pope and at other celebrations where the Pope was present. His role was not to judge the wines consumed but to protect the Pope from being poisoned. In other words if he didn't collapse in agony, then the Pontiff could proceed with the celebration of mass or drinking his wine at a dinner. Many may have feared accepting the responsibility but no record exists of any *pincerna* ever suffering any ill effects.

Pope Clement V Pope Clement V, formerly known as Bernard de Got and Archbishop of Bordeaux deserves a double entry in this chapter. In 1300 AD, whilst Archbishop, he received a donation to the church from his brother, and invested it in what became known as the first-ever Bordeaux wine chateau. Situated in Pessac in the Graves region, it was later named Chateau Pape-Clement.

At the beginning of the 14th century there was a schism in the Catholic Church, known as *The Babylonian Exile* and a second papacy was declared at Avignon. In 1310 Bertrand de Got was appointed Pope Clement V at Avignon and was apparently urged to select a site for a papal summer palace. Having already been attracted by one wine chateau he now searched for suitable land for another. Observing that the gravel on the surface of the soil at the first property absorbed the heat of the sun by day and reflected it back over the vines by night, thereby encouraging further growth, he looked for similar possibilities near Avignon. It might be logical to anticipate his choosing a cooler location than the steamy southern Rhône Valley, but land near Orange was his preference, because it was covered by a bed of smooth pebbles. These were left from a prehistoric inland sea and would provide even more support for a vineyard, especially one that was expected to grow red grapes.

Unfortunately Pope Clement died in 1314 and the benefits of the *Chateauneuf-du-Pape* or *New Castle of the Pope* were passed to his successor John XXII who didn't really show much interest. It was left to Clement VI, who succeeded in 1342, to proclaim the wine from the vineyard outstanding. He was a Frenchman who also appreciated Chianti and knew a good wine when he tasted it.

Urban VII Urban VII, not to be confused with the third century martyred Pope and Saint Urban, was a contradiction in wine terms. During his papacy from 1623-1644 he regularly encouraged public celebration by having the fountains of Rome filled with wine. However he countered this apparent generosity by taxing the population for its consumption.

Wine Celebrities

Fidel Castro One of the highlights of the Cuban dictator's trip to Portugal in October 1998 was a visit to Taylor Fladgate & Yeatman, widely acknowledged as being the Rolls Royce of Port houses. Adrian Bridge, then Marketing, now Managing Director escorted him around the premises. At one stage a brief explanation was given of how neutral brandy is added after 3 days of fermentation, thus retaining 50 per cent of the natural grape sugar. Castro became quite animated, assuming he had found a new market for Cuban cane sugar. Fortuitously, another member of the party, King Juan Carlos of Spain, offered his services as an interpreter and explained that only naturally residual sugar from the grapes is permitted.

Gérard Depardieu The internationally acclaimed film star has been a wine lover for most of his life and is reputedly the owner of 3 superb private cellars. One of these is said to contain the finest existing collection of Chateauneuf-du-Pape. When Gérard became a movie legend with his inspired performance as Cyrano de Bergerac, the wine authorities of the town quickly made him a proposition to officially endorse their wines, by offering him his own vineyard in the Bergerac region as remuneration. They must have been a little disappointed when he declined saying that he already owned a fine vineyard in the Loire Valley. He was referring to Chateau de Tigné his property in the Anjou appellation, which he purchased in 1982 and which covers some 90 hectares (225 acres). He also owns part shares in Chateau Gadet in Bordeaux, as well as Domaine Alain Paret in Condrieu, and is currently interested in starting a winery in the Languedoc region.

Queen Elizabeth The Queen Mother Her late Royal Majesty was reputed to enjoy a little tipple and her 101-year life span suggests she thrived on her favourite drinks. According to the UK wine trade there were several of these. For many years it was the general opinion that she enjoyed a large glass of Sandeman Royal Corregidor Sherry before lunch, whilst others declared that she always partook of a couple of drams of J&B Rare Scotch Whisky after her meal. To add to the list some courtiers confided that her preference was for Dubonnet Vermouth and others for Gin. Perhaps the most extreme claim came from a broadcast journalist, who when reflecting upon her life, advised that *The Queen Mother always kept US$150,000 (£100,000) worth of Champagne Veuve Clicquot in her cellar*. The statement was quickly denied by the Champagne house's agent but it did admit that Veuve Clicquot produced a special sweeter cuvée (blend) exclusively for the Queen Mother, called *Rich England*. After all she was quite a rich *veuve* (widow) herself.

Mark Inglis The head winemaker at the Montana Brancott winery in the Marlborough region of New Zealand may not be well known outside the country. Nevertheless he deserves celebrity status for the extraordinary feat of courage, fortitude and resilience that he demonstrated on January 7th 2002, let alone for the determination displayed during his normal everyday working life. On the day in question he succeeded in reaching the 3,764 metres (12,320 feet) summit of New Zealand's highest peak, Mount Cook, on prosthetic limbs, 19 years after he lost both his legs to frostbite on the very same mountain. He is reported to have commented that he had returned to finish what he had started.

Sam Neill The Kiwi film star of *Jurassic Park* fame is the head of his family-owned Two Paddocks Vineyards, which was founded in 1993 on the South Island of New Zealand. It is situated at the eastern end of the Gibbston Valley in Central Otago, which is the most southerly wine region on Earth. The family also owns another, smaller vineyard, called Alex Paddocks at Alexandra above the Earnsleugh Valley, which was planted in 1998. Working in vineyards that have magnificent backdrops of snow-capped mountains, they are already achieving some encouraging results with Pinot Noir.

Cliff Richard, that boyish 60 something year old English pop star, may have surprised some of his fellow Evangelical Christians when he launched the first release of his Quinta do Moinho red wine with the 2001 vintage. The vineyard is situated in Portugal's Algarve holiday region. With the help of Australian winemaker David Baverstock, who has worked in Portugal for many years, Sir Cliff is producing a blend of 50 per cent Aragonez and 50 per cent Shiraz. Fans swooped to purchase bottles immediately the wine was put on sale.

Apparently in the days before his knighthood, Sir Cliff had been inspired by a visit he made to Hardy's vineyards in McLaren Vale, South Australia.

Greg Norman has an appealing range of wines, which was launched in 1999 in partnership with Beringer Blass. The wine company says that Greg Norman and chief winemaker Chris Hatcher personally select the wines from the various wineries belonging to Beringer Blass. There has been widespread recognition in the Wine Industry that Greg is playing more than a sleeping partner role.

Of course the arrangement has led to a variety of jokes, such as which wine goes best with white shark?

Francis Ford Coppola The famous Hollywood film director has been gradually adding to his vineyard in the heart of the Napa Valley since 1975 and he claims it is the largest single estate for fine wine in the United States. Known as the Niebaum-Coppola estate, it has gained a justifiable reputation for some excellent red wines with good aging potential. With some satisfaction he tells friends that his most significant vineyard purchases were acquired with his profits from Bram Stoker's Dracula, a fact he remembers by hanging a portrait of that evil character in the hallway of his Napa home.

Sir Winston Churchill The great British wartime Premier was a man who took much pleasure in fine wines and several claims have been made about his favourite selections. His family has made it abundantly clear that Champagne Pol Roger was his first choice and in 1984 members of the family were present at Blenheim Palace for the launch of The Sir Winston Churchill Special Cuvée, as the prestige label of the house.

There is a charming story about a time when Sir Winston made a visit to the Pol Roger mansion, where he was entertained by head of the house, Odette Pol-Roger. It is reported that he complained to her about the nagging of his American wife, Clementine. Sir Winston loved to drink Pol Roger for breakfast but Clemmie insisted a whole bottle was excessive. He, on the contrary, considered a half bottle too small, so they compromised and he drank the Champagne in pints, a bottle size which is no longer available, but which was provided for him by Pol Roger. Sir Winston lived until he was 91.

Shane Warne American and Canadian readers of this book are likely to say Shane who? without realising that they are talking about one of history's all-time greatest sportsmen. In cricket terms Shane Warne ranks with baseball master Roger Clemens and basketball legend Michael Jordan. He is the greatest bowler of leg-breaks, googlies and flippers the cricket fields of the world have ever known. His record number of over 400 Test cricket dismissals speaks for itself.

Shane also has a reputation as a gourmand and the need to watch his waistline, hence his decision to market two dry wines. In 2002 he launched the little-known Zilzie Wines from Victoria. Reports spread rapidly that Shane's signature on the labels had sent sales soaring. The Chardonnay was described by one wine journalist as *doing a little through the air* and the

Shiraz as *plum LBW* and one UK publication wrote that his wine will carry a *loud appeal*. None of the comments were intended as back of the hand compliments.

Fess Parker Long time retired film star and TV actor Fess Parker owns a popular 285-hectare (714-acre) vineyard and ranch in California's Santa Barbara region. Famed for his heroic roles as Davy Crockett and Daniel Boone, he saw no frontiers to a late career in wine. His enterprise has become a serious operation under the guidance of top winemaking consultant Jed Steele, with its Chardonnay and Syrah (Shiraz) winning plaudits. Fess Parker Winery must be one of the most profitable as well, as tourists arrive *en masse* and leave with cases of wine and bags full of raccoon skin hats.

Dom Pérignon, the celebration of Champagne In the early 20th century the combination of the Temperance Movement, American Prohibition and the loss of its biggest-ever export market of Tsarist Russia, caused a devastating drop in Champagne sales. By 1931 matters were desperate. Many houses had seen their export sales dip by around 80 per cent and so a committee was formed to take some radical action. Headed by the mayors of Épernay and Hautvillers and the deputy-mayor of Reims it anxiously sought new ideas. The suggestion was put forward that 1932 would be the 250th anniversary of Dom Pérignon's invention of sparkling wine. Hence it was decided that this would be the ideal platform for publicising the King of Wines. (See **Benedictines** in Monks, Popes and Wine.)

The event, scheduled for Tuesday June 28th 1932, drew journalists and politicians from several neighbouring countries. Also the famous newsreel cameras of the era filmed the proceedings which began with the Archbishop of Reims blessing the statue of Dom Pérignon.

This was followed by a superb outdoor lunch with numerous tables spread amidst the mulberry trees of the Abbey of Hautvillers. Each was headed by a director of one of the Champagne houses and a point was made of pouring the Champagnes of many different houses at every table. A London journalist commented that on one table, hosted by a director of Champagne Louis Roederer, Heidsieck (both Piper and Charles), Mumm, Ruinart, Pommery, and more Roederer were poured.

British MPs were sent invitations which announced *arrangements have been made for a special fleet of Air Liners to convey guests to Reims on the morning of Tuesday, June 28th, returning to London the same evening*. An addendum read *N.B. Breakfast will be served from 7.30am at the Dorchester Hotel, Park Lane, W.1, and cars will leave for Croydon Aerodrome punctually at 8.15am*. The MPs, various members of the House of Lords and an assortment of journalists flew to Reims where they were conveyed by pony and trap to Hautvillers for the celebrations. The itinerary included the drive from the airport through the woods and vineyards, the crowning of the Princess of Champagne, the luncheon itself, the return horse-driven journey and the flight back to Croydon. Just before take-off the plane was filled with numerous ready chilled bottles of Champagne and glasses. Understandably several honourable gentlemen appeared to have lost their passports on arrival in England.

The event was a great success. Newsreels of it were shown all over Europe and the United States, the newspapers provided extensive coverage and questions were even asked by sober politicians in the House of Commons, demanding what could be done to help our struggling Champagne friends in France. It is a historical fact that from that date Champagne sales made a recovery, but would that have happened if God had not blessed everyone with a dry, sunny day.

Perry Mason – the cases he lost Millions will recall hours spent watching the television character of Perry Mason, the brilliant defence lawyer who never lost a case. Played by Raymond Burr, the series became the subject of daily conversation around the globe and Raymond, a confirmed gourmet with a great love of fine wine, amassed a sizeable bank account. In the 1980s he used some of his profits to invest in a vineyard partnership in California's Dry Creek Valley. Sadly he died shortly before the first (1990) wines were ready for release and never really knew how good they were.

Thomas Jefferson - the sad truth Stories about the historic figure of Thomas Jefferson and wine are never ending. It is a fact that he loved the subject and studied it with a relish. Indeed he was able to take advantage of his privileged position as the United States first-ever Ambassador to France to research the wines of Bordeaux in some depth and was made welcome at many of the top chateaux. He purchased the finest wines and shipped them home to age in his Monticello cellar and his name was usually stencilled onto the bottles with white paint.

One such 1787 Chateau Lafite was auctioned for a world record price, exactly 200 years later in 1987, when the late multi-millionaire Malcolm Forbes, then owner of Forbes magazine, paid US$187,000 (£105,000) for it. (Information courtesy of Christie's, London, England)

Being a generous man Forbes kindly loaned the bottle to a friend, the owner of a New York City wine shop. It was to be put on display under lock and key. The inevitable happened when an important customer entered the shop. The owner gave in to temptation, opened the display cabinet, lifted the bottle and walked across the floor to show it to his customer and tripped, dropping the bottle, which smashed into various segments. An anonymous report of the incident tells of sales assistants racing forward with coffee spoons to try and taste the few remaining drops but alas too late, for the world record price Lafite had obviously been oxidised for many years.

Regrettably details of the telephone conversation between the shop owner and Malcolm Forbes were not recorded.

Ferruccio Lamborghini The late Ferruccio Lamborghini first made his name piecing together tractors from scrap metal with his bare hands. Immediately after the Second World War components were simply not available, so Ferruccio created his own solution. He scoured the battlefields of central Italy for abandoned tanks and military vehicles to find the scrap metal items he needed. Weeks were spent constructing each tractor, which he would proudly drive into the local square on market day and offer for sale. From this humble start he developed the most prestigious tractor company and subsequently became the producer of one of the most illustrious makes of sports cars. When eventually Ingegnere (Engineer) Lamborghini, as he liked to be called, sold his businesses he retired to Lake Trasimeno in Umbria, where he planted some 120 hectares (300 acres) of vines and made an agreeable red Torgiano wine. Yet wine never really became the central focus of his life. Instead he kept a collection of his beloved tractors and simply enjoyed spending hours tinkering with them.

Following his death in 1993 the wine estate passed to his daughter Patrizia, who has achieved excellent results and has transformed the quality and character of the wines. She hired leading winemaker Dr. Ricardo Cotarella and under his influence Lamborghini Campoleone Rosso (50 per cent Merlot and 50 per cent Sangiovese) has been consistently winning plaudits from the international media. Ingegnere would have been proud of the results.

Flying Wine Men

There are many examples of winery owners or senior personnel having small planes or executive jets but the following are some of the more unusual connections between flying and wine.

Pelee Island icewine pickers The Pelee Island Winery buildings are actually situated at Kingsville, Ontario on the north coast of Lake Erie in the most southerly wine region on the Canadian mainland. Its name derives from vineyards it owns on Pelee Island around 40 kms (25 miles) further south, in the middle of the lake. The winery produces some outstanding Icewine for which it uses only grapes that are picked manually, when frozen by nature to a minimum temperature of -8°C (17.6°F). Over the years winery president Walter Schmoranz has found that all the experienced pickers – whom he prefers – live on the mainland. So at the appropriate time, he flies teams of pickers to the island in the middle of the night.

Flying Winemakers Flying Winemakers have been active for around twenty years. Names like Kym Milne, Peter Bright, John Worontscheck and Gerd Stepp have regularly appeared on the back labels of wines from an assortment of countries. They could be described as first generation flying winemakers. Today they have been succeeded by a second generation, with names too numerous to list. The term encompasses both men and women, with a multitude of winemaking talents, who share their expertise and experience within developing wine regions/countries and with long-established wineries wishing to adopt new styles. Australians can be found working in France, New Zealanders in Romania, French in South Africa, Germans in Italy and Californians in Chile.

Sometimes Flying Winemakers arrive shortly before the harvest, to ensure only the ripest, healthiest grapes are picked, then supervise the winemaking and selection of barrels or other storage, before flying out again. Experienced professionals are usually able to arrange their schedules to permit them to visit wineries and vineyards several times a year, in order to oversee the entire winemaking cycle. Probably the best-known example is Michel Rolland of France, who has literally turned his winery employers around the world into fans of his winemaking skills.

Flying Wine Man A nickname given to the author in 1984, live on WAVE-FM by the former Louisville, Kentucky radio host Rick George. Rick explained that the Galloping Gourmet Graham Kerr had just appeared on the show as a guest, and suggested the Flying Wine Man as a suitable title for my lifestyle as an itinerant wine journalist. His description is certainly more memorable than Andrew Jones and helps to demonstrate that I am not going to be snobbish about wine; it also gains me a little recognition.

It was definitely more helpful than the error made by the Internet service of Barnes & Noble, the giant US book retailer. It published a biography to accompany my *Wine Talk* book and described me as a long-time retired former US Air Force pilot, who had served in World War II and who wrote books on DIY. My wife can assure readers that I have expertise in neither direction.

Ed King Junior, the octogenarian President of King Estate in Oregon, is an excellent example of the great American success story. His parents were sharecroppers, on a farm just outside Dodge City, Kansas, who survived the terrible dust-bowl days of the 1930s.

From a tender age he would ride on horseback to a wooden two-roomed school at nearby Laurel. He proved an exceptional pupil and later entered Kansas State University, where he studied aeronautical engineering. In the years that followed he developed great expertise in aircraft radio equipment. In 1959 he founded the King Radio company which became synonymous with small aircraft communications. He was already a qualified pilot and soon gained his *jet rating*. At peak production he employed some 4,000 people.

In 1985 he sold his company *for a fortune* and invested in his own private jet but leisure soon became tedious to a man who had been so active. Subsequently when his son Ed King III called him to say that he and a colleague had purchased some vineyard blocks in Southern Oregon, Ed King Junior simply said *let's start a winery*, which is exactly what the father and son partnership did. They founded the largest winery in the state and constructed the buildings *to last 150 years*. Although Ed no longer takes the controls of a plane, he still amasses thousands of miles a year, not exhibiting his famous radio equipment but marketing their stylish King Estate Pinot Gris and enchanting Pinot Noir.

Dave & Holly Nelson The most rewarding achievement for this husband and wife team was to learn that their Nelson Estate Merlot had been selected for the first-class service of Northwest Airlines. Their satisfaction was justified by Dave's previous career as a Northwest pilot and Holly's continuing work as a flight attendant for the famous airline. Of course the obvious happened when, on a trip to Hawaii, Captain Dave had flirted with his pretty young colleague. The romance was continued later over a bottle of wine and both realised that the subject was a mutual interest. Twenty years later their Sonoma wine label has developed a reputation as a high flier for Merlot, Cabernet Franc and Chardonnay.

Mercier balloon In 1880 the French Champagne house Mercier decided to undertake a little novel promotion of its brand in central Paris. Eugène Mercier personally organised a tempting offer to consumers, but no-one could have predicted the unusual turn of events.

Mercier hired a hot-air balloon and a pilot, and tethered it by rope to a fence near the Eiffel Tower. Passers-by were offered a complimentary glass of Mercier Champagne if they would step into the balloon's basket. The promotion proceeded for several days without any problems, but then one morning when the basket was filled to capacity the unpredictable happened. A gale arose and a strong gust of wind snapped the mooring, leaving an astonished pilot, nine passengers and a waiter rising helplessly into the air. Skimming the rooftops the balloon hurtled east soon leaving the Paris suburbs behind and heading for the Champagne region. It gained in altitude and speed as it continued its flight before landing intact 16 hours later in the Alsace region, which was then annexed to Germany. The bewildered occupants had one more shock to suffer when they found themselves surrounded by police who threatened them with prosecution as illegal immigrants. Fortunately, the charge could not be justified and the only action taken was fining Champagne Mercier 20 crowns for failing to declare 6 untouched bottles that were found on board the balloon.

The story made headlines around the world and Eugène Mercier claimed it was the cheapest publicity he had ever gained, costing *less than a centime a line*.

Montgolfier brothers Joseph and Jacques Montgolfier, who invented the hot-air balloon, were two of sixteen children from a family of paper-makers in the small town of Annonay near Lyons in eastern France. Apparently their idea arose from a discussion they had about one of their brothers' shirts billowing as it dried in front of a furnace. In 1783 they demonstrated the world's first hot-air balloon which reached a height of around 2,000 metres (approx. 6,500 feet). Inevitably the balloon lost its impetus and fell to earth in a Burgundy vineyard. Subsequently more than one village in Burgundy has *a rue Montgolfier* and claims that it landed in their vineyard appellation.

Wine & Animals

Baboons-Remedy A South Africa has a problem with sweet-toothed baboons decimating some of its finest vineyards. They can inflict so much damage that some growers have resorted to extreme measures to rid themselves of the creatures.

At Tulbagh in the Western Cape, one of the oldest wineries called Twee Jonge Gezellen has a policy of planting the Pontac variety in the first 2 rows of the vineyard, where it borders the Veldt (wild mountainous area). Unlike the classic red grape varieties, such as Cabernet, Merlot, Pinotage and Shiraz, which have red skin and white flesh, Pontac has red skin and red flesh. For that very reason it is banned from wine production in many regions, as it can be used to artificially enhance the depth of colour in a red wine. The Tulbagh growers only plant the Pontac to deter the baboons.

In the dry season the baboons descend into the valleys intent on enjoying the crop, so the farmers entice them with succulent red bunches of Pontac. Being naturally lazy, the animals gather the first healthy fruit they notice. Screeching with happiness they tear the grapes with their hands only to recoil with horror, mistaking the red juice from the Pontac grapes for blood, and run screaming back into the hills.

Baboons-Remedy B In the 90s, just after Nelson Mandela became President, one South African winery whose name begins with the letter V, developed another tactic. In view of the fact that it was situated in one of the only regions to retain the old-style white nationalist rule, its methods might be seen as ironic.

The owners of the winery were so frustrated by one particular family of baboons stealing their healthiest grapes, that they held a conference to plot their downfall. Hampered by the animals being a protected species, they literally took the law into their own hands. One morning a team of men, carefully camouflaged, lay in wait for the anticipated return of the baboons. They took great care to surround the baby of the family and then charged forward noisily, scaring off the rest of the animals. Netting the small creature they roped it towards them. Out came their brushes and they simply painted it white *from head to toe* and then released it. Several years later they claimed not to have seen another single baboon.

Bears, mountain lions and moose For first-time visitors, walking through the magnificent parks and forests of the Rocky Mountains in Colorado can be quite an experience, especially when coming across a notice which advises how to react when confronted by a bear. After all it is quite a relief to learn that if a bear attacks, always fight back, because this often startles the creature and it might well run away. So it is not surprising that the Terror Creek winery in Paonia, with the highest altitude vineyard in North America at 1,969 metres (6,400 feet), finds it a little difficult to recruit pickers at harvest time. For not only do the local bears love rich, ripe grapes but so do the mountain lions and occasional giant moose that comes loping in for a feed.

Proprietors John and Joan Matthewson have retaliated by constructing a wire cage, which covers the entire vineyard and allows the pickers to work safely inside the mesh while the animals hopefully, remain outside.

Other unpopular animals Amongst other large animal pests in vineyards are kangaroos. Ten years ago some growers in Padthaway, South Australia became so harassed by kangaroos posing a danger to traffic on the main road running through the middle of the vineyard region, that they attempted to solve the problem in a simple way. They set up feeding points for them in the centre of the vineyards and treated them like pets. Apparently the accident rates reduced dramatically.

Parrots are both hated and loved. Hated because of the grapes they plunder, and loved because some say their droppings make an ideal fertiliser.

Growers in some of the less populated states in America have problems with wild turkeys eating their fill of the ripest grapes. Sometimes this doesn't prove too much of a problem in *huntin' and shootin'* country and it is rumoured that wild turkey stuffed with Riesling makes the tastiest dish.

No pest has caused more devastation than *phylloxera vastatrix* the tiny aphid, which first threatened the existence of the European vineyards during the 19th century. Only two wine producing countries are phylloxera free; Chile because the aphid cannot cross the Andes and the island of Cyprus because it cannot survive lengthy journeys over the sea.

Bye Bye Fuddle Duck Situated in a location that has been called *the most northerly desert in the world*, the Mission Hill winery in the Okanagan Valley of British Columbia has an exemplary reputation for international class wines. It has won medals in many countries and in 2001 it was named Canadian Winery of the Year. A complete reversal of the situation when owner Anthony Von Mandl and his family purchased the winery in 1981. At the time it was better known for its down-market labels *Fuddle Duck* and *Hot Goose*. Anthony quickly removed them from *the menu* and began serious work. Mission Hill surprised the judges when it won a gold medal in the 2002 *Chardonnay du Monde* competition in Burgundy, France with its Reserve Chardonnay icewine.

Exploding bunny The vineyards of Central Otago are the most southerly in the world, and certainly amongst the most beautiful, with many stunning mountain backdrops. They are also home to some serious rabbit problems which cost vineyard owners both time and money. In 2002 one anonymous grower became so irritated by these hopping pests that his fiery temperament could take no more. With a little careful planning he trapped a rabbit, tied a stick of gelignite to it and lit the fuse, before releasing the alarmed animal into the entrance of the warren. To his astonishment the rabbit raced out of another exit and headed straight for shelter underneath the grower's brand new, four wheel drive vehicle. The result was a draw, or if you prefer a loss to both sides. The poor rabbit was ready only for a casserole and the rear of the vehicle had been blown to smithereens.

Moscato Curioso Lou Preston, owner of Preston Vineyards in the Dry Creek Valley of California's Sonoma region is one of those enterprising wine producers who is prepared to experiment. On one occasion when he decided to grow some Muscat vines it took a little time to find the style his customers preferred. Being a lover of French wines he started with an Alsace-style *Muscat* that was not bone dry but his supporters were not impressed. Next he tried a *full-bodied creamy sweet late harvest dessert wine à la Muscat de Beaumes de Venise*. This is a popular fortified wine from France's southern Rhône Valley. This second Preston Muscat did not find many takers either. His philosophy then crossed the border from France into Italy as he developed a slightly frothing, aromatic medium-sweet fizz and it virtually walked out through the door.

The reason for the transformation was down to a little *cat marketing*. He hired artist Dian Zepeda to create a poster that *played up the seductive quality of Muscat*. The result was a cat design, which became the label of his new wine style known as *Moscato Curioso*. The word quickly spread amongst the feline lovers of Sonoma and these days a regular sight at Preston Vineyards is a line of cat owners come to replenish their supplies.

Champagne mice Images of giant mice pouring magnums of Charles Heidsieck down their throats are slightly exaggerated, but it is a matter of historic fact that for more than 100 years mice were responsible for ruining much good Champagne. However even their misdemeanours were the catalyst for an advance in cellar management.

From the time of Dom Pérignon in the late 17th century until the early 19th century mice in Champagne cellars were a real nuisance. In those days the corks were secured by tying them onto the bottles with string, and the mice, tempted by dried spillage on the string, would nibble through it and cause the bottles to pop open. Eventually this resulted in the development of thin wire cages to secure corks – a practice still in use today.

Quiltro Quiltro is the name given to wild street dogs in Chile, those snarling, sniffing animals that survive on anything they can steal or scrounge. Three vicious-looking barking street dogs adorn the Quiltro wine label of Chilean wine. *Wine scavengers* aka humans who look for the keenest bargains, can take their pick of Quiltro or Street Dog Chardonnay, Sauvignon Blanc, Merlot or Cabernet Sauvignon. The latter apparently goes extremely well with a T-bone steak.

Of course we should not forget the expression *every dog has his day* and Quiltro have introduced a premium level range of wines for such occasions, suitably named *Top Dog*.

Sherry mice The classic Sherry house of Gonzales Byass is famed for the quality of its wines and is also justifiably proud of its cellars. Indeed one of its prize exhibits is the now unused Eiffel bodega with its unique wrought iron framework. At the other end of the scale, and much humbler, for many years the house offered visitors a lunch-time mouse circus act.

In the early 1980s the foreman of one of its stone-built bodegas was an animal lover who gave in to temptation and fed crumbs from his sandwiches to a cellar mouse. Being sympathetic to the little creature, he also decided to treat it to a tiny glass of Sherry which the gastronomic rodent seemed to genuinely appreciate. Soon the small – but growing – mouse began to appear at noon each day for a repeat performance. So the foreman constructed a little stairs and taught the mouse to climb it to reach the lip of the glass. In due course the mid-day act became an item on the visitors' tour, that is until someone brought their cat to work.

Stoffel the wine tasting dog Stoffel, a Jack Russell and Bull Terrier crossbreed, is the pet dog of Frans Smit, head winemaker at the historic Spier Estate near the South African city of Stellenbosch. Since he was a puppy, Frans has taken Stoffel to work with him every day at the main Spier cellars, and so this canine oenophile has developed a love of wine from his earliest years. Stoffel begins the morning relaxing in the open rear section of Frans' 4 x 4 but the moment tasting time arrives a familiar whistle brings him briskly to his master's side. Whenever Frans spits out a sample or empties a glass Stoffel simply snaps up the wine before it hits the ground. Unfortunately he has become a trifle elitist and no longer shows any interest in white wines but merely devours every available drop of red before he returns to the 4 x 4 for a little snooze.

Wild boars of Tuchan The French word *terroir* implies a combination of soil, micro-climate, geographical position, atmosphere and other local characteristics which make a vineyard and its wine individual. Few other vineyards can be blessed with such an unusual local influence than the one responsible for a tasty, full-bodied red known as Terroir de Tuchan. The wine is made by the co-operative at Mont Tauch in the Fitou appellation in southern France, who cheerfully outwit their foes – the wild boars of Tuchan – which live alongside the vineyard in the biggest natural reserve for their species in France. Curiously the *sangliers* or wild boar are not over enthusiastic about eating the grapes. They prefer to roll on their backs and scratch themselves against the vines subsequently flattening the vineyards. So the co-operative has adapted an electric cattle fence by lowering it and using it to keep animals out, rather than in! Apparently, if any of the beasts do break into the vineyard, local growers consider the most satisfying response to be wild boar stuffed with grapes and washed down with Terroir de Tuchan.

Wine & Art

Almost free Rembrandt In November 2000 Rembrandt paintings worth US$25 million were stolen from a Scandinavian museum in a well-planned operation. Detectives investigating the case could immediately deduce that the thieves were probably not lovers of the most successful Rioja Gran Reserva from Spain, because the top-rated house of Faustino has reproduced an authentic Rembrandt on the label of its Faustino I Gran Reserva for over a century. It is a 1641 portrait of Nicholas Van Rimbeek, a Dutch wine merchant. Instead of risking lengthy imprisonment the criminals could have just purchased a few cases and had Rembrandts wherever they looked.

Champagne Perrier-Jouët One of the best-known examples of wine art is the ornate flower bottle which holds the house's delicious prestige blend. It is generally known as the Belle Époque Cuvée but in the USA it is called Fleur de Champagne. Each bottle is hand decorated and baked in a small oven at a tiny glassworks in a suburb of Paris. The design was taken from an original magnum painted with white anemones, created for Perrier-Jouët by the celebrated Belle Époque artist Emile Gallé in 1902. Sadly it was smashed in a Paris street riot in 1968.

Frogs in Riesling is the title of a painting by John Olsen, reproduced on a Riesling label from Leeuwin Estate at Margaret River in Western Australia. It is an amusing, somewhat zany picture of a goggle-eyed frog, surrounded by frogspawn, swimming through Riesling. Leeuwin's Art Series covers 5 varietals: Chardonnay, Cabernet Sauvignon, Riesling, Pinot Noir and Sauvignon Blanc. It *represents Leeuwin's finest wines from each vintage.*

His Eminence's Choice One of the most colourful of traditional Old World labels is found on bottles of 10 Year Old Tawny Port from the distinguished house of Delaforce. Called *His Eminence's Choice* the label is a facsimile of an original oil painting by the Parisian artist Borion. It shows a Roman Catholic Cardinal raising a tempting glass of tawny Port to the light. Ironically Delaforce is an old Protestant family whose ancestors were Huguenot refugees, but the house is perfectly happy to show ecumenical sympathies by allowing Protestants to make the Port and Catholics to drink it.

Navarro Correas is a long-established Argentine wine house in the Mendoza region, founded in 1798. It has recently attracted compliments for the delectable Cabernet Sauvignon in its Coleccion Privada range. In fact the range could easily be re-named the house's *Art Collection*. For some 25 years Navarro Correas has sponsored talented Argentine artists to paint original works for use on its labels. The wine comes in a stylish, silvery gift can with the artwork for the current vintage on the front and from previous vintages on the back. The 2000 vintage shows the Ombu tree painted by Garcia Uriburu. This highly unusual tree, which thrives in the pampas grass, may well be the only one in the world that grows five trunks.

Missing season In 1979 the Etchart winery in Cafayate, Argentina commissioned the artist Ducmelic to create a painting as the basis of a new label for their aromatic dry white Torrontes wine. The 3 Etchart brothers requested the use of the theme of nature as revealed in the annual cycle of the vine. When Ducmelic presented them with his completed work, the brothers were delighted with its beauty, but baffled by his logic. The painting was meant to represent the 4 seasons and yet it only featured 3 vine leaves of different colours. The artist explained that his painting was quite straightforward, as the 3 leaves represented 3 seasons. The first was green to represent the new growth of spring, the second was golden for the heat of summer and the third was a rusty red denoting autumn after the grapes had been gathered. When asked why there wasn't a fourth leaf to represent winter, the artist simply rejoined that in winter there aren't any leaves, so he hadn't painted one.

Marlboro Country If you visit Benmarl Vineyards, nestled between the Berkshire Mountains and the Hudson River in Marlboro, up-state New York, you are likely to be pleasantly surprised. You will not just find a humble winery but also a unique art museum. Both are the love children of veteran owner Mark Miller, a former Hollywood film artist.

His work first became popular in romantic magazines and Mark's *Gallery in a Vineyard* speaks volumes about the life and times of the 60s and 70s, an era when his work was most acclaimed. Visitors are invited to see his portraits of Elvis Presley, The Beatles and Richard Nixon, and copies are available for sale.

Another claim to fame is that Benmarl Vineyards holds the first winery licence ever granted in New York state.

Monarch Every autumn the Pelee Island Winery in Ontario, Canada is invaded by thousands of migrating Monarch butterflies on their 2000-mile journey to the mountains of Central Mexico. The winery marks the flight with its Monarch label painted by Rosalyn Pettinato which is found on its medium-dry white Vidal.

Naked lady When Kenwood Vineyards in Sonoma, California decided on their first Artist Series of labels in 1975, they submitted their initial proposal to the Bureau of Alcohol, Tobacco and Firearms for approval. It was a simple painting by San Francisco artist David Goines, of a naked woman perched – it would seem – a little uncomfortably on a vineyard slope. The following was the reply *The drawing of the young lady must be deleted. More specifically, the Bureau regards the picture as 'obscene and indecent' under regulations 27cKR 4.39 (a) (3).* Nineteen years later censorship had waned and The Naked Lady finally made her debut in 1994, without a brushstroke added or a regulation quoted.

Naked lady neighbour Clos Pegase in the Napa Valley, a reasonably near neighbour of Kenwood, experienced a similar problem. In 1992 the winery wished to publish a painting called *Bedecked Nude* by French artist Jean Dubuffet on the label of its 1988 Napa Valley Hommage Artists Series Cabernet Sauvignon. It also ran into trouble with the Bureau of Alcohol, Tobacco and Firearms, which ruled that the painting of its naked male was indecent. The authority later reversed its decision and eventually in winter 2002 Clos Pegase released the full version – of what looks like a robot with male genitals – on its 1998 Hommage Artists Series Cabernet Sauvignon.

Questions might be asked about the marketing benefits of publishing it at all. Consumers might find the sight off-putting as they slice a gigot of lamb and sip the Cabernet.

Rejected by the Baron Chateau Mouton Rothschild, the great first growth Bordeaux, has probably provided the best-known artists' labels of their kind. The late Baron Philippe de Rothschild first commissioned one from the French painter Jean Carlu in 1924. Then in 1945, for the Victory vintage, he began the practice which was continued until the year 2000 of using different illustrations for each vintage. These have included works by Dali, Cocteau, Chagall and Moore. Few have probably realised that the Baron, a most upright and honourable man, according to his former general manager Philippe Cottin, occasionally rejected the works of some of the world's most renowned artists. As with his other contributors he always paid them in full with wine, but the works that he disliked were simply hidden away in a locked room and are probably still there.

With the 2000 vintage the Baron's daughter, the Baroness Philippine de Rothschild, took the concept a stage further and attempted to make the entire bottle a *collector's item*. The front of the bottle was printed with a golden ram design, copied from the *Augsberg Ram*, a 1590 AD drinking vessel exhibited in the museum of wine at the chateau. Some may be disappointed at her decision to digress from the Baron's initial idea. In fact the British wine trade magazine, Harpers, described the work as *Mouton dressed as ram*.

Taittinger Collection Taittinger can justifiably claim to be one of the great Champagne houses and also the creator of one of the most prestigious *art* collections. 1983 saw the beginning of the collection with the introduction of the magnificent *gold* bottle by Victor Vasarely. At the time of writing 9 artists have been privileged to decorate bottles for the Taittinger Collection. Viera da Silva produced his striking *blue* bottle in 1988, followed by Hans Hartung's elegant *silver* example in 1992, but perhaps the most vivid and memorable was the *red bottle* painted by Toshimitsu Imai in 1994. Other artists commissioned have been Arman, André Masson, Roy Lichtenstein, Corneille and Matta.

Toulouse Lautrec Chateau Malromé, which makes an attractive range of Bordeaux wines in the village of Saint-André du Bois, exhibits one of the largest collections of fake paintings, and the owner Philippe Decroix beams with satisfaction as he shows them to his guests. They were all painted as copies for use in the 1998 French film *Lautrec* and purchased by the astute M. Decroix immediately filming had been completed.

The mother of the deformed artist, the Countess Adèle de Toulouse-Lautrec acquired Chateau Malromé in 1883 and her son Henri de Toulouse-Lautrec made it the scene of his summer visits for many years and, in fact, died at the chateau in 1901. His classic posters, such as *Ambassadeurs* and *La Revue Blanche* are also remembered on the labels of the chateau's wines.

As the writer was leaving the property, he accidentally stumbled against another painting that was standing against the wall of the entrance. Apologising profusely, he was assured by M. Decroix that there was no need to worry, *it is merely a Van Gogh!*

Wine Countries

Here are a few of the less well-known wine producing countries.

Algeria The only Algerian wine that seems to be generally available is a brand called Sidi Brahim. But 50 years ago, in Algeria's heyday as a French colony, viticulture was a thriving and prosperous activity. The coastal strip, with its Mediterranean climate, provided an excellent environment for red wines in particular, and names such as Domaine de la Trappe and the unfortunately named Lung, were widely compared with the finest reds from France's Rhône Valley. By the late 1950s Algerian wine production had reached an all-time record with an average of around 1,820 million litres (400 million gallons) per annum.

The Romans planted the first vineyards there and the practice continued on a modest scale until around 1880. When Algeria came under French rule it proved an ideal place for the hasty retreat of French winegrowers, desperately trying to outrun the phylloxera aphid that threatened to wipe out their country's vineyards. Ironically, within a few years the pest had found its way there, but it never became anything like the threat it was in Europe because it disliked sandy conditions. It is estimated that from 1880 – 1990 Algerian wine production increased by 1,000 per cent. Today Algeria maintains strict Moslem law and one wonders where exactly the source of wine for Sidi Brahim can be.

Bolivia This landlocked, mountainous country in South America has the highest altitude vineyards in the world. In the Tarija region, it is claimed that all the vines lie between 1,600 metres (5,200 feet) and 2,850 metres (9,262 feet). The whole country possesses 2,000 hectares (5,000 acres) of planted vineyards.

Bolivia has an ancient wine-producing heritage which dates back to 1609, when the earliest vineyard is recorded near the city of Tarija. The first wines were fermented in large earthenware jars and were produced for *liturgical purposes in Mizque (Cochabamba)*, which then had one of the very first Roman Catholic Archbishops in the entire Americas. Today the best-known wineries are Prudencio and Pinedo, who make international class wines and use qualified oenologists to supervise the most modern winemaking techniques. The former has imported vine cuttings from the University of Davis, California and specialises in Cabernet Sauvignon.

Ethiopia has ancient Christian and Jewish traditions and consequently planted vineyards to make wine for religious rites. Best-known of contemporary vineyard operations is the Guder winery to the east of Addis Ababa, some 1,000 kms (625 miles) north of the Equator. Its reputation is quite widespread in its own country and its greatest international claim to fame is that for a couple of years its winemaker was Carlo Corrino. He was originally winemaker at Montrose Vineyards in Mudgee, New South Wales and later at the historic Marchesi di Frescobaldi estates, in the Tuscany region of Italy, and clearly a man who can claim to have wide experience.

Madagascar Jesuit missionaries brought the first vine cuttings to this large island in the Indian Ocean from the Alsace region of France late in the 19th century. Today there are a number of active wineries, of which Clos Malaza and Fontaine-aux-Anes are the most prominent.

Clos Malaza, situated slightly north of Moromby, describes itself as a *tropical vineyard at an altitude of 1,400 metres (4,550 feet)*. It produces white, rosé and red styles using Villard Noir, Chambourcin, Petit Bouchet, Varousset for red and Couderc Blanc for white. Fontaine-aux-Anes (*The Donkey's drinking place*) uses Chasselas for white and Gamay for red.

Moldova For a brief period prior to the crumbling of the Iron Curtain in 1989, Moldova (sometimes known as Moldavia) was actually the 5th largest wine producing country/state in the world. It had literally become the big, bulk, inexpensive wine supplier for the Soviet Union. The demise of the USSR brought a massive drop in demand. Further hampered by adverse economic circumstances, wine production has fallen dramatically, leaving former co-operatives desperately trying to privatise and compete in the real world. There must be some hope for future revival if sufficient foreign investment can be found, for growers and winemakers in Moldova still talk of the legendary green *Cotnari* wine that brought fame to the land in the 19th century. In the meantime a few potential stars are beginning to emerge, such as the Zubresti winery that is working minor miracles with its dry white Aligoté and Rikatselli wines, and its sweet fortified Muscat.

Norway The Hallingstad Vineyard must be entitled to call itself the most northerly vineyard in the world. It is situated slightly south of the village of Horten near Oslofjord at 60° north, a site that was chosen with meticulous care by owner Sveier Hansen for its relatively mild micro-climate. Planting of the vineyard, which covers 2 hectares (5 acres), began in 1992 and further land is available for expansion if needed.

The wine is called L'esprit d'Edvard Munch after the painter of the same name, who purchased a small sailor's house in a nearby village. The principle varietal is Pinot Noir, although there are some small plantings of Chardonnay, Riesling and Viognier.

The first wines, with their impressive labelling, have become collectors' items, resulting in the bizarre situation that very little of the wine is consumed. Those who have tasted the Pinot Noir have commented on its good colour and bouquet of wild raspberries.

Thailand Several modern wineries are progressing in Thailand, fuelled by a burgeoning interest in French wine and gastronomy. Chateau de Loei in the northeast has a French winemaker and is producing some dry white Chenin Blanc. Another property, called Chatemp with vineyards in the Chaophrya River region and also in the River Kwai valley, is making a dry white, partly oaked blend of vinifera grapes. It may the first wine in the world to carry the vintage on its label according to the Buddhist calendar. For example the Gregorian date of 1997 is actually labelled 2541.

Uganda In 1998 the writer literally stumbled into what is believed to be the only cultivated vineyard situated on the very Equator at 0°. It is a one hectare (2.5 acres) experimental vineyard owned by William Mukaira, a retired school-teacher, at Bushenyi in the mountains of Western Uganda, at around 4,600 feet. William took cuttings from vines that had been abandoned on monastery land by The White Fathers, who were missionaries from France and Italy. Earlier in the 20th century the fathers had brought cuttings from their homelands in order to produce sacramental wine. When a new generation of Ugandan-born fathers replaced the Europeans they didn't maintain the same traditions. So William seized his opportunity with everyone's consent.

He planted his first few vines in 1995 and his aim is to see if viticulture can be developed into a new agricultural industry, to boost the economy of a region that suffers from extreme poverty and disease. His task is complicated by a weather pattern of two wet and two dry seasons, meaning two separate vintages in March and September, plus an average daily temperature that varies little from 26°C (79°F).

Vin

Vin French for wine.

Vina An Indian stringed musical instrument, which has a fretted fingerboard mounted on two dry-blown gourds.

Vinaceous Wine coloured.

Vinaigrette A salad dressing, French in origin, comprising wine vinegar, oil, herbs and seasoning.

Vinay Small vineyard sub-region in Champagne, France.

Vincalottes Wine village in the Yonne region of France, near Chablis.

Vincelles Village in Champagne region of France.

Vincent Patron Saint of wine producers.

Vincentia A little-known wine from Mudgee, New South Wales.

Vincorp This Victoria, Australia winery wins the prize for the most boring name.

Vindaloo Rather hot Indian curry that kills all attempts to drink wine with it!

Vindecision Whether or not to open the next bottle.

Vin de Garde Wine for aging.

Vindelible Wine stains on white shirtfront.

Vinden Estate A small Australian winery in the Hunter Valley with an attractive Semillon.

Vindigo Lovely deep purple colour of Australian Shiraz.

Vindiscretion Regrettable behaviour under the influence.

Vindividual Selfish person who keeps all his wine to himself.

Vin Doux Naturel French term normally used for fortified sweet wine.

Vine Term used to represent life throughout The Bible.

Viné Old French word for fortified.

Vinedresser Nineteenth century term for a person who cultivated vines.

Vineland Small city in American State of New Jersey which has no great claim to wine fame.

Vinegar Wine that has gone sour, usually deliberately. It is generally used for pickling, or as a condiment.

Vinery A greenhouse for growing vines.

Vines Wooden climbing plants which bear grapes that can be trained into bushes, lines, pergolas and trees.

Vinetto Italian for lightweight wine.

Vinexpo Major International wine trade exhibition held in Bordeaux.

Vineux French word for wine that is a little high in alcohol.

Vineyards Land where vines are planted. Term has been used since Old Testament days.

Vinfruco Exciting Stellenbosch, South Africa winery producing Arniston Bay and other competitive, Cape blends and other wines.

Vin Gris So-called *grey wines* that are slightly pink.

Vinho Portuguese for wine.

Vinicide Derogatory English term used by lovers of old wines when referring to inexperienced or ignorant drinkers who consume great wines many years before they have peaked.

Viniculture Entire subject of wine production.

Vinifera The most important species of vine.

Vinification General term for everything involved in the making of a wine.

Vinillo Spanish for lightweight wine.

Vinjest A joke about wine that you have just read.

Vinland Name for Eastern coast of North American continent, given by first Viking settlers.

Vin Liquoreux Term for sweet wine that is made from late-picked grapes in south-west France.

Vin Moelleux Term for sweet wine that has the texture of marrow.

Vinny Jones Archetypal *hard man* of celluloid fame, best known for *Lock, Stock and Two Smoking Barrels*. He was also a prominent English Premier League soccer player with a reputation for controversial behaviour. A *rum* character, rather than a *wine* one.

Vino Italian and Spanish for wine.

Vinobatics A term used to explain the dramatic helicopter flights by Christian Moueix during the rain-diluted 1987 vintage at Chateau Petrus, which some rate as the finest red wine property on Earth. He used the down draught from the rotor blades to dry excess moisture from the grapes immediately before they were gathered. Much to the terror of some of the pickers!

Vino Noceto Outstanding producer of Sangiovese in Amador County, California.

Vinopolis Wine Theme Centre in London, England.

Vinot A rather light red from Piedmont in Italy made in a novello style.

Vinothèque Library or collection of bottles.

Vinous Displaying wine-like characteristics.

Vin Paillé or **Vin de Paille** White wine pressed from grapes that have been allowed to shrivel on straw mats.

Vinsanteria The roof space or attic where Italian wine producers age their *holy* wine called *Vinsanto*.

Vinsobres Amusingly named village appellation in the Côtes du Rhône.

Vintage The year a wine was produced.

Vintage Champagne Most respected houses make a small proportion of their production as Vintage Champagne only in outstanding conditions, approximately 3 times in every 10 years. It is normally from their finest vineyards.

Vintage Port Classic long-aging style of Port that needs to age in bottle, on its lees, for 12-20 years or more. It is only made in outstanding vintages. Top names are Taylor Fladgate, Fonseca, Croft, Grahams, Quinta da Noval, Churchill.

Vintagewise Classic wine book written by André Simon (1945).

Vintina Estate A small, promising Victoria, Australia winery hoping to produce good Pinot Noir.

Vintitulist Collector of wine labels.

Vintner A person who sells wine.

Vinumvirat Austrian wine from Röschitz.

Vinzelles Wine village near Macon, France.

Wine Help

Experiment This is probably the most important single word of advice for beginners and wine enthusiasts. There is no better way to learn than by tasting and one should experiment with wines from different varietals and blends, from different regions and countries and different price points. Conversely, it is wise to keep a small stock of consistent favourites for everyday drinking.

Champagne in the fridge door It may come as a surprise to learn that you can place a half-consumed bottle of Champagne, or any other bottle-fermented sparkling wine, in a fridge door without any stopper - and it will still be fresh and fizzy the next day. That is often the ideal opportunity to pour a Mimosa (Buck's Fizz) for breakfast.

Sweet wine in the fridge door Good quality sweet white wine keeps longer than any other style when left in a fridge.

Everyday restaurants By all means order a glass of fizz, Chardonnay or Dry Riesling as an aperitif but if possible delay ordering your main wine selection until you have selected your menu. Then it will be much easier to find a wine on the list that will match well. It sounds like common sense but many diners let themselves be rushed into ordering their wine as soon as they sit down and then find it doesn't always suit.

House wines House wines in many chain restaurants often tend to be chosen as an economic decision. It is wiser not to order a house wine unless you feel confident that the owner or management has a serious interest in wine.

By contrast, if you are actually in a wine-growing region, always ask what the house, or pouring wine, is. If it is some unknown local wine then it is probably well worth trying. The reason is, the restaurant owner is likely to know several local producers and it would serve no purpose to purchase anything inferior.

If you are wondering about ordering a house wine, be cheeky and once you have placed your meal order, ask if you can have a free tasting sample. If you meet any resistance remind the waiter how much you have just spent and if that doesn't work then don't trust the house wine. Try it, be cheeky – it seldom fails.

Restaurants/price level The eminent writer and gourmet Hilaire Belloc travelled extensively through France during the late 19th and early 20th century and passed on the benefit of his experiences to his readers. One sound piece of advice he gave was that he *always drank the second cheapest Claret (Red Bordeaux) on the list, because that was probably what the proprietor drank himself*.

Restaurants/wine waiters Many people become nervous when faced by a professional wine waiter or sommelier, often feeling they risk revealing their ignorance or mispronouncing the name of a wine. The majority of wine waiters really do wish to be helpful but a few are a bit pushy, so here are a few ways to deal with these problems.

In the first place always take command of the situation. When you are approached, immediately ask for help, which will attract attention. Then state the style of wine you wish to select, such as a dry white or red wine. For this example we will presume that the reader wishes to choose a dry white. Simply ask the wine waiter for the best value dry white in the lowest 40 per cent of the wine list. There is no likelihood that he, or she, will admit that the restaurant only sells inferior wines at that level, and subsequently will go to some trouble to offer the best example.

Restaurants/foreign wine names There is usually no need to get into difficulties with foreign language wine names. If looking through a list with a wine waiter you come across a name like Castelgiocondo Brunello di Montalcino, or Reichsgraf von Kesselstatt Piesporter Goldtropfchen, just ask how it is pronounced and put the onus on the vendor, rather than the buyer. However don't be too concerned if the waiter has very limited language ability, because that does not necessarily reflect on his, or her, wine knowledge.

Restaurants/Champagne Be careful about ordering small bottles of French Champagne. If you are offered the choice of splits (quarters), half-bottles, bottles or magnums, always aim for the largest size that suits your needs and budget. There are two factors that influence the quality of buying Champagne in these circumstances. First, the sales of splits and half-bottles are frequently much slower than standard bottles. Second, the larger the volume of the bottle the better the Champagne ages. Subsequently if you are dining as a couple a standard bottle is the wiser purchase, or as a group the choice should be a magnum.

Restaurants/treating a business guest If you do not know your guest well but wish to please him or her, be quite open and inquire in advance about their personal preferences. Then telephone your choice of restaurant and give that information to the wine waiter. Also stipulate your budget and ask for suggestions. Then agree to one of the wines offered and, if necessary, ask for it to be decanted prior to service. Your guest will probably be impressed with both the wine and the service and will be unlikely to know the cost.

The prominent Dallas, Texas wine journalist Darryl Beeson tells of an experience when he was the sommelier and wine manager for the famous Adolphus Hotel in that city. A regular business diner telephoned him to say that he would be dining the next day with a most important guest and wished the wine selection to impress him. Darryl inquired as to the choice of menu, which was a fish course and subsequently selected a Trimbach Cuvée Frederic Emile Riesling, one of the world's most elegant dry white wines and yet one that most experts consider very reasonably priced. It was a magnificent wine and a superb match but the customer complained that he was disappointed with the service. When asked why, he replied the *wine wasn't expensive enough*.

Always remember that your guest may know a great deal more about wine than you. So, if you waste an absurd sum on a bottle of Chateau Latour that is only 5 years old, when it needs a minimum of 15 years aging, or likewise with a young Henschke Hill of Grace Shiraz, then your guest is likely to think you have more money than sense.

Letting a wine breathe This is an endless source of controversy and over the years varying opinions from experts have left consumers in a great state of confusion. The writer adds his own recommendations based on personal experience.

Only still wines need to breathe. Sparkling wines will simply lose their fizz.

In general red wines are more likely to benefit than white.

You are unlikely to harm any young wines by letting them breathe.

Just removing the cork is not enough to allow a wine to breathe, because the actual area of wine exposed to the air is tiny. To let a wine breathe properly it should be decanted, or poured into a wine decanter, or if you do not possess one, use a water jug, or large glasses. The object of the exercise is to expose as much of the surface area as possible to the air.

If a wine has sediment and you do not have a wine filter, then use a coffee filter, or even a makeshift filter using a tea strainer or something similar.

Most young reds will benefit by breathing for one hour, but reds that have been aged for a long time in small oak barrels will improve with two hours' breathing. The finest old style Rioja Gran Reserva wines from Spain, like Faustino I are examples that will gain from as long as four hours. Perhaps the process should be seen as analogous to waking up in the mornings. The vast majority of us need time.

Opening fizz without losing any wine Always remove the capsule and metal cage carefully without shaking the bottle. Then place the bottle upright, in your right hand, at a 45° angle with the cork in your left hand. Next, gently but firmly turn the cork in one direction and the bottle in the other. Providing you don't have a problem cork, your fizz should give a light pop and not overflow. If you have a problem cork, read the next item.

Removing that problem Champagne or sparkling wine cork Many of us have experienced a problem with dry corks that will not move despite all attempts by hand or using metal grips. The answer is to find the toughest, hardest door in your home and place the cork at a 45° angle between the back of the door and the frame, exert pressure to grip the cork tightly and then turn the cork in a clockwise direction. With sufficient pressure and a little patience the cork will begin to move. Complete the task as above.

Removing that problem cork from a still wine If the cork will not move at all, then place the neck of the bottle under a hot water tap to warm the glass. Normally the glass will expand slightly allowing the cork to be released. If you still cannot move it, then take it back to your supplier for a replacement.

At the inaugural meeting of *The Mystere Wine Club* in Cardiff, South Wales, in 1980, the late BBC journalist Chris Howell and the writer used two house bricks to remove the frail cork from a bottle of Chateau Cos d'Estournel 1911, which had moved a little but then refused to be withdrawn. In other words don't be frightened to use your initiative.

How to get the best value Of course taxation on wine varies from country to country but most other basic costs differ very little. For instance, when you buy a cheap bottle of wine you are paying for the glass bottle, cork, capsule, the front and back labels, transport and so forth. These overheads are pretty much the same as for a more expensive bottle; therefore, it stands to reason, that the value of wine will be greater in the dearer bottle.

Frequently Asked Questions

Can you chill red wines in summer? It is perfectly acceptable to chill lighter bodied reds such as Pinot Noir and Gamay, also lighter styles of Merlot and Grenache-Shiraz blends. It is wiser not to chill Cabernet Sauvignon, Shiraz or fuller-bodied Merlots.

How long can you leave a bottle of wine in a refrigerator? Seven days should be a maximum. Twenty years for a bottle of Champagne, claimed by a BBC Radio Kent (England) listener, is probably a world record. It also resulted in a wasted bottle of flat fizz. Chilling gradually dulls wine, causing it to lose its flavour and vitality.

Is my old bottle any good? The writer has had the privilege of taking telephone enquiries from listeners in several countries, and has regularly been asked whether the contents of certain specified old bottles will still be suitable for drinking. The world of wine is now so large that no expert can possibly remember the records of every good long-aging wine. Therefore much advice has to be general.

There is no simple answer but it should be understood that around 95 per cent of wines are made for immediate consumption. It could be said that most bottles bought in France are drunk within 7 weeks, in the UK within 7 days, in the USA within 7 hours, in New Zealand within a couple less and in Australia within 7 minutes. By contrast some fine wines are made with the intention of being aged for several, or even many, years before being drunk. Generally speaking these are upper-mid priced and high priced wines.

There are not so many examples of dry white wines that are made for long aging. Possibly the best-known category is finer quality White Burgundy from France. In many ways sweet whites, like late-harvest wines, those affected by botrytis, (such as some Grand Cru Classé Sauternes), great late-picked Rieslings from Germany, better quality Tokay and icewines from several countries, offer greater aging potential. Amongst fortified wines, Vintage Port from Portugal is the only widely available category that ages well and as a style it probably has a better track record for longevity than any other wine. Names like Taylor's, Fonseca and Croft excel.

Reds need a good structure, ample tannins, ripe fruit and a reasonable balance of acidity to mature well and in fact more red wine is aged than any other category. However you can have a bottle with all these ingredients, which – for instance – has come from over-rich soil, that will not improve with aging. A major factor is the length of the fermentation. It has been said that the slower the fermentation, the longer the aging potential.

There are a few basic guidelines: such as don't waste time aging popular everyday wines. They are not made for that purpose but for early consumption and in most cases, if you leave them for 15 years, you will discover an unpleasant solution of colour, wood and water that will not even benefit your next casserole.

If you have always owned the bottle concerned, then of course you will know if it has been kept under suitable conditions (see **I don't have a cellar** below). A greater risk exists if you have bought the wine when several years old, because you are unlikely to be aware of where and how it has been aged. It is really surprising how many listeners call about bottles of famous wines that they have kept standing upright in warm living rooms since their initial purchase.

If a wine had satisfactory aging potential and has been aged properly then you have a good chance of excellent results and there are many vintage charts published on the Internet and in books, which will guide you concerning the maturity of your wine.

Are the most expensive wines always the best? No, not necessarily. Price is often influenced by market demand for a wine with small volume production. As the reputation of a great wine spreads, so more consumers wish to purchase it and just like a rare gem or valuable painting, so its price will rise.

Also – sad to relate – many great red wines like top Bordeaux chateaux, Penfold's Grange and the finest Napa Cabernets are often consumed by inexperienced but wealthy buyers years before they reach their peak. This reduces the volume of fully mature fine wine available in auction sales and fine wine merchants. It also causes price increases.

Who is Robert Parker? Robert Parker is the legendary Baltimore-based wine expert whose subscription publication *The Wine Advocate* was the first to introduce a 100 point rating scale. He has a reputation as a brilliant taster and has attracted tens of thousands of wealthy American and international followers. Many of these immediately order any wine to which he awards high marks, resulting in an unprecedented demand for the vintage concerned and usually creating a sudden major increase in price.

Are the old rules about matching white wines with fish and red with meat still wise to follow? Yes and No. In general terms such guidelines continue to be helpful, especially for beginners. However some fish dishes like fresh tuna or salmon will match with Merlot, or Pinot Noir, while Cabernet Sauvignon marries well with dark/bitter chocolate. Much discussion and many competitions have taken place to find the best match for freshly shucked oysters. A recent US competition saw King Estate Pinot Gris being selected as first choice, though others will swear by Marlborough New Zealand Sauvignon Blanc, while French connoisseurs argue for Muscadet or

Alsace Riesling. The choice of wines to match various cheeses is a constant matter of debate. Try Sauvignon Blanc with goat's cheese, Cabernet with Cheddar and late harvest sweet wines with blue veined cheese.

Some French Champagne houses claim that the *King of Wines* matches all food courses but most serious wine folk would disagree. In fact the great house of Perrier-Jouët always serve Red Bordeaux with cheese at the end of lunch for their guests.

The nitty gritty of matching food and wine is that your palate is personal and if you prefer to drink Chardonnay with rare steak, or Pinot Noir with barbecued shrimps, then only you know how much you enjoy these flavours together and you should feel free to maintain your choice. On the other hand the single most important word in wine appreciation is *experiment* and that applies equally to wine and food matches.

What is a blend? First and foremost, it is a much misunderstood word and should never be used in any derogatory sense. In wine terms it means that wines made from different grape varieties have been blended together. Most major French Champagnes are a blend of 3 varieties: Pinot Noir, Pinot Meunier and Chardonnay. The extremely popular Australian wine, Jacob's Creek Red, is a blend of Shiraz and Cabernet with more Shiraz and less Cabernet. Interestingly it began the other way round but the wine producer found that more consumers preferred the softer, fruitier style of the Shiraz, so its proportion was increased and the Cabernet decreased.

What is blending? Blending is the mixing together of different wines to achieve a final product that is considered a finer and better balanced wine than any of the initial ingredient wines. Blends are made from different grape varieties, different vineyards or even different vineyard blocks. It helps winemakers to achieve consistency and produce the best possible balance of flavours. It is one of the most important skills. In Europe, centuries ago, some producers used to blend by putting different grape varieties together in required proportions before pressing them in the same lot. The small, traditional house of Champagne Alfred Gratien still does this at Epernay using what it calls the *conche* system.

Wine for a child's 21st birthday The first rule is that, if you are not an expert yourself, you should request the advice of one, although you personally can make a substantial contribution to the correct choice by providing some useful information. This requires some research work on your part. If you then give your expert the results of that research and an approximate budget, he or she should be able to produce some very helpful suggestions. Remember that you should not be purchasing subjectively for your own future pleasure, but trying to forecast the likes of the recipient at maturity – particularly difficult if you wish to give the wine to a new-born baby. Also advise your expert whether the choice of suitable wine is your priority, or if more attention should be paid to its potential value as an investment. If the latter, then you don't really need an expert, just somewhere to buy first growth Red Bordeaux.

The next step is to consider the taste buds of the child now, to assess whether they show any dry or sweet tendencies. It is normal for children under about 12 years to prefer sweeter tastes but you may find an individual with drier preferences, therefore you should choose them the driest wines with good aging properties, and this means really fine reds like Cabernet, Shiraz and Merlot from highly reputed vineyards. If the child's palate is sweet, consider the taste buds of any adult relatives. These are likely to be a general indicator, although there may always be exceptions. If you suspect that there will be a tendency to sweetness, then be quite sure that you do not purchase any red wines. A much wiser choice would be Vintage Port, many examples of which peak at around 20-25 years.

If you are convinced that sweetness needs to be the selection then enquire about late harvest and noble rot wines but be sure they are in full-sized bottles, as the greater the volume in the bottle the slower the aging process. Just a few top French Champagnes can make an excellent choice as they will age superbly and prove to be an attractive financial investment. Dom Pérignon, Louis Roederer Cristal and Krug all mature well and have good investment potential. However your 21-year-old may not like Champagne.

Part of the fun is to acquire the exact vintage of the recipient's birth and sometimes this means avoiding wines from a favourite region. For example Coonawarra Cabernets, which possibly would offer as good a balance of value and aging potential as any reds on Earth, would be best avoided from the 1995 vintage, as they don't have the necessary structure and concentration to peak in 2016. On the other hand 1995 was an excellent vintage from the Western Cape of South Africa and much of Northern Italy and very good for Barossa Shiraz. So sometimes one has to move around the world to get the best vintage potential.

Remember also that it is wiser to purchase the wine concerned sooner rather than later, due to availability and price. One of the most frequently asked questions of wine journalists is where to buy bottles that are 20 years old. Not easy to answer.

She loves sweet white, I love red Often a wine journalist is asked for help with this problem and the answer is simple. Just purchase a wine saver like Vacu-Vin which will allow you both to enjoy the bottles of your choice without the need to guzzle all the wine in too much of a rush. Probably the best advice is to spread the contents over 3 sittings, because every time the stopper is removed air gets at the surface of the wine and it begins to oxidise.

I don't have a cellar. Where should I store my wine? There are a few basic rules for those who are unable to have their own cellars but wish to keep a reasonable stock of wines.

1. Keep your wines out of both daylight and artificial light. Exposure to artificial light for a couple of hours for inspection purposes will not cause any problems.

2. Ensure your wines are nowhere near anything that vibrates, like a washing machine, refrigerator or water pump. Your wines need to settle to encourage gentle, steady aging.

3. Keep all bottles on their side, so that the corks remain moist and do not shrink, which would allow air to oxidise the wine.

4. Do your very best to maintain a reasonably consistent temperature which should be no more than 17°C (65°F).

5. Remember that if you have some really valuable wines and you seek perfection, you should maintain the same consistent temperature, even when you are away from home.

What does *corked* mean? The advent of artificial corks and the return of screw-capped bottles have complicated the issue. *Corked* has become a term that covers a host of wine faults but really it should indicate that a wine has deteriorated due to being exposed to TCA (Trichloroanisole), which is an infection of natural cork and which affects a small but annoying percentage of wines. It grows more offensive with age. It can often be detected by a smell of old damp magazine paper.

Famous Fizz Flat – Help! Wine on the Web receives a regular stream of enquiries which are answered as quickly and helpfully as possible. Probably the most difficult enquiry came from a reader who said he had purchased a case of a prestige Champagne some months earlier but had only recently opened the first two bottles, both of which were *flat*, being totally without fizz. He had complained to both the retailer and regional wholesale distributor, neither of whom would help. What would we advise?

It has to be said that we had never heard of such a problem concerning this extremely famous brand. It just might be the situation that the reader had purchased the case, drunk two bottles and then regretted the substantial price he had paid and was trying to bluff his way out of trouble. In wine terms it might need *The Wisdom of Solomon* to settle the dispute. One of the major difficulties in resolving such an issue is that one can only do so by opening each remaining bottle to inspect the condition of the Champagne.

Subsequently our advice was that he should write to the two parties explaining the problem, supplying a receipt or credit card confirmation and also to copy everything to the Public Relations Manager of the Champagne house in France. Then to invite representatives of both local parties to meet him at the retailer's premises to open all the bottles on the under-standing that if others are found to be *flat* that his money would be refunded in full. If our reader was bluffing we considered it likely that he would withdraw. For if the Champagne was found to be satisfactory then it could be a really serious problem trying to stopper it temporarily, to put it mildly.

Wine Temperatures

Air-conditioning Remember that if you have a cellar or stock of wine in your home, it is important to keep it at a reasonably cool and consistent temperature, around 18°C (64°F). All is well until you go on holiday, shutting off your air conditioning. The rapid changes in temperature in switching off and on again, will be harmful to your wine and have a dulling effect. You either have to leave the air-conditioning on – an expensive choice – or organise your storage in a confined and protected space which can be cooled independently.

Back of the hand test for red wine Use the back of your hand as your personal wine thermometer. For red wines you should feel the lightest chill when placing the back of your hand against the shoulder of a bottle. Try it once and if you decide the wine is a little too warm or too cool, then allow for the touch to be adjusted the next time.

Correct temperatures The following advice has been extracted from an assortment of books, wine guides and back labels. It is appreciated that few consumers have a wine thermometer. These are often difficult to find. The UK company Cellardine has a neat model that wraps around a bottle.

Champagne or Sparkling wines	4.5-7°C (40-45°F)
White	7-10°C (45-50°F)
Rosé or blush	10-12°C (50-54°F)
Light reds	12-13°C (54-55°F)
Medium reds	12.5-15.5°C (55-60°F)
Full-bodied reds	18-19°C (64-66°F)
Oak aged reserve reds	18-20°C (64-68°F)

Common sense should tell you that Champagne and sparkling wines are refreshing and should be served well chilled. Nothing is less palatable than resuming a half-consumed glass of fizz which is lukewarm. There is a habit in the Champagne region of France of serving a *freshener* which is to top up half-drunk flutes with more, well chilled Champagne.

Try an experiment with your next bottle of Chardonnay. Of course it will take a little self-control. Pour everyone present a half-glass and ask them to taste it immediately, then to put their glasses down and not to resume drinking for a full 10 minutes. In something like 80 per cent of instances you will find substantially increased aroma and better developed palate. It's not easy though!

It is a cliché that rules are made to be broken but often by breaking traditional wine rules you make delicious discoveries. For instance, on a hot Barossa day Jacob's Creek head winemaker Philip Laffer can often be found with a large ice cube in a chilled Grenache-Shiraz.

Ice buckets-the golden rules Appalling sights are seen in some restaurants with wine perched on top of the ice in large buckets with only the base of the bottle making partial contact with the ice. First, take an empty ice bucket and put your bottle in it. Fill it almost to the top with ice. Finally, add cold water to within a couple of inches of the top. The result will be that the ice will chill the water and the water will provide a consistently chilled surface to the bottle. Remember that the neck of the bottle will protrude from the chilled water: so be polite, as in the tradition of French aristocratic gentlemen when pouring Champagne, and serve the first lukewarm glass to yourself.

Icewine or Eiswein There are two styles. The first is sweet, almost always white wine pressed from grapes that have been picked when frozen. Best-known countries are Canada and Germany but many others now produce it. Usually a minimum temperature is required for the picking of the grapes of -8°C (17.6F). Often the grapes are picked in the early hours of the morning to ensure the coldest temperature. The water content of the grape juice is removed as ice, leaving the concentrated fruit pulp to be pressed. Riesling and Scheurebe produce the finest results in Europe and Vidal in Canada.

The second method does not involve picking under such conditions but requires tank chilling. It is a clever compromise but does not appear to produce the same quality.

In the Northern Hemisphere When Christmas comes bringing cold winter weather, there is often a lot of competition for space in the refrigerator and complaints about the number of wines occupying space. If you can trust your neighbours, the best answer is to leave your bottles out of doors overnight. If you can't do that, then place them in the boot (trunk) of your car. Of course some southerners do have similar experiences at another time of the year.

Rapid Ice A simple gel-filled sleeve invented by the Schneider brothers of Delft, Netherlands, which should be placed in a freezer overnight. It is then fitted over a bottle and chills a white wine suitably in about 5-6 minutes. A slightly different sleeve also works ideally for Champagne and sparkling wines, taking about 7-8 minutes.

Terracotta Coolers These are not intended for chilling wines but for insulating the existing temperature. Subsequently they are popular in some restaurants, since they allow a bottle taken from a refrigerator to maintain its cool temperature.

Therm-au-Rouge A first look at this fascinating wine sleeve in operation is a case of *seeing is believing*. Therm-au-Rouge (meaning *warm the red*) literally warms cold red wines to an acceptable temperature in as little as 6 or 7 minutes. With a touch of Harry Potter mystery, just place the sleeve over the lower half of the bottle, bend the magical silver clicker backwards and forwards, and it releases a catalyst into the fluid in the sleeve. This initiates a harmless chemical reaction, which gives off heat. The sleeve expands and gradually heats up, gently warming the whole bottle. Peter Dunne modestly disclaims being an inventor, *just a developer*, he says. But understandably he has a patent registered on his little development.

The Queen's Grasshopper In 1972, during the state visit of Her Majesty Queen Elizabeth the Second and the Duke of Edinburgh to France, an official presentation was made to them of a giant wine cooler in the form of a grasshopper. The fascinating work of French designer François-Xavier Lalanne, the grey and green metal insect is larger than the average man. It is not known how many bottles it will chill, or how effective it is, as ever since it arrived at its English royal home of Windsor Castle no-one has been quite sure what to do with it and it has been displayed as a unique ornament just inside one of the main entrances.

Wine at the most suitable temperature Over the years a few enthusiastic winebibbers have been known to bring traditional glass thermometers to the table to calculate the precise temperature of wines to be consumed. Most wine lovers think this is going too far and that one should simply serve wine to suit your preference. Who can say that a chilled Merlot is wrong on a hot summer's day but one might be wise to ensure it is a moderately priced example.

Many Champagnes and sparkling wines thrive on being fresh and so benefit from being drunk well chilled. But Champagne that is more than 15 years old often becomes tranquil as it loses some of its fizz and settles. Therefore it should not be as well chilled.

For red wine lovers the arrival of the modern metallic wrap-around thermometer has become much more practical, since they are unobtrusive whilst displaying the temperature quite clearly.

Wine in refrigerated cabinets Be careful, be careful, be careful! Some retailers and restaurants overdo the use of refrigerated cabinets for stocking wine. There is nothing the matter with using these to hold fast turnover bottles like Jacob's Creek Semillon-Chardonnay or Sutter Home White Zinfandel because they won't remain in a fridge for long. But leaving a Corton Charlemagne or Champagne Louis Roederer Cristal, which may take a few months to sell, under such conditions is a sad mistake, for even after a few weeks refrigeration begins to dull wine. The result is comments along the lines of *Well, I didn't think that was so special*.

Date of Origin

The foundation date of a winery, often printed on the front or back label of a bottle of wine, can sometimes give a clue to the best value when considering lower and mid-priced wines.

Australia It is interesting to note that the majority of leading brands in Australia were founded about 150 years ago. They either had free land grants or purchased their land at a very low price. As their businesses developed so did the size of their vineyard holdings. Prime examples are Wyndham Estate (1828), Lindemans (1843), Penfolds (1844), Jacob's Creek (1847), Yalumba (1849), Hardy's (1854) and McWilliams (1877). The capital cost of their early land acquisitions has long since been paid; subsequently it is easier for them to offer competitive prices than it is for many newcomers.

First New Zealand vineyard This was planted in 1819, at Kerikeri on the North Island, by an Anglican missionary the Rev. Samuel Marsden. But the first real signs of an emerging wine industry came in the early 20th century, when settlers arrived from the Balkan countries to dig gum. Later, the 1970s brought a major transfor- mation, when declining demand for dairy products saw a steady stream of farmers change to grape growing and wine production. In the 1980s, the cool climatic conditions helped achieve the rapid success of the Sauvignon Blanc varietal. It soon attracted international acclaim and the following 2 decades have seen New Zealand confirm itself as one of the most exciting and consistent wine producing nations, adding Chardonnay, Pinot Noir and Shiraz to its achievements.

Chile In Chile there was a surge in the number of wineries during the second half of the 19th century. This was, to some degree, influenced by the phylloxera epidemic in Western Europe that threatened to destroy many of the world's most famous vineyards. Realisation dawned that Chile was one of the very few countries that the aphid was unlikely to reach, the Andes constituting a formidable barrier. Plus, Chile had an ideal climate. Many of these wineries were founded by farming families and entrepreneurs who acquired the land they needed for virtually nothing. Often these have remained independent wineries and have long since paid off the capital cost of their land. In reality the first Chilean vineyard was planted by the monk Francisco de Aguirre, at Copiapo in 1548. It was the first successful vineyard in the Southern Hemisphere.

In contrast, as the reputation of Chilean wines began to improve in the 1980s, new names arrived in the country including several from overseas. These parties either had to purchase new land, enter into partnership with established growers or buy their grapes from existing vineyards; all of which practices create capital costs that the wineries founded in the 19th century do not have to bear.

Therefore it appears logical that wine from the older wineries will offer better value than wine from the newcomers.

The conclusion is that if you are seeking the best value from Chile it is wise to look for foundation dates in the 1800s; many of these will also identify independent family-owned wineries.

Undurraga (1885), Errazuriz (1870), Concha Y Toro (1883), Santa Carolina (1875), Valdivieso (1875) and Santa Rita (1880) are good examples.

Europe Similarly, in Europe, there are many long-established wineries, but frequently it is not only the foundation date that is important. Often finding long-term family ownership is more likely to suggest a pattern of consistency. Wineries like Bertani in the Verona region of Italy, famous for its Amarone and Valpolicella, which was founded in 1857 had the benefit of early land purchase, as did Faustino in Spain with its outstanding Rioja, which was founded in the same year. The impression gained is that these wineries do not have to rush aging, as both mature their top wines for a minimum of 6 years. It can be argued that the benefit of their early land purchases has allowed them to invest in time and trouble. The oldest recorded continuous winery in the world is the Josephshofer vineyard in Germany's Mosel Valley, belonging to the Reichsgraf von Kesselstatt estate. Documents in the museum of Trier Cathedral prove its existence in 596 AD when it was ceded to the monks of Saint Martin. Remarkably it remained in their possession for 1,193 years until 1789.

It has only recently been proven that Roman vineyards existed in **England** and it is quite possible that they also did in **South Wales** but little research has been undertaken. In 731 AD the great monk historian, known as The Venerable Bede, wrote of vineyards thriving in England and Ireland and Roger Crisp, author of *Vineyards, The Wessex Series*, has confirmed the existence of many Saxon vineyards in the south and west of England. When the Normans conquered Britain they went on a building spree, erecting hundreds of churches and castles and encouraged the cultivation of vines. Another monk-historian, Geraldis Cambrensis, wrote during the middle of the 11th century of the first recorded vineyard in Wales, when he described his father's castle at Manorbier.

The dissolution of the monasteries by King Henry VIII in 1536 meant the destruction of the monastic vineyards, which were the largest in Britain. It was not until 1875 that the Scottish-born Third Marquess of Bute attempted a revival on land alongside Castell Coch near Cardiff. The satirical magazine *Punch* sneered at his attempt *if the wine is ever made it will take four to drink it, two to hold the victim down and one to pour it down his throat*. Today around 350 wineries battle against the elements, the majority depending upon French and Germanic hybrid vines. The best-known names include Cariad, Denbies, Chapel Down, Carr Taylor, Hidden Spring and Three Choirs.

Finding comparable examples in **the United States** is hampered by the intervention of Prohibition from 1920-33, an era when many vineyards were grubbed out. The oldest continuous winery in America is Mirassou Vineyards at San José, California, which was founded in 1854 but even they couldn't produce wine for commercial sale during Prohibition.

Prior to the American Wars of Independence the 13 English colonies saw various attempts at professional vine cultivation. The first publicly acknowledged real success came in the early 19th century, when Nicholas Longworth planted a vineyard at Cincinnati, Ohio in 1840. His chief claim to fame lay with a *Sparkling Catawba*, a name which would cause most wine enthusiasts to balk today. Catawba is a foxy native American variety, believed to originate in the Carolinas. It is often made in a medium-sweet style and its main distinguishing feature is a complete lack of finesse. By 1845 many other growers had followed suit and the state of Ohio produced 300,000 gallons of wine in that year. By 1860, as viticulture spread to southern Ohio, the state achieved the largest volume of wine production in America. But just as suddenly as the vineyard boom started, it collapsed in 1864 with the outbreak of the Civil War. The men of Ohio literally left and most of the vineyards went untended. When the stragglers returned the challenge didn't seem as attractive. In the meantime the Gold Rush had taken tens of thousands of European immigrants west to

California. Many of these had lived on the land, which usually meant they were experienced in viticulture. Few found gold, many preferred to stay in California than return home, and inevitably the state's first wine industry began to develop.

South Africa should have benefited from the fact that many of its wine estates date from the 17th century when the early Dutch settlers arrived. But this advantage has been undermined by the events of the second half of the 20th century, when its wine industry became trapped in a time warp by Apartheid. Just as Australia, New Zealand and California were beginning to inspire the wine market with their delicious, New World, fruit-forward wines, South Africa found its export markets frozen by political sanctions and was largely bypassed by the first couple of generations of modern winemaking. Only when Nelson Mandela came to power did the rush to learn begin, with the realisation that for centuries many vines had been planted in the wrong regions. There are now many new projects involving the up and coming generation of young winemakers, who have trained abroad, and/or the hiring of experienced foreign winemakers. An excellent example is Bellingham, which was founded by Hollander G Vuuren in 1693. Under the control of young winemaker Graham Weerts, who has worked in five countries, it is now producing exciting Chardonnay and Merlot in the cooler Coastal Region away from its fairly hot estate in Paarl.

Growing the Grapes

This can be a significant factor in controlling the quality and calculating the retail price of a wine.

Some producers grow all their own grapes. Inevitably these are often small operators or owners of single estates. Legal requirements differ considerably between countries as to what can be called an estate wine, but often you can learn the true situation from the back labels. These will normally indicate that the wine has been made exclusively from estate-grown grapes, but do not be fooled that this will guarantee the superiority of the wine.

In contrast it is virtually impossible for many large volume producers to grow sufficient grapes to meet the demands for particular wines.

Some producers grow some of their own grapes and purchase the balance from other growers.

Some producers grow and purchase grapes and also buy both grape juice and wine.

Some producers don't own any vines and buy all the grapes they require from grape growers.

An excellent example of this last method is the great French Champagne house of Charles Heidsieck, which produces outstanding results without owning any vineyards. Its late legendary winemaker Daniel Thibault won numerous awards for his blending skills without having a single Charles Heidsieck grape to press.

In some parts of Europe, sometimes due to Napoleonic law, many thousands of individuals have inherited tiny vineyard blocks that can be even smaller than 0.04 of a hectare (a tenth of an acre). Such growers usually belong to co-operatives where they share their grapes and the facilities with others. An example of this is the

Citra co-operative in Central Italy, renowned for its Montepulciano d'Abruzzo.

Also during the 1960s and 70s various German blends like Blue Nun and Black Tower attracted huge sales worldwide. If it hadn't been

for the inheritance laws they could never have found the volume of wine needed.

The Jacob's Creek winery based at Rowland Flat in the Barossa Valley of South Australia is a prime example of progress in grape management. Head winemaker Philip Laffer explains to visitors how matters have changed since 1990, when the brand was just beginning to rise as an international star. Originally all their grapes were picked during the day and by hand. Now they are all picked during the night between about midnight and 8am and by automatic harvesting machines. The reasons are that the average daily temperatures in their Australian vineyards during the harvest can be in the high 30s or even low 40s Celsius, while at night they will drop into the mid or lower 20s. The cooler conditions enable the grapes to retain freshness and good acidity in their juice which means better wine. Also there have been many improvements in automatic picking.

Many readers might be surprised to learn that when the harvest is at its peak, it is unlikely to find any winemakers in the Jacob's Creek home winery. They will be scattered amongst the tens of thousands of acres of vines, carrying out the most basic tests by literally picking grapes and biting them to detect whether they have the correct balance of freshness and ripeness. Philip Laffer says *there is a 1 to 2 day window of opportunity, pick too early and the grapes will be green and acidic, pick too late and they will be dull and Port-like*. Of course Port can be world class, but if you want to make a lighter, fresh, fruit-driven wine, then picking too late is not the answer, for the grapes will be overripe.

Much has been written about the famous Bordeaux chateaux. The actual buildings vary from fine castles to near rubble. One definition, from some 30 years ago, stated that for a property to be entitled to call itself a Bordeaux chateau the wine must be made from grapes grown within one estate on which there must be a habitable *heraditement*. Clearly there are many exceptions but, in all fairness, the French have become stricter and more precise in their use of the term *chateau*. Prior to the involvement of the United Kingdom in the European Union many barrels of Bordeaux chateau grown wines were shipped to British wine cellars, where they were aged and later bottled. Now all such wines must be bottled in the region of production and many carry the term *mis en chateau* indicating that they have been bottled at the original chateau. In contrast it is still possible for a First Growth from Pauillac to include a limited volume of wine from small vineyard parcels in a neighbouring appellation.

In all likelihood we probably worry far too much about where the grapes come from. The quality and character of the wine should be the real priority.

Some producers of sparkling wines in Mediterranean climates, in Australia and California, deliberately pick their grapes underripe in order to have sufficient acidity. This method can achieve attractive results but never compares with fully ripened grapes that due to cool climatic conditions are finely balanced.

Wine Books

First written reference to wine The Babylonian epic of Gilgamesh, circa 1800 BC mentions a mystical vineyard in its 10th tablet.

Roman wine writing Cato (233-149 BC), Varro (118-29 BC), Virgilius (70-19 BC), Columella (2 BC-65 AD) and Plato (23-79 AD) all wrote of wine and vines with Columella's works being regarded as the most significant on the subject.

First wine books Expert opinion varies, but the 2 generally recognised claimants for this position both date from 1478 AD. They are the *Tractatus de Vino et Ejus Proprietate* whose author is anonymous and *Liber de Vinis* by Arnaldus de Villanova. Copies of both are held in the British Museum.

Others claim the distinction for the fourth section/book of *Opus Ruralium Commodorum* written by the Italian, Petrus de Crescentiis (1230-1310 AD). It was published as a wine book after his death by order of the French King Charles V in 1373. However some do not regard it as a book in its own right.

First English language wine book *A new Boke of the natures and properties of all wines that are commonly used here in England*, written by William Turner, was published in London in 1568 by William Seres. It was the first English language book to deal solely with the subject of wine.

Smallest wine book The smallest wine book is called *Wine The Universal Drink* and is published by Ariel Books, part of Andrew McMeel Publishing of Kansas City, Missouri, USA. It is a hardback edition containing 28 pages, measuring 5.5 x 4.5cms (2.16 x 1.77 inches) with a depth of 1.27cms (0.5 inches), and is printed in Singapore.

Largest wine book *The Chateaux of Bordeaux* by Charles Mozley and Hugh Johnson, published in 1975, measures 49.53 x 62.23cms (19.5 x 24.5 inches.) It was limited to just 50 copies. Another edition was made by placing loose pages in a box measuring 68.58 x 53.34cms (27 x 21 inches), but it is generally considered to fall outside the category because it was not bound.

Heaviest wine book Believed to be *O Portugal Vinicola* written by Cincinnato da Costa in 1900. It tipped the scales at 13kgs or 28.6lbs.

Best Seller It is widely recognised that the on-going publication of Hugh Johnson's *Pocket Wine Guide* is the best-selling wine book. The publishers report that sales are approaching 7.5 million copies. At the time of writing it is in its 26th edition.

Number of wine books known A 1985 bibliography *Wine into Words* by James M Gabler lists over 3,200 English Language wine books but includes editions on viticulture, home made wine making and wine related poetry. It is likely that since that year the figure has more than doubled.

Curious wine titles Wine and wine-related words prove useful for the titles of books of all

C000072253

AIR
BAND
RADIO
GUIDE
Third Edition
Graham Duke

IAN ALLAN
Publishing

Acknowledgements

My grateful thanks are due to the many organisations and individual persons who have helped with the preparation of this publication. Although it is not possible to mention everyone, special thanks are acknowledged to the following:

Aerad, London; The Aviation Hobby Centre; Civil Aviation Authority, London (Public Relations Department); Flightdeck (The Aviation Shop); Garex Electronics; Javiation; Jeppesen, Frankfurt; Lowe Electronics; National Air Traffic Services (NATS) — London ATCC, NATS — Scottish and Oceanic, NATS — Frequency Management Division, Nevada; Radiocommunications Agency, London; Radio Research, Stoke-on-Trent; Royal Air Force, No 1 AIDU, Northolt; Sandpiper Communications; Servisair, Bramhall, Cheshire; Shannon Aeradio, Ireland and Steepletone.

Once again, my special thanks to Enid and Yvonne for their assistance with the preparation of the manuscript.

Contents

First published 1992
Reprinted 1993
Second edition 1995
Reprinted 1996
Third edition 1997

ISBN 0 7110 2501 0

Published by Ian Allan Publishing

an imprint of Ian Allan Ltd, Terminal House, Station Approach, Shepperton, Surrey TW17 8AS. Printed by Ian Allan Printing Ltd, at its works at Coombelands in Runnymede, England.

Code: 9704/E2

Front cover:
Airbus A340, G-VBUS, of Virgin Atlantic Airways Ltd, and a map showing high level routes across the UK. *Virgin Atlantic/Eurocontrol*

Back cover:
Yupiteru VT-125, one of many airband receivers available. *Nevada*

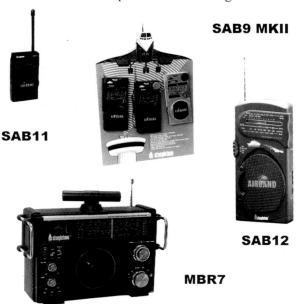

Introduction

Advances in computer technology and electronics have led to the availability of a whole range of sophisticated and comprehensive radio receivers at affordable prices, even though this can sometimes result in overcomplication for the average listener. Many receivers today are capable of a vast spectrum of frequencies and modes, usually well beyond the needs of the air band listener. It is unfortunately true that even the most sophisticated and complicated receiver does not necessarily provide the best reception of aeronautical frequencies, since the wide-range design means that the end result is a compromise. The current fashion is to produce wideband multi-mode receivers which, whilst being superb pieces of equipment, may not provide better reception of air band traffic than their simpler and less expensive counterparts.

This guide is for those readers who simply wish to have some impartial advice on what air traffic control transmissions are all about, and how to go about choosing a suitable receiver. Then, having decided upon the most appropriate piece of equipment, the book deals with the next question raised by most readers — how can we improve the reception of the messages by the use of external antennas, amplifiers and tuners?

Although many aviation enthusiasts have no interest in radio as a subject, the ability to receive commands and responses between ground-based controllers and aircrew is desirable in order to understand and develop the hobby of aviation and air band listening. How this is achieved is of secondary importance, in the same way that someone choosing a television set needs no technical expertise on the theory of the subject.

The author is not a radio expert. However, experience over many years of air band listening and numerous receivers has provided a wealth of practical knowledge which is passed on through this handbook. As with the first edition, I have been able to draw on the experiences of a great many people who regularly listen to aeronautical radio. Some of them are expert in the technology surrounding radio and associated subjects, but just as many are simply interested in the hobby of air band listening without having any particular knowledge of the technical side. In every case their comments and opinions have been greatly valued and hopefully this book will reflect this.

The manuscript for this book will have been completed many months prior to publication; much of the detail will, of course, be earlier than that. It is therefore inevitable that information on particular pieces of equipment may well be out of date by the time you come to read the book, and it is essential, for this reason alone, that you

check with your supplier before deciding on a purchase.

The variety of available air band scanners is changing so quickly that it is almost impossible to produce an up-to-date and meaningful guide covering individual models. Instead, the comments on receivers are of a general nature rather than being specific. The reception of ATC transmissions on VHF and UHF is determined by several factors: height above sea level; proximity of features which can restrict reception; type of antenna system employed; distance between the transmitter and the receiver; the sensitivity of the receiver; the strength of the signal; and, last but not least, the weather.

In other words, the most expensive, sophisticated and sensitive receiver will produce very disappointing results if the location and the antenna system are inadequate. Conversely, a low-cost general-purpose set will give surprisingly good quality reception if it is located near to the transmitter — for example, when used at an airport or connected to a properly designed antenna system. On the other hand, HF or Short Wave radio reception is not influenced to the same extent by these considerations. Long range reception can often be achieved with the simplest of antenna systems.

In conclusion, this book is restricted to general advice on the principles of air band scanners, hopefully providing guidance and help on what to look for, in preference to actually comparing receiver A with receiver B. There are several other publications available which are eminently suitable reading for anyone who is interested in the technical aspects of radio.

Air Traffic Control in the UK

The United Kingdom is covered by three Air Traffic Control centres covering regions which are entitled *London, Scottish* and *Manchester.* These are located at West Drayton, a few miles north of Heathrow; at Prestwick in Ayrshire, Scotland; and at Manchester International Airport.

The London and Scottish areas are known as Flight Information Regions (FIRs), and the Upper Airspace (above 24,500ft) as Upper Flight Information Regions (UIRs).

The London FIR extends across Wales and England to 55° North, approximately in line with Newcastle upon Tyne.

North of this line is the Scottish FIR which covers all of Scotland and Northern Ireland. Both FIRs extend to the boundaries of the adjacent European FIRs to the south and east of the British Isles. The Scottish FIR controls a large area of the sea north of Scotland.

The Manchester centre covers a large part of central England up to FL 195.

Except for Northern Ireland, Ireland's air traffic is handled by the Shannon FIR, with the control centre located at Shannon.

The Control System

The air traffic control system in the United Kingdom is subdivided into several categories of service which vary in degree according to the kind of airspace in which the flight is operating.

Information Services

The simplest air traffic service is one in which pilots are given information concerning the local weather and details of other flights in the vicinity; the responsibility for remaining clear of other aircraft rests with the pilot. Any decisions to change level or heading will be at the discretion of the pilot, although the ATC unit will normally expect to be kept informed of any such manoeuvres. An Information Service will be non-radar, although sometimes it will be backed up by a radar unit, but as not all flights in the area may be seen on radar the service is often limited.

Information Services are provided for low-level general aviation flights routeing across the country, mostly in good visual conditions. Normally the service will be provided by local airfield controllers, either civil or military, complemented by a non-radar service given by the air traffic control centres in London and Scotland. These are known respectively as 'London Information' and 'Scottish Information'.

Advisory Services

An enhanced level of service is provided by a Radar Advisory Service, although the responsibility for remaining clear of other traffic still remains with the pilot.

The ATC unit will provide advice on other traffic to assist in avoiding other flights but the pilot does not have to accept that advice; therefore the decision as to what action to take is not that of the controller.

Radar Advisory Services are provided by a network of military and civilian airfields and also by the three centres to various flights operating outside controlled airspace.

Controlled Airspace

Regions of airspace in which the controller has responsibility for ensuring that air traffic is safely

Opposite:
One of the high-power radar stations providing a service for UK airspace. *Civil Aviation Authority*

Right:
Yupiteru MVT-7000 multi-band receiver. *Nevada*

separated are referred to as Controlled Airspace. Pilots are only permitted to fly in such areas if they are qualified to fly on aircraft instruments, rather than visually. Pilots have to comply with instructions given by air traffic control regarding headings and changes of level.

Most controlled airspace in the UK is in the form of 'airways', usually 10-mile-wide corridors with a base level around 3,000ft and an upper limit of 24,500ft. The airway centre lines are based on straight lines between radio navigation beacons, and they link major airports and provide cross-country routes for intercontinental air traffic.

Above 24,500ft the whole of the airspace is subject to positive control, although the major routes still follow the same tracks set out by the airways in the lower airspace.

All airspace in the United Kingdom is categorised by a series of letters defined by the International Civil Aviation Organisation. The airspace which is subject to the highest degree of control is known as Class A airspace and this includes the system of airways which exist below FL 245 (approximately 24,500ft).

All airspace above FL 245 is Class B and aircraft are always subject to a control service.

At the moment there is no Class C airspace in the UK but other classes (D, E, F and G) are in use and cover the entire country. The airspace with the least control is Class G which is also known as Free Airspace. However, none of these categories are referred to by pilots or air traffic controllers when talking to each other. The only phrases that are used are 'controlled' or 'uncontrolled' airspace.

Around airfields, aircraft at lower levels will be handled by controllers at the airfield itself, even though not all the flights will actually land at the airfield.

Below:
Airport Control at Zurich airport. *Siemens Plessey Systems*

Opposite:
Yupiteru MVT-8000 multi-band base station. *Nevada*

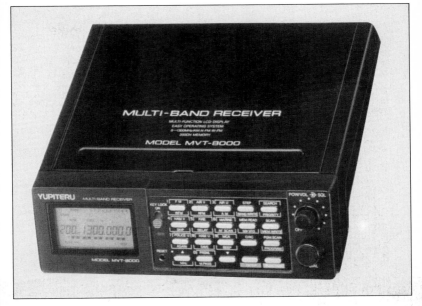

Oceanic Airspace

Away from the populated areas of Europe an entirely different control system exists; this is because VHF radio waves are limited in range, and also because radar cover also depends on the line-of-sight principle.

Flights which are out of range of land — for example when crossing the North Atlantic — do not use VHF or UHF radio for communicating with the control centres. Instead, High Frequency (HF) radio is employed since this has an almost unlimited range, although it is less predictable in quality and reliability. However, the use of HF is gradually reducing as datalink via satellite becomes more widespread. These systems allow the rapid and reliable transfer of information between aircraft and the ground and there is little doubt that HF radio will play only a small part in aviation in the future.

As the flights cannot be seen on radar, the control process is achieved by obtaining radio reports from the aircrew on the position of the aircraft and comparing them with the flight plans to ensure that the required separation is maintained throughout the crossing.

The control centre for the Atlantic region is located at Prestwick in Scotland, but the actual messages from the aircraft are handled by a radio station at Ballygirreen, near Shannon in Ireland, from where they are sent by telex to Prestwick. Any replies from the control centre are transmitted to the aircraft by the Ballygirreen station.

Plans are already in hand for replacing the use of position reports and HF radio on busy oceanic routes with satellite-based air traffic control which will do away with the present system in many parts of the world, but probably not before 2010.

Trials with satellite communications have been continuing now for several years but so far no firm implementation dates have been announced for the system to replace current arrangements.

Communications

The various levels and categories of the control process require the use of numerous radio frequencies, and the new listener will probably have difficulty in following the variety of messages passing between pilots and controllers.

With practice, however, a pattern will gradually develop and experience will provide the listener with something resembling a sixth sense for locating the correct frequencies.

Further Reading

This brief introduction to the system of air traffic control in the United Kingdom has merely touched upon the outline of the very complex and ever-changing methods by which flights are handled by ground controllers.

If you would like to know more about the detail of the procedures and systems in use today you will probably find the companion publication *abc Air Traffic Control* useful.

1 The Legal Position

It is essential that anybody contemplating using a receiver to listen to ATC transmissions should be clear about the legal position.

Any apparatus designed for the receipt of aviation messages is considered to be an aeronautical station under the terms of the UK Air Navigation Order and as such requires the approval of the Civil Aviation Authority. The CAA, however, only recognises receiving stations that are required to provide an aeronautical service as being suitable for approval; therefore any other person or organisation will not be successful in applying for such authorisation.

The Air Navigation Order (ANO) and the Wireless Telegraphy Act 1949 both specifically prohibit the use of radio apparatus capable of receiving aeronautical messages — if you use, or intend to use, such equipment you can be prosecuted by the Civil Aviation Authority (through its agents) or the Police under either or both sets of legislation. The Police are becoming increasingly concerned about the number of scanners in use, particularly those which are used by criminals in order to monitor Police frequencies and those which are used for the purpose of monitoring private telephone conversations. They have a certain degree of training in the use of scanners and are quite capable of examining a receiver to determine which frequencies are stored in the memories. If it is found that a particular frequency is stored in the memory, the Police will assume that the intention is to listen to that particular channel and will use this as evidence in a prosecution.

The Wireless Telegraphy Act 1949 (amended by the Post Office Act 1969 and the Wireless Telegraphy Act 1967) states in section 5:

'Any person who... otherwise than under the authority of the Secretary of State, uses any wireless telegraphy apparatus with intent to obtain information as to the contents of any message... shall be guilty of an offence.'

Furthermore, with certain exceptions, it is an offence under Section 1 of the Interception of Communications Act 1985 if a person 'intentionally intercepts a communication in the course of its transmission by post or by means of a public telecommunications system'.

However, there is still some doubt concerning the attitude of the courts in reaching a decision in such cases. In the House of Lords on 4 June 1987 a case between Rudd and The Secretary of State for Trade and Industry resulted in a prosecution failing since the intent of the person involved was in doubt. Further cases as late as 1995 have followed the same principle and no convictions have arisen.

The Broadcasting Bill also covers the unlawful use of scanners. Section 147 states:

'Any person who has any station for wireless telegraphy, or apparatus for wireless telegraphy in his possession, or under his control, and intends to use it in contravention of Section One of this Act shall be guilty of an offence.'

All of this means that you must not listen to any frequency that is not being broadcast for the benefit of the public at large, and for which you do not possess a certificate of approval. The very act of listening is itself contrary to law. Air band receivers have been confiscated in the UK, although there is no record of any person being prosecuted for listening to ATC transmissions, at least in the UK.

One of the latest and most sophisticated scanners which covers a very wide range of frequencies has a new feature, namely the inclusion of a bank of memories which require a password in order to gain access. Obviously this is intended for those frequencies which the listener wishes to remain confidential.

Bear in mind that many foreign countries take a much more serious view of air band listening than Britain, and even the sale of receivers capable of receiving air traffic control frequencies is prohibited.

Anyone considering taking a radio receiver abroad should be aware of the strictly applied regulations of some countries regarding unauthorised listening. At best, the authorities might confiscate the equipment. You might find yourself in serious trouble if you take your air band scanner to certain countries.

If any person chooses to disregard the law and listen to non-broadcast frequencies, then this must be at the risk of being found out and prosecuted. If you choose to act in this way, keep the receiver discreetly out of sight and use an earpiece or headphones when listening.

Using a receiver in the public areas of an airport lounge, for example, on maximum volume is likely to attract the attention of the authorities as well as causing annoyance to other people — not everyone is interested in ATC messages!

At the present time, the authorities appear not to take very much interest in people who choose to listen to ATC frequencies, but there is a risk that a blatant disregard for the law may result in the position changing to the detriment of all those who pursue the hobby with no more than innocent interest.

Showing off your ability to receive the messages of controllers and pilots on your air band scanner could possibly result in everybody being penalised in the long run.

2 What Can I Hear

Equipped with any of the currently available receivers listed in the appendices it will be relatively easy to hear ATC messages in most parts of the UK. Even though there are numerous special phrases and words which are unique to aviation, once these are understood the language is not difficult to follow.

It is obviously essential that the provision of air traffic services are closely co-ordinated on a worldwide basis: to achieve this there are areas of ATC responsibility dividing the world's surface into manageable regions. These control areas coincide approximately with the countries of the world, while sparsely populated regions and oceans are usually the responsibility of more than one of the adjacent nations.

Flight Information Regions
The UK forms part of a European network of control areas with two regions of control covering Scotland, England, Wales and Northern Ireland. There is a separate centre based at Manchester Airport which covers a large area of central England up to FL 195 (approximately 19,500ft).

England and Wales fall within a control area known as the London Flight Information Region, while Scotland is covered by another control area known as the Scottish Flight Information Region.

Within each Flight Information Region (FIR) the control area is divided into several types of airspace — for example, airfields, air routes, military training areas, danger areas and so on.

Air Traffic Services
Most, but not all, of the aircraft which fly in each of these separate kinds of airspace will be in radio contact with air traffic controllers whose function is to ensure maximum safety allied to the most expeditious flight profile. Some of the airspace does not require radio communication between the aircraft and the ground.

Although referred to by the general term 'controllers', they do not necessarily have direct control over the aircraft to which they may be speaking.

According to the type of airspace in which the aircraft is flying the air traffic controller may be merely providing appropriate information or advice to the pilot, who must then decide on what action, if any, to take to remain safely clear of other nearby traffic. It is only in certain types of airspace that the controller becomes responsible for the proper separation of the flight — generally this is referred to as 'controlled' or regulated airspace. Aircraft and flightcrews must be suitably qualified and technically equipped before being allowed to operate in such areas.

Below:
Terminal Area Control, London Area and Terminal Control Centre. *Siemens Plessey Systems*

It follows therefore that the messages between controllers and flightcrews will vary in content according to the kind of service being provided. Furthermore, the controllers' messages will be transmitted from numerous ground stations dotted all over the country. Most of these will be located at civil and military airfields, where the personnel will offer a service to flights using the airfield or passing through the area.

As well as these 'local' operations, there will be numerous long-distance, high-flying aircraft criss-crossing the region en route to distant destinations. Many of these will be overflying the London or Scottish FIRs between the American continent and Europe.

Control Centres
These high-level flights will be controlled from one of two Air Traffic Control centres. The centre for the London FIR is located at West Drayton (near Heathrow Airport), while the centre for the Scottish FIR is at Prestwick in Scotland.

Because VHF and UHF radio signals operate on a line-of-sight principle, it would not be practical to locate the transmitters for the whole of the UK at West Drayton or Prestwick — the effectiveness of the signals would be so poor that flights at the perimeter of the regions would be unable to receive the transmissions.

For this reason it is necessary to locate the transmitters at strategic points throughout the regions where they are able to provide the most effective radio cover to aircraft within their jurisdiction.

To avoid any possible interference and confusion between controllers and flightcrews, the system is designed with separate radio frequencies for the different functions across the control areas, and the country is also divided into sectors of airspace both on plan and horizontally with separate groups of controllers responsible for each sector.

Frequencies
It is obviously essential that the same frequency is never used where it might be overheard by a controller or pilot for whom it is not intended. As it is possible to receive VHF or UHF signals up to 150 miles distant it requires careful planning across a region, and even between adjacent countries, to ensure that interference is minimised, if not eliminated.

Although there are hundreds of available frequencies for aeronautical use, the organisers of the congested airspace of Europe are finding it increasingly difficult to plan the distribution of frequencies effectively.

Below:
Boeing 747-400 of Singapore Airlines. *Singapore Airlines*

Those parts of the UK with the highest traffic density will, of necessity, employ the greatest number of separate sectors and frequencies and the most transmitters, so the reception of messages will present no difficulty for the air band listener. This is the case in London and the southeast of England. Furthermore, the relatively flat countryside means that the messages are uninterrupted by high ground as in other parts of the country.

On the other hand, listeners who live in the more remote and rugged areas, such as North Wales and the Lake District, will undoubtedly suffer the problems of difficult and limited reception caused by high ground combined with few transmitters, although, of course, there will be fewer difficulties in receiving messages from aircraft in flight.

This, then, is the framework against which ATC messages are passed between ground personnel and flightcrews.

Airfield controllers deal with low-level flights close to the field — at most 50 miles away — therefore the transmitters they use are not required to be very high-powered. It follows that an air band receiver which is beyond this distance will be unlikely to receive ground transmissions from airfields, although it is possible to greatly improve reception by the use of suitable aerials.

High-level long-distance flights are handled by civilian and military controllers at one of the air traffic control centres; each team of controllers has responsibility for a separate area (or sector) of airspace and certain dedicated frequencies are allocated to each of the sectors.

The transmitters for the control centres are located on suitable sites remote from the centre, where they are able to provide the most efficient service to the flights in the area. The difference between these transmitters and those used at airfields is affected by the flight levels of the aircraft. Whereas the low-powered equipment at airfields has to be effective only as far as local traffic is concerned, the en-route transmitters must be able to cover a far greater range because all the flights dealt with are at a relatively high level.

There are only a few en-route transmitters in the UK; listening to high-level traffic on an air band receiver often results in messages from the aircraft being heard without difficulty, whereas the ATC responses are unlikely to be heard unless the receiver is somewhere in the vicinity of one of the transmitters.

Frequency Details
The frequency of a radio signal is measured in cycles per second; one cycle per second is known as a HERTZ; one thousand cycles per second is referred to as one KILOhertz, and one million cycles per second is known as one MEGAhertz. Thus, one thousand Kilohertz (kHz)

is the same as one Megahertz (MHz). For example, one popular frequency used by flights crossing the North Atlantic is '5649'. This is either 5649 kHz or (more properly) 5.649MHz or in other words 5MHz and 649kHz.

All the frequencies used between air traffic controllers and aircrew are in Megahertz, grouped into three blocks. The lowest frequency is 2MHz, the highest 400MHz. More details on this are given later.

The way in which frequencies are quoted can sometimes be confusing. Frequencies used by flights over the North Atlantic for instance are given in Kilohertz which means they consist of four or five figures (eg 8864 or 10069). However, receiver specifications normally state the range of frequencies in Megahertz — in these cases the range falls between 8 and 11MHz.

For example, a receiver which is advertised as having a range between 150kHz and 60MHz is the same as saying that the receiver covers .15MHz to 60MHz or, alternatively, 150kHz to 60,000kHz.

Aeronautical Frequencies
The frequencies used for aviation messages are in three groups:

■ *Group One — High Frequency*
This is used where it is necessary to pass messages over long distances. The range is between 2MHz and 23MHz, although not every frequency is allocated for aeronautical purposes. Groups of frequencies within the range are designated to other uses. This group is sometimes called 'Short Wave' but the modern term is High Frequency, abbreviated to 'HF' by controllers and pilots alike. The use of HF for aeronautical purposes is declining with the advent of datalink and satellites providing ATC with much more accurate and reliable communications with aircraft.

■ *Group Two — Very High Frequency*
Civil flights and certain military flights transmitting across short distances — perhaps 100 miles or so — will use frequencies between 118MHz and 136.975MHz. This group is referred to as Very High Frequency or VHF. Some pilots, especially those on military flights, describe the VHF range as 'Victor' frequencies.

■ *Group Three — Ultra High Frequency*
Military flights transmitting over distances of around 100 miles or so (the same distances as for VHF) are allocated frequencies in a range between 225MHz and 400MHz. This group is known as Ultra High Frequency or UHF, often known as 'Uniform' frequencies to pilots.

There are certain other frequencies outside these ranges which are used for other specialist purposes, mainly navigation beacons,

instrument landing systems and so on. These are between 108MHz and 117.950MHz in 50kHz spacings.

Another group of frequencies (455.475-455.975MHz NFM) are used as repeater stations at airfields by ground operational staff who are able to listen to ATC instructions at the same time as communicating with each other.

Which Receiver?

Most newcomers to the hobby of air band listening buy a receiver suitable for the second group of frequencies, which is the one used by all civilian aircraft in London and Scottish airspace. They are likely to be the least expensive, readily available (particularly on the secondhand market), give good results and (important for beginners) the amount of air traffic on individual frequencies is far greater than with any other aeronautical band.

Although the density of traffic varies considerably in different parts of the country, listening to transmissions on VHF can often result in an almost continuous stream of messages during the day.

Some VHF receivers are also capable of receiving transmissions on the third group of frequencies (the Ultra High Frequency or UHF range) in addition to VHF. Receivers for UHF exclusively are not normally available — but check with your supplier first.

The extent of military transmissions on the UHF band is far less than is usually experienced with civilian air traffic on VHF. This is partly because there are a very much larger number of available frequencies (if every frequency between 225MHz and 400MHz were in use at 25kHz spacings there would be 7,000 channels!) and partly because military aviation transmissions are allocated frequencies not only related to the location of the flight but also the function of the flight — in other words, the kind of task the aircraft is performing often determines the frequency to be used irrespective of the area in which it is working.

Military flights tend to operate mostly during weekday periods; the number of flights taking place during the night and at weekends is very much reduced.

High Frequency (Short Wave)

The transmissions on the first group of frequencies (High Frequency) can be received only on a certain type of receiver, and because the principles involved are quite different from those used for VHF and UHF the subject is dealt with separately in Chapter 6.

There are now several hand-held receivers on the market which cover all three aeronautical ranges.

Where to Look

All the frequencies in use for air traffic control purposes in the UK are readily available to the public by a variety of means. Apart from those official publications which are produced for the aviation world, there are also several manuals specifically intended to give ATC enthusiasts the detail they require in an easy to understand style.

The official publications consist mainly of two formats. First there are charts used for air navigation purposes, covering individual airfields, airways, high-level air routes, oceanic areas and terminal control areas; each has the principal radio communication frequencies printed on the sheet, often grouped together in one corner of the chart. Of course, the frequencies on the individual sheets are limited to those which relate directly to the area covered by the chart, so to obtain full coverage of all frequencies necessitates the purchase of a great number of charts, obviously an expensive exercise.

The second official group of publications from which frequencies can be obtained are known as the *Communications Supplements*, published by the Royal Air Force or by Aerad. Each organisation produces its own version, both being very similar in content. They cover a great amount of detail about aviation procedures, as well as frequencies, but they are a little on the expensive side for the amateur.

The other source of information on frequency allocation are the numerous books produced specifically for this purpose. There are several publications which specialise in providing very detailed listings of VHF and UHF aeronautical radio frequencies, usually classified into airfields, airways and other useful categories such as 'company' frequencies. None of the official publications provide the same level of detail as these specialist books, so they are probably a 'best buy' as far as total coverage is concerned.

Most of the frequencies in use in UK airspace are listed at the end of this book, although it is inevitable that some of these will have been superseded by the time of publication.

Of course, many pilots have difficulty in being aware of some of the new frequencies. However, every change of frequency is notified to the pilot by the controller, who will be fully conversant with any changes. The air band listener can adopt the same approach, listening out for new frequencies given out by the air traffic controllers over the radio. Experienced air band enthusiasts will quickly spot any new frequencies as soon as they arise; their need for official publications on frequency changes is therefore very limited.

What Can I Hear?
First-time listeners to an air band receiver are likely to be bewildered by the various transmissions they hear; some of the messages will not be concerned with Air Traffic Control. Many of the 760 channels on VHF and the 7,000 on UHF are allocated to several categories of service provided by ATC in terms of positive control, advice or simply information, depending on the circumstances.

Obviously the primary allocations are for transmissions between flights and controllers, perhaps locally where airfield conditions prevail, or 'en-route' for high-level traffic under the control of a major control centre.

The transmissions will be in one of the following categories:

Radio Navigation Beacons
These are Very High Frequency Omni-Directional Radio (VOR) or Doppler Very High Frequency Omni-Directional Radio (DVOR). These are the main navigation facilities located at important points on airways. The identity of the beacon is transmitted in Morse Code, continuously throughout the day and night, on the frequency indicated on radio navigation charts. The name of each of the beacons is known as its 'designator' — for example, Clacton VOR in Norfolk is designated Charlie Lima November (CLN) and transmits on frequency 114.55MHz.

All VHF beacons operate on frequencies between 108 MHz and 117.950MHz. They are listed in Appendix V.

Airfield Conditions
There are four VHF frequencies which broadcast current details for UK airfields, each of which gives a variety of information on a continuous basis.

The information provided in this way is known as 'VOLMET', and the broadcasts cover the following locations:

■ London Volmet Main — Frequency 135.375 — Amsterdam, Brussels, Dublin, Glasgow, London/Gatwick London/Heathrow, London/Stansted, Manchester, Paris Charles De Gaulle.

■ London Volmet South — Frequency 128.6 — Birmingham, Bournemouth, Bristol, Cardiff, Jersey, Luton, Norwich, Southampton, Southend.

■ London Volmet North — Frequency 126.6 — Blackpool, East Midlands, Isle of Man, Leeds-Bradford, Liverpool, London/Gatwick, Manchester, Newcastle, Teesside.

■ Scottish Volmet — Frequency 125.725 — Aberdeen, Belfast/Aldergrove, Edinburgh, Glasgow, Inverness, London/Heathrow, Prestwick, Stornoway, Sumburgh.

The broadcasts are compiled from prerecorded voice segments which cover all possible combinations of weather conditions. These are automatically linked together by computer to give a very realistic continuous message for each airport covered. The broadcasts are continuous throughout the day and night, with automatic updating as new details of conditions are received.

Weather broadcasts, including those on HF, are detailed in Appendix VII.

Automatic Terminal Information Service (ATIS)
Many of the larger airfields in the UK broadcast details of local weather conditions on a continuous basis on specific frequencies; these are published in various documents relating to airfield facilities, details of which are covered in the appendices.

The popular airfields with continuously broadcast information are listed but by the time this book is published some of the frequencies may have been changed and other locations will probably have been added. Small airports will not be provided with a dedicated airport information frequency; instead the weather and other relevant details will be passed, on request, by ATC personnel to individual flights.

As airfields become increasingly busy, the 'air time' taken by controllers in reading out weather

details reaches a level whereby an alternative method becomes essential. The solution is to provide a separate frequency used purely for the continuous broadcast of local conditions. (It should be noted that 'continuous' may not mean that the full 24 hours will be covered. In some cases, the transmission times may only be, for example, between 0900 and 2100 UTC.)

Airfield information transmissions are known as 'ATIS' (Automatic Terminal Information Service). The message is preceded by a letter (for example 'Hotel'). The broadcast will continue on a repetitive basis until one of the aspects included in the message is changed. The revised information will then be broadcast in an updated format prefixed with the next letter of the alphabet — in this case 'India'.

When pilots first contact the airfield they are able to identify the information they have obtained on their second radio by reference to the particular letter — for example, 'Information India received'.

Company Frequencies

It is essential that aircraft crews are able to make contact with their operating bases on dedicated radio frequencies rather than pass messages through the channels used for ATC purposes. In fact, controllers will usually refuse to handle non-ATC messages (except, of course, in an emergency) but will instead request the caller to select one of the frequencies notified for such use.

The major airlines will have at least one frequency in the UK for company use. Virtually all company frequencies are in a range between 129MHz and 132MHz, although by no means every channel will be used for this purpose. A small number of company frequencies are contained within the band between 136MHz and 136.975MHz.

Smaller airlines which are not based in the UK, or which choose not to establish their own base station, may use the company facilities of one of the larger airlines or a specialist handling company such as Servisair.

Company transmissions generally concern flight departure times, arrival times, passenger numbers, requests for wheelchairs, medical assistance, technical advice and so forth.

Some of the frequently used company channels are listed in the appendices.

Gliders, Microlights, Hang-Gliders, Balloons and Parachutists

Each of these categories of flight has been allocated VHF radio frequencies so that pilots may communicate with each other and with their bases. These are as follows:

- Gliders: 129.90
- Hang-Gliders: 129.90
- Balloons: 129.90
- Parachutists: 130.30

En-Route Traffic

The UK is the main gateway to the North Atlantic for European air traffic, with a significant proportion of traffic overflying the region at high levels. These flights are controlled from West Drayton or Prestwick on VHF or UHF frequencies reserved for the major air routes. The same frequencies are used for internal UK flights using the airways system or the upper air routes. As flights cross the country they pass from one sector to the next and each time this occurs there will be a frequency change given by the controller.

The current published frequencies are listed

in the appendices.

Most of the frequencies within this category will be transmitted on the 'offset' principle, which is described in Chapter 7.

North Atlantic Clearances

Before a flight is permitted to enter the airspace of the North Atlantic it is a requirement that ATC clearance be obtained. Pilots can be heard on one of three VHF frequencies requesting Oceanic Clearance from the Oceanic Control Centre at Prestwick. (The particular frequency used by the flight is related to its country of origin.)

The frequencies currently in use are 123.95MHz, 127.65MHz and 135.52MHz.

The ATC responses are transmitted from Dundonald Hill (Scotland) and Davidstow Moor (Cornwall). Therefore, unless the receiver is located in a position within reasonable distance from one of these transmitters the controller will not normally be heard on an air band receiver.

Oceanic Tracks

The tracks themselves vary on a daily basis. They are identified by a letter with westbound tracks commencing with Track Alpha as the most northerly, and eastbound tracks using Track Zulu as the most southerly. The daily track message is given an identification number representing the day of the year, starting with 001 on 1 January. Details of track allocations are sent to airlines by a system of teleprinter networks.

Flight Information Services

Flights outside controlled or regulated airspace may request an information service on one of several frequencies for London or Scottish airspace as detailed in Appendix VIII.

These services are 'procedural', ie not assisted by radar, so the degree of service is limited. Also, due to staffing difficulties, the availability of controllers providing the service from the Scottish or London ATC centres is restricted.

Local Airfields

Most airfields in the UK are allocated two or more radio frequencies for dealing with air traffic arriving at or departing the airfield, or for those flights overflying the airfield within the jurisdiction of the local ATC unit.

The control of traffic landing or taking off is handled by controllers in the Visual Control Room on the 'Tower' frequency. Flights away from the airfield itself will be dealt with by the 'Approach' controller, usually assisted by radar.

Busier airfields may be provided with separate 'Ground' and 'Clearance Delivery' frequencies, dealing with the movement of all traffic on the runways and taxiways, and also flight plan clearances.

At military airfields there are even more subdivisions, each related to the type of service being provided. Often different military frequencies are referred to as 'studs', a term used to indicate pre-set frequencies which can be chosen instantly by the pilot by selecting the appropriate button or 'stud' on the radio.

Most military airfields also have a range of VHF frequencies for those flights which are not provided with UHF radio.

Large and complicated airports such as Heathrow have several other frequencies, each allocated to specific tasks within the airport structure, enabling the airfield to operate smoothly and safely. Large airports simply could not function with only two or three frequencies in use.

Fire Service Vehicles

Virtually all airport fire service vehicles operate on frequency 121.6MHz (VHF) when within the airfield boundary.

Distress and Diversion

Aircraft which are in trouble of any kind — for example, lost with engine trouble or any other emergency situation, can contact the Distress and Diversion unit at the control centres of West Drayton or Prestwick on the international emergency frequencies of 121.5MHz (VHF) or 243MHz (UHF).

In fact, flights which are already under the control of an air traffic control unit will report their problem to the controller on the frequency which they are currently using; the distress frequencies are normally used by aircraft outside regulated airspace.

The popular name given to the Distress and Diversion cell (D and D) is 'Mayday'. There are in fact two levels of emergency — 'Mayday' is for flights in real distress, whereas the lower level of distress, known as 'Pan' is for flights which need assistance or guidance without the urgency of a full-scale emergency situation.

Pilots can often be heard on the distress frequency simulating emergencies with the radio call 'Practice Pan — Practice Pan — Practice Pan'. This gives pilots and controllers an opportunity to practise real life situations without the urgency of real time situations. Obviously if a genuine emergency arises during the practice that will immediately take precedence.

For pilots wishing to confirm their position, a separate 'fixer' service is available through the distress and diversion cell, using the same frequencies.

The possibility of hearing a distress message is, in fact, quite rare. The receiver can be tuned to the emergency frequency for hours at a time without a single transmission being heard. The most likely way to detect such messages is by the use of a voice-activated tape recorder — details of such systems are covered in Chapter 7.

3 Features For VHF/UHF Receivers

This chapter covers the various facilities provided on many of the radio receivers available today suitable for the reception of aeronautical transmissions.

Scanners

This is a general term used to describe a receiver which is either capable of automatically switching from one specific memorised channel to another, often at high speed, in order to detect any transmissions which may be taking place on any of the memorised frequencies, or which can search across all the available frequencies regardless of the memorised channels. If a transmission is detected, the scanning/searching stops. When the transmission is over, the scan continues, although most modern receivers can be set to remain indefinitely on the frequency on which the initial transmission was received.

Scanning usually refers to the receiver systematically stepping through the memorised frequencies programmed into the receiver by the user. Only those frequencies stored in the memory are checked during the scanning operation.

Searching

This term describes the ability of the receiver to step rapidly through all the frequencies, either on VHF or UHF, stopping when a transmission (or any other source of sound) is heard. Usually the search commences at the lowest frequency and proceeds through the entire range to the highest frequency, after which the process is repeated. Many scanners also have a facility of searching between any two specified frequencies chosen by the listener. The ability to search has obvious advantages, allowing the listener to find and record unknown and little-used frequencies. It is particularly helpful when locating 'company' frequencies, which are almost all confined to 80 channels on the VHF band between 130.00MHz and 132.00MHz. By programming the scanner to search between these two limits any company transmissions will be detected. As many of the frequencies are used only occasionally, this can be an efficient and rewarding way of finding the transmissions.

Lockout or Pass

Often, during a scanning or searching operation, the receiver will lock onto a frequency which is giving a continuous unwanted transmission. The receiver will therefore stop at the particular frequency and will remain there until the instruction is given to continue the search/scan.

Above:
Yupiteru MVT-7100 wideband scanner. *Nevada*

Opposite:
Trident TR 2400 wide-range receiver. *Waters and Stanton*

Where unwanted signals are being received, a lockout facility will enable any specific frequency to be eliminated from the process of scan or search — in other words, 'locked out' by the press of a key.

Any frequency locked out can be reinstated just as easily at the press of the appropriate key. Lockout is sometimes referred to as 'Pass'.

Hand-helds

A modern self-explanatory expression, describing receivers which are completely portable. They will be battery powered, of small dimensions, with a simple antenna supplied with the receiver.

Modern technology ensures a sophisticated and comprehensive range of facilities, even in the smallest sets.

Some receivers can be plugged into the electrical circuit of a car, via the cigarette lighter socket, as an alternative to using batteries, or from the mains via a transformer. Another option is to use rechargeable batteries which can be recharged from mains power, sometimes without the need to remove the batteries from the set.

'Hand-helds' are mainly VHF or VHF/UHF, making them particularly suitable for use at airfields or at airshows. There are a small number of 'hand-held' receivers capable of receiving all three aeronautical frequency ranges — VHF, UHF and HF.

Base Stations

Receivers are normally kept at a permanent location, invariably mains operated, and with an antenna system far superior to the portable type used with 'hand-helds'. Usually the receiver is of a 'table-top' design with a large keypad for frequency entries and a large clear display for the actual frequencies.

A modern trend is to combine the functions of 'hand-helds' and base stations into one versatile receiver which can meet the requirements of both types. Many receivers can be operated from any type of power source with any type of antenna connected to it. Specially designed stands incorporating a recharging unit are available to support the 'hand-held' set when used as a base station, helping to overcome the problem of small lightweight sets remaining upright and at the same time easy to operate.

Squelch Control

Virtually all good quality VHF or UHF receivers are provided with a 'squelch' control, a device which is adjusted to eliminate the continuous background noise which can be heard between messages. When a transmission takes place the squelch is automatically opened.

Frequency Steps

Until several years ago the separation between frequencies on both VHF and UHF air bands was 50kHz — for example, 127.000MHz, 127.050, 127.100, 127.150, etc.

Because of the need to increase the number of available channels on VHF it was then decided (in 1976) to double the number of frequencies by reducing the separation to 25kHz, thereby giving twice the range for VHF operations. The examples quoted earlier therefore became 127.000MHz, 127.025, 127.050, 127.075 and so on. In 1992 the separation between UHF frequencies was also reduced from 50kHz to 25kHz.

All VHF receivers on the market today have 25kHz spacings (or 'steps') while UHF receivers have 50kHz steps as a minimum. Check with your supplier that the UHF range is provided with 25kHz steps.

An acute shortage of VHF radio frequencies in the congested airspace of northern Europe will result in a significant change to the channels available. In 1994, at a regional meeting of the International Civil Aviation Organisation (ICAO) held in Vienna, a decision was reached on the action to be taken to deal with the problem. In 1995 the ICAO Special Communications Operations Division concluded that channel spacings in Europe would be reduced from 25kHz to 8.33kHz and that the implementation date would be 1 January 1998. The new channels would be restricted initially to flights at FL 200 and above. It was also decided that, although the new channels would be applicable in UK airspace, this would not take place until 1 January 1999 at the earliest and even then only in the southeast of England where traffic is at its busiest.

In order to implement the changes it will be necessary for some existing frequencies in the 25MHz range to be moved. Airspace will be planned so that certain routes will operate with the new spacing whilst others will stay as they are. It will not be possible to mix 25kHz and 8.33kHz channels on the same routes and there will not be any arrangements for accommodating traffic which does not have the necessary radio equipment fitted. There will be short-term measures to deal with the implementation of the new frequencies and it is probable that new radio receivers fitted to aircraft will have the ability to switch between one mode and another.

As far as the air band listener is concerned, this does not mean that existing equipment has to be changed. The present system will remain as it is for many years and even when the change to the new channel spacing takes effect it will be limited to the southeast of England and the central areas of northern Europe. At present it seems unlikely that the new spacings will be implemented before the year 2000. Nevertheless, there is no doubt that the changes will take place eventually and any purchaser considering a new air band receiver may wish to select one which has the ability to cope with the new channels.

One point to remember when listening to VHF or UHF aeronautical messages is the standard method of describing individual frequencies. Where the frequency consists of six characters, the last digit is never spoken. Also if the fifth digit happens to be zero, it is not spoken. The following examples should clarify the correct phraseology:

■ 127.100 is spoken as — 'one two seven decimal one'
■ 135.375 is spoken as — 'one three five decimal three seven'
■ 118.050 is spoken as — 'one one eight decimal zero five'

Throughout this book frequencies may be given as five or six digit numbers but the above rules will always apply.

Frequency Range
Every receiver will have a range of frequencies specified by the manufacturer. Unless otherwise stated, it may be assumed that the range between the lowest and highest frequency will be 'continuous' — that is to say there will be no gaps. If there are any gaps, then this must be stated by the manufacturer.

Unfortunately, some air band receivers are still advertised as (for example) being suitable for UHF/VHF, whereas in fact the complete range of frequencies is not covered.

Another point to bear in mind is the incorrect frequency range often published for a particular receiver, sometimes to the disadvantage of the manufacturer! It is not uncommon to see a published top frequency of 136.00MHz for a VHF receiver whereas in fact the range extends beyond 137.00MHz.

One further area of interest for the air band listener is the repeater frequencies used at airports. These are Personal Mobile Radio channels in the Narrow FM range which enable airport staff (Ground Engineers, Fire Crews, Vehicle Drivers, Police, etc) to listen to messages from Air Traffic Control and aircraft.

They operate on the duplex system; that is, the base station and the mobile transceiver send and receive messages on different frequencies.

Many air band scanners are not provided with NFM mode, therefore tuning in to these channels will not be possible, but this should not deter one from purchasing a particular receiver since the additional interest is very limited.

Frequencies are usually in the range 453.0000 to 456.0000MHz. Details for individual airports are given in specialist scanning handbooks.

Below:
Trident TR 980 scanner. *Waters and Stanton*

18

4 What to Look For in a VHF/UHF Receiver

The many descriptions used in portraying the various features available on air band receivers can sometimes be difficult to follow and are often confusing; therefore the prospective purchaser may find it useful to have a basic understanding of the terms used by the manufacturers, so that a sensible choice can be made.

Advertisements are often a maze of very descriptive phrases which, at first glance, give the impression that a piece of equipment with so many features must surely be the best value and the most comprehensive. Sometimes in fact the essential detail for the air band listener may be difficult to determine, so before rushing to the telephone to place your order consider carefully what it is you actually want and then check by asking specific questions about the performance of the particular model. This is especially important if your interest is confined to the aeronautical radio frequencies used by civilian and military flights using VHF and UHF.

Remember that there are many excellent sets available on the secondhand market, and purchases made this way are likely to give excellent value for money. The only drawback is that you will not usually be able to return the set if it turns out to be unsuitable for your purpose. On the other hand you are likely to get some first-hand comments on the performance of the set from the seller. Many of the receivers described in Chapter 8 are available only on the secondhand market.

A number of retail outlets do now agree to give a full refund if the receiver turns out to be inadequate, for whatever reason, provided, of course, it is returned in perfect condition within a specified time. Some shops have a sample set which can be loaned to prospective purchasers on a trial basis.

The following checklist is really applicable to receivers which are at the top end of the market (not necessarily meaning the most costly!) from the point of view of their specification.

It is very easy to assume from technical specifications, full of detailed statistics, that the scanner is capable of receiving virtually all that the air band enthusiast can ever require. Careful examination might reveal, however, that although the characteristics of the particular receiver might well be superb it does not necessarily mean that the frequencies cover the entire air band range, or that performance in the air band channels gives the best results.

■ Some sets are said to cover 'VHF and UHF air bands' whereas in fact there can be gaps in the

Above:
Yupiteru VT-125 dedicated VHF air band receiver.
Nevada

frequencies which can actually be received.
■ Bear in mind that the same model receiver produced by the same manufacturer at different times may have an updated range of frequencies on the later model. Also sets on sale abroad may not be equipped to the same standard as UK models since air band frequencies are illegal in many parts of the world.
■ The advice, therefore, is to be quite specific in your questions as to what the new purchase will actually do — ask the seller to state categorically whether each of the requirements is provided.
■ All aeronautical transmissions are in the Amplitude Modulation mode (AM) and this must be confirmed when checking the specification of a receiver.

Very High Frequency (Civil) Coverage
The frequencies which are essential in the VHF range start at 108.000MHz at the lower end and 136.975MHz at the top end, in 'steps' of 25kHz — this means that individual frequencies are separated by 25kHz, the standard difference

between VHF frequencies used throughout the world for air traffic control transmissions. For example, 134.450 is separated from adjacent frequencies by 25kHz, giving 134.475 and 134.425, the channels above and below 134.450. Frequencies between 108.000 and 117.975 MHz cover radio navigation beacons.

25kHz is the normal separation between VHF frequencies fitted to aeronautical radio receivers in civil aircraft, and virtually all modern scanners are capable of selecting the separate channels. It is possible to obtain dedicated VHF air band receivers and generally these give very good results.

Summary: Lowest VHF frequency to be 118.000MHz. Highest VHF frequency to be 136.975MHz. Steps to be 25kHz as a minimum.

Ultra High Frequency (Military) Coverage
If your interest is in the military side of aviation, you might wish to consider the purchase of a receiver which is specifically designed to receive aeronautical transmissions between 225MHz and 400MHz. There are a number of models on the market which are described as being suitable for military use but a careful check is advised before a decision is made since not all receivers are capable of covering the complete military band. In fact, a few scanner advertisements which claim suitability for military use are misleading since only part of the range of frequencies is provided.

Take care to ensure that the set in question does have the full cover between 225 and 400MHz at 25kHz spacings, a total of 7,000 channels.

Also, remember that military air traffic messages tend to be far fewer than those on the civil frequencies; at weekends, bank holidays and during the night the volume of military air traffic is considerably reduced, and there are likely to be long periods of silence between transmissions.

There are several military frequencies used for civil flights which take place, in fact, on VHF, being operated by London or Scottish Military Control. In addition, military flights which are using the normal airways system will do so under the control of the civil air traffic controllers on the normal VHF channels.

Scanners with VHF and UHF air bands exclusively are available, but UHF sets exclusively are virtually unheard of.

Facility for 5kHz Steps
Most air band receivers are designed to operate at frequencies which are 'stepped' (ie separated) by 25kHz, the normal spacing used in aviation voice transmissions.

For technical reasons, ATC messages for high flying en-route civil or military traffic are often transmitted on frequencies which are slightly higher or lower than the published frequency. These can be 2.5, 5.0 or 7.5kHz higher or lower than the promulgated frequency quoted in ATC documentation.

If your scanner is receiving transmissions from a transmitter operating on one of these frequencies (known as 'offsets') it is possible that reception will be improved if the receiver can be tuned to a frequency slightly higher or slightly lower than the published one.

If the signals are strong, the offset will not have any effect on reception, but if the signals are weak (due perhaps to the distance between the receiver and the transmitter) the slight difference can improve matters considerably.

An air band receiver provided with a facility for selecting a frequency higher or lower than the published one can therefore be a positive advantage.

Another use for this feature is to 'tone down' a particularly strong and distorted signal from a transmitter located near to the receiver.

Some of the latest scanners can be programmed to step down as low as 1kHz or as high as 999kHz so that the user can select any frequency across the entire range with an accuracy of 1kHz.

For practical purposes, however, the ability to tune in 5kHz increments gives good results and is available on many modern receivers.

Summary: Ability to select 5kHz steps (or even lower) is a positive advantage, especially in those areas remote from the transmitter stations.

Memories
Most modern air band receivers are capable of storing a number of frequencies, ranging from 10 to 1000. This feature simply ensures that those frequencies chosen by the listener can be stored in the receiver's memory, ready for selection whenever needed.

Naturally, the ability to store frequencies has no effect on the quality of reception of the individual receiver — it merely makes the selection of frequencies much more convenient and relieves the listener of the chore of finding separate channels each time they are needed.

Some receivers separate the memories into groups which can be selected independently. These are known as 'banks'.

For example, air band scanners provided with 100 memory channels usually have 10 'banks', or groups, each of 10 memories. These can conveniently be used for separate purposes, ie VHF en-route frequencies, UHF frequencies, 'company', local airfields, Heathrow, Gatwick and so on. As each bank can be monitored independently of the remainder, this facility has obvious advantages.

A receiver provided with a memory facility can also be used with another function known as 'scanning' which is covered next.

Summary: Choose a receiver with memories; although these obviously have no effect on the quality of the messages received, they do make life easier!

Above:
Visual Control Room, Birmingham International airport. *Civil Aviation Authority*

Scanning

Frequencies stored in the memory of a receiver can be rapidly stepped through in turn to check whether any transmission is taking place. If a signal is detected, the receiver will remain on the individual frequency for as long as the signal is transmitted, after which the receiver continues to check the memorised frequencies in turn for the next transmission. The ability to carry out this process is referred to as 'scanning' or occasionally 'memory scanning'. Receivers with this facility are often advertised as 'scanners'.

Most receivers that are able to scan are also provided with a choice for the listener when using the scanning feature. It is possible to decide, when a signal is detected on a particular frequency, whether to remain on that frequency indefinitely even though the transmissions have ceased (known as 'Hold') or whether to continue the scan after a predetermined interval. It is also a common feature to be able to delay the period before scanning restarts.

When the scan is set to 'Hold', the receiver will stop scanning once a signal is detected and

will remain on that frequency indefinitely until the user decides to continue the scan. If the scan is set to 'Delay', the receiver will cease the scanning process once a signal is detected. It will then remain on that frequency until the end of the signal, after which it will stay on the frequency for a few seconds, waiting for any further transmissions. If no such signal is detected, the scan will be resumed until the next sound is heard. Some receivers can be programmed to adjust the delay at the end of a transmission between 2 and 10sec.

Summary: A scanning feature is useful, especially to first-timers, but not absolutely essential. It is available only on receivers with memories.

Search

The ability to search through frequencies is similar to the scanning mode referred to earlier, and the two terms are, in fact, sometimes confused.

Scanning applies to memorised frequencies,

whereas searching is concerned with stepping through *all* channels between an upper and lower limit.

Some sets can only scan between the lowest frequency and the highest frequency, stepping through every channel in sequence until a transmission is heard.

More sophisticated receivers can be programmed to search between any two frequencies, which are decided by the listener. The ability to 'Delay' or to 'Hold', as described earlier under the heading *Scanning*, also applies to the 'Search' mode.

There are a number of receivers on which it is possible to transfer any frequency on which transmissions are detected directly into the memory of the set — this applies both to the 'Scan' and 'Search' modes.

Summary: The ability to search is a positive advantage, but not essential. It is probably of most use to the beginner who is unsure of individual frequencies.

Below:
Great Dunn Fell radar station in the Pennines.
Author

Lockout or Pass
Scanners with facilities for searching or scanning are often provided with a 'lockout' function.

As the receiver will, of course, stop at any sound it detects, it is often the case that some of those signals will not be wanted by the listener — for example, continuous weather transmissions, airfield information transmissions or simply interference.

Whenever the set stops at an unwanted frequency the 'lockout' key is pressed. The search (or scan) then continues, the locked-out frequencies subsequently being ignored by the receiver. Any frequency which has been locked out can be brought back into the circuit by pressing the lockout key again.

Summary: Lockout or pass is a feature which applies only to receivers with Scan or Search modes. Most sets with Scan/Search will be capable of lockout.

Changing Frequency
One question often overlooked concerns the simplicity of changing frequency.

It is usually possible to step manually through memorised frequencies, both forwards or backwards, or similarly to move in either direction through the entire range by manually switching from one frequency to the next.

In other cases, it may be necessary to enter every individual frequency, as required, by manual means. The frequencies selected will, of course, vary depending on the steps programmed into the receiver by the user.

Some scanners have a feature which allows frequencies to be changed forwards or backwards by means of a rotary tuning knob.

Summary: A relatively minor consideration, but one which can make listening far more convenient.

Power Supply
There are several alternative methods of providing power to your air band receiver.

■ *Batteries*: These can be ordinary dry cell batteries or the rechargeable type.

Normal batteries are expensive for everyday use, especially if the receiver is used mainly as a base station in the home or in a car.

Rechargeable batteries are very economical in use, once the initial cost of purchasing the recharging unit and at least two sets of batteries has been met. (The second set of batteries is necessary so that the receiver can still be used while the first set is being recharged.)

These batteries can be recharged hundreds of times at a very low cost, although their 'life' in the receiver is quite low — perhaps a few hours — so they are not the most suitable type for sets used almost continuously.

Some receivers are provided with the means for recharging the batteries while still in the set. The recharging unit also serves as a power supply source which operates the receiver directly. The recharger, therefore, operates the scanner when it is in use, and continues to recharge the batteries when the receiver is switched off.

Again, the rechargeable batteries will only be effective for no more than a few hours, so if it is intended to use the set outside for a longer period it is preferable to use normal long-life batteries instead of rechargeables. Remember that most base station receivers are not designed to operate on batteries.

■ *12 Volt Car Power:* Most modern scanners are provided with a connection for an external power source and this can be used for an adapter which can be connected to the cigarette lighter socket of a vehicle. The adapter must be switched to the correct output voltage appropriate to the receiver, and it is also important to ensure that the polarity of the connections are matched to the set. Car power adapters are usually provided with a reversible polarity socket, so the 'plus' and 'minus' connection to the receiver can easily be fitted incorrectly. Care must be taken to match the connections correctly so that the set is not damaged.

■ *Mains Operation:* Similar to the car supply is the adapter operating from the mains supply. Obviously this provides the easiest and most economic method of supplying a continuously stable and reliable source of power for receivers operating from a home base.

Most of the top manufacturers of air band receivers are able to supply a mains adapter suitable for that particular product, but sometimes it will be necessary to obtain a separate adapter from an independent supplier, in which case care is needed to make sure the unit is compatible with the receiver. It is advisable to purchase such items only from reputable outlets as it is possible to damage the receiver by the use of unsuitable equipment.

Summary: Decide on which power supplies you are likely to need according to the type of use you anticipate.

Antenna Connections
Virtually all popular air band monitoring receivers are provided with an antenna which is connected to the set by either a PL259-type fitting or a BNC-type fitting.

The BNC-type is neater and smaller and therefore less cumbersome for the smaller receiver, while the PL259 is a heavier unit. Most modern scanners are now provided with the BNC type of antenna connection. Both types can be used with antennas or receivers because each one can be adapted by the use of the correct fitting. In other words, a BNC socket on a radio receiver can be used with an antenna with a PL259 plug with the correct adapter; the opposite also applies. Both these connectors are used with co-axial cable.

Suitable adapters for converting from one type of connector to another are available from any radio equipment supplier with comprehensive stocks. Both BNC and PL 259 connections can be fitted without the use of solder.

Some receivers are supplied without an antenna — the purchaser is expected to select a suitable antenna system most appropriate to the set, bearing in mind the location where it will be used, the proximity of transmitters, and so on. Of course, any receiver with one of the usual connections can be fitted with more than one antenna — perhaps one for mobile use and one for use as a base station.

Summary: Try to choose a receiver with one of the popular kinds of antenna connection — the BNC or the PL259.

Squelch
The squelch control is a rotary switch which is used to eliminate background noise and interference. Without this facility reception is spoiled by 'hiss' and interference. In addition,

the search and scan functions will not operate while any background noise is present. Also, tape recording with a voice-activated recorder will be difficult, if not impossible.

Although it may appear to be an obvious requirement in a modern expensive receiver, it is advisable to check specifically that the set does have a squelch facility.

Summary: Check that the set you are considering does have 'squelch'. Not all of them do!

Priority Channel
When a receiver is operating in either Scan or Search mode, it is possible with some models to allocate one or more frequencies as a 'priority'.

This means that whenever the receiver is scanning a range of memorised channels, or searching through a sequence of frequencies, the priority channel will be sampled at regular intervals (usually about one or two seconds) to determine whether a transmission is taking place. If a signal is detected, the receiver will remain on the priority channel until the end of the message — it will then revert to the Search or Scan mode as appropriate.

The question might be asked 'Which frequencies are likely to be chosen as a priority?' Each listener could select his or her own special interest channel — for example, the emergency frequency of 121.5 (VHF) or 243.0 (UHF) which is used only very occasionally — but apart from this kind of use the priority channel is unlikely to be of special use to the air band listener and, in any case, such attributes do not enhance the performance of the receiver.

Summary: Priority channel can be useful but is not essential.

Reception Mode
Transmissions between aircraft and ground-based controllers, whether on civil or military radio frequencies, take place on a system known as amplitude modulation or AM. When you are considering which particular receiver is your 'best buy' there will be no need to consider any other method of receiving the radio signals — AM is the only mode on which VHF and UHF operate. Sometimes this causes confusion to purchasers who are not familiar with radio terms. For example, domestic broadcasting stations in the United Kingdom, ie BBC Radio Two, which broadcasts on the Frequency Modulation Mode (or FM), is often referred to as VHF, but a receiver with FM as an advertised reception system will not be suitable for aircraft listening.

Advertisements often make reference to phrases such as 'wide band', 'narrow band FM', 'wide band FM', and so on, but none of these facilities has any relationship with the VHF or UHF aircraft bands, so there is no advantage in

choosing such a receiver if only the air bands are of interest.

The ability of a receiver to receive air band VHF transmissions, UHF transmissions, or both, is sufficient information for the purchaser as far as 'mode' is concerned. References to any other mode are of no relevance to the air band listener, although airport repeaters operate in the NFM mode. For more details see Chapter 3.

Summary: VHF and UHF aeronautical transmission are all AM. It is more important to establish the actual range of frequencies to ensure full coverage.

Inexpensive Receivers
Many people who are starting out in the field of air band listening are understandably hesitant about spending perhaps £200 on a receiver when they are unsure about the quality of the messages they are likely to receive in their area. Also, being a new hobby, they will wish to test the water before reaching a decision on whether to move up-market into the realms of the sophisticated sets described earlier.

Apart from the fact that modern expensive receivers are often difficult for the beginner to master, there is also the consideration that the newcomer will almost certainly be unaware of the aeronautical activity in the area; therefore the probability of being able to get the best results is slight.

A possible solution in such situations is the low-price receiver (probably no more than £50 at 1997 prices) which will at least enable the listener to hear some of the VHF transmissions in the area.

The method of tuning such receivers is 'continuous' (that is, the same as an old-fashioned domestic radio receiver which operates by simply shifting a pointer across a waveband dial) so that the full range of VHF frequencies can be covered very quickly, backwards and forwards, until a transmission is detected.

Whenever a pilot or controller is heard, it is well worth noting the position on the dial by using a strip of adhesive paper across the top of the scale, suitably marked as each of the frequencies comes through.

In practice, because of the design of the receiver, it is inevitable that more than one individual frequency will be heard at each position on the scale, since this kind of set is not able to separate each frequency.

It is therefore reasonably certain that several messages will break through at each point on the scale. Whereas the sophisticated crystal-controlled sets are able to separate every individual channel at 25kHz spacings, this is not so with the lower priced receivers.

For the beginner this is not necessarily a drawback. In fact, most newcomers to the subject of air band listening simply want to hear as many conversations as they can — long periods of absolute silence are not for them! Beginners need the interest of hearing pilots and controllers talking to each other in order to whet the appetite for the later pleasure of hearing the more interesting and occasional titbits of information which rarely happen on the airwaves.

Many people who are first-time air band listeners often tune in to the 'company' range of frequencies between 130 and 132MHz — they are more likely to hear interesting messages in this range, but also, more importantly, there will almost certainly be far more of them by comparison to the normal ATC frequencies.

Because of the receiver's simple design, the overlapping of frequencies can mean that 20 or more channels are covered by one position on the dial, resulting in a considerable spread of transmissions being received instead of a single one being detected as on the more sophisticated set.

One of the drawbacks is the strength of the transmission on one particular frequency overpowering those on other adjacent frequencies, which can sometimes be annoying, especially if the lower strength message was more interesting. However, this does not seem to be significant to air band listeners who are starting out with the hobby. The most important factor for the newcomer is the ability to hear as many messages as possible. This is just as likely with a set costing £30 as with any other.

Of course, there are drawbacks to the simple low-cost set, and as time passes the listener tends to become more frustrated and anxious to switch to one of the more up-market models.

Inexpensive receivers tend to suffer badly from local interference, with unwanted signals breaking through and obliterating aeronautical transmissions. Police messages and those of other similar agencies can often be heard, as well as other incomprehensible blasts of static.

They are not usually fitted with a squelch facility, so background noise can be a problem as well.

A further drawback is the lack of sensitivity with low priced receivers, meaning that the range of the equipment will be far less than with one of the more sophisticated models. For this reason such sets are generally at their best when fairly close to a transmitter — at an airport for example.

It is also unusual to find such receivers with BNC or PL259 connections for external aerials, although this can be easily overcome by the use of a simple metal 'crocodile' clip for attaching the aerial cable to the receiver. Even with the lowest cost receiver, connection to a suitable external aerial will often result in a much better signal, although these will include more interference just the same as other transmissions.

The slightly more advanced design of air band receiver combines the low cost of the simple continuous tuning model with the sophistication of the 'quality' type which is capable of accurate tuning to a number of specific frequencies.

This is achieved by providing the basic receiver with a small number of crystals, each being manufactured to suit a particular frequency, and each chosen by the purchaser to suit the particular transmission which the listener wishes to hear. Each crystal is plugged into the receiver and can be changed at random as often as desired. The benefit of the crystals is that the specified frequencies can be selected accurately, with very little risk of breakthrough and no overlapping of frequencies, so that the result is a receiver with good general qualities plus a selection of specific frequency channels chosen by the user.

As with all compromises, of course, there are some drawbacks, the main one being that only those frequencies selected by the purchaser can be received. If the set is used in another part of the country the crystals will be useless, unless of course replacement crystals for the new alternative frequencies are purchased.

The other problem is that the crystals themselves are not particularly cheap. The cost of crystals can soon add up to the extent that it would probably be more sensible to look out for a secondhand crystal-controlled receiver which will have the benefit of all the frequencies being accurately selectable. This type of receiver is now available only on the secondhand market.

At the time of writing, none of the lower priced air band receivers are capable of receiving military transmissions on UHF. All the inexpensive models are for civil VHF air band, probably with the additional frequencies for the usual broadcast bands of BBC1, BBC2, etc.

To summarise, many first-time air band listeners are not prepared to part with considerable sums of money in return for a receiver which might turn out to be a grave disappointment. Instead, a low-cost alternative might be quite acceptable and sufficient to enable the listener to decide whether to continue with the hobby.

One of the best ways to become an owner of an air band receiver is to consider a secondhand purchase through the advertising columns of radio enthusiasts' magazines or from one of the country's main radio stockists.

Both sources are ideal for the first timer, provided the purchaser asks sensible questions first concerning frequencies, frequency steps, and so on, as described earlier.

Summary: Low-priced simple receivers are often quite acceptable for the beginner. It is not always necessary to buy expensive sets for listening pleasure.

5 Antennas

No radio receiver can be expected to perform at its best without an antenna system which suits the particular range of frequencies being received.

The antenna (or aerial if you prefer — the meaning is the same) can have a remarkable effect on the ability of a receiver to bring in stations which would otherwise be unavailable.

You may be fortunate to live in an area where ATC transmitters are nearby, with plenty of air traffic as well, and good quality reception of controllers' and pilots' messages. Even so, a good aerial system is still worth considering if only for the increased range it will provide.

Anyone who spends money on a quality air band receiver is likely to be disappointed if there is a lack of attention to the design of the antenna system. Consider, for example, the difference in the quality of television pictures when a suitable aerial is used compared to no aerial at all. Obviously, no one would dream of using a television set in an area of poor reception without the right aerial.

The message is, therefore, to give your antenna installation some careful thought if you want to obtain the best results.

Airband antennas are actually quite simple in design and their construction is well within the capabilities of the average DIY person. The same comments apply to antennas as to receivers — spending more and more money on the antenna often has no significant effect on performance. Often the best all-round results are provided by the simplest home-made systems made up from discarded television or radio aerials at virtually no expense.

Another point to remember is that all VHF and UHF transmissions are generally line-of-sight. The most expensive receiver used in a location where there is no line-of-sight to the transmitter will give poor results, even with the best antenna. Alternatively, a basic low-price receiver, located in a suitable position close to a transmitter, can perform well even with the simplest aerial.

Before looking at antenna design for VHF and UHF air band listening, there are a few basic points to bear in mind as far as 'systems' are concerned — a system being the overall design and location of the antenna, its installation, the feed to the receiver, the various connections and, of course, the receiver itself.

First, there are two kinds of antenna — one which is capable of receiving signals from every direction in equal strength, known as 'omni-directional', and the other which is designed to concentrate the received signals, and amplify them, from one particular point (probably an en-route transmitter or an airport) so that the

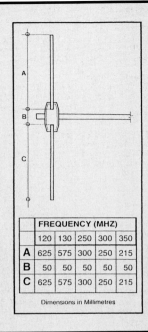

	FREQUENCY (MHZ)				
	120	130	250	300	350
A	625	575	300	250	215
B	50	50	50	50	50
C	625	575	300	250	215

Dimensions in Millimetres

strongest possible signal is heard. These are known as 'directional' aerials.

In areas of good overall air band coverage, with ATC transmitters relatively close and with the receiver in a good location, the omni-directional system will perform quite adequately. Other locations, surrounded by high ground, massive buildings or simply remote from airports or transmitter stations, may well benefit from a directional type of antenna which can at least be pointed towards an airport or an en-route transmitter so as to obtain the best possible signal, even though it may be less than perfect.

Whether you decide upon an omni-directional antenna or one which is directional will, of course, depend upon your particular listening base and your individual requirements.

If you are listening in an area which is generally poor in reception terms, then you may well consider an antenna which can be pointed towards an en-route transmitter or an airport so that any available signals can be detected at the best possible level. The locations of ATC transmitters across the UK are given in the chart.

The drawback, of course, is the fact that when using a directional antenna any other transmissions not in line with the antenna will probably be heard at a much reduced level.

However, it is impossible to give positive advice for every situation. So much depends upon the local circumstances and the relative positions of aircraft, airfields, transmitters and other features likely to affect reception.

Antenna Design

We will now look at the various types of antenna available under the two headings. To begin with, omni-directional antennas fall into two basic designs:

■ Single element vertical designs, often referred to as Marconi-type aerials, or
■ Dipoles, consisting of two separate halves of a vertical aerial which act together as a single antenna.

Opposite:
Simple but effective dipole antenna for VHF or UHF reception, cut to the lengths shown depending on the frequency.

Below:
Folded dipole, also for VHF or UHF use. The dimensions are the same as those for the simple dipole.

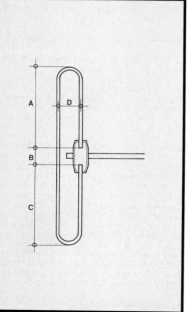

Marconi Antennas
The single vertical type is designed to operate at a particular frequency according to the length of the element. The appropriate length is arrived at by calculating the dimension of the element according to a simple formula, 75 divided by the frequency in Megahertz, which gives the length of the antenna in millimetres, although for best results 5% of the length should be deducted.

The frequencies used for aeronautical communication range between 118MHz at the lowest end on VHF, to 400MHz at the highest on UHF. By using the formula for single element vertical antennas the lengths vary from 603mm to 178mm (75 divided by 118 and 75 divided by 400 respectively, less 5%).

Obviously as it is not practical to design the antenna for these two extreme frequencies, it is more sensible to choose an average rating appropriate to the most popular frequency in your area.

When deciding upon the antenna length, unless there is a specific frequency of particular interest, a mid-range average can be used, probably around 127MHz for VHF (giving a dimension of around 600mm) and perhaps 300MHz for UHF (resulting in a dimension of approximately 250mm).

There is no need to worry too much about being accurate about the exact measurements. The final result will be influenced to a far greater extent by other factors (such as the height of the antenna, good clean connections and so on) so the dimensions should be looked upon as no more than a guide.

Ground Plane Antennas
The single element antenna will operate much more effectively if it is provided with a system of radials (usually four) at its base (known as a ground screen). An antenna of this design with a vertical element and radials is known as a 'ground plane'.

Each of the radials should be cut to the same length as the vertical element and angled downwards at approximately 45° to give the best results.

The centre core of the co-axial cable should be connected to the vertical element, with the outer braid connected to the ground plane elements. The vertical element and the ground screen must be insulated from each other.

Dipoles
Perhaps the most popular 'do-it-yourself' antenna is the dipole. This consists of two single elements (as described earlier) mounted vertically, one above the other, with the centre core of the co-axial cable connected to the upper element and the outer braid connected to the lower element. Again, it is essential that the antenna is constructed in such a way that the two elements are insulated from each other.

This can be achieved by fixing the elements to a base board of rigid plastic, for example, or by the use of a suitable cable connector box which can be purchased from shops dealing with television and radio aerials.

Each of the two elements should be cut to the length which is appropriate to the chosen frequency, using the formula given earlier. The overall length of the antenna is therefore twice that of the single element type.

If it is required to have an aerial system suitable for listening to both VHF and UHF transmissions, two Marconi-type antennas, or alternatively two dipole antennas, can be erected side by side in a location as high as possible, with separate co-axial down-leads to the receiver. The two antennas must be designed for the respective UHF and VHF frequencies, and the leads will have to be switched from one antenna to the other according to the station being received.

It is, of course, quite feasible to use one single antenna, of either design, cut to an average length midway between the two optimum dimensions suggested for VHF and UHF — say 425mm. This will give an acceptable performance and may well be suitable if the location of the receiver is reasonably close to transmitter sites. Obviously an 'average' design can never be as good as one prepared specifically for a narrow range of frequencies, so the decision as to how the problem is tackled is one for each individual listener according to the circumstances.

If it is the intention to listen only to VHF or only to UHF transmissions then a single antenna

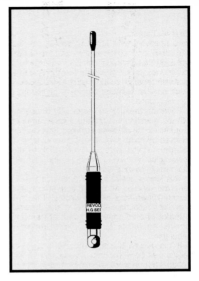

designed for the required frequencies will be easy to manufacture. Do not be misled into assuming that because these simple antennas are relatively easy and cheap to make that they are less effective than other antennas advertised and sold by specialist companies. Experience shows that they are very efficient and can be just as good as those which can be purchased ready made. In fact, some air band listeners maintain that their home-made antennas give a performance which is better than the professional models.

Folded Dipoles
A marginally more efficient version of the dipole antenna is the type known as a 'folded' dipole in which a normal dipole design is provided with an additional element which connects the two extreme ends, resulting in an antenna with slightly improved capabilities when compared to the normal dipole. The dimensions of the two arms are calculated by using the same formula as given previously.

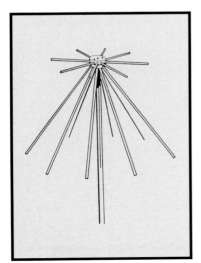

Left:
'REVCO' nest of dipoles provides a wider range of reception on VHF and UHF.

Above:
'REVCO' mobile antennas give better performance than the simple whip antennas provided with the receiver.

Nests of Dipoles

For a relatively wide range of frequencies, as with VHF and UHF, it has already been explained that separate antennas, designed in accordance with the simple formula, can be used with separate co-axial leads to the receiver which can be switched between the required frequency bands.

However, there is an easier way of dealing with the question of handling a wide range of frequencies for air band listening; this can be achieved by combining several different lengths of antenna elements, cut according to the frequencies required, and fed to the receiver with a single co-axial lead.

This kind of antenna consists of a number of separate dipoles and for this reason it has become known as a 'nest of dipoles'. This type is available commercially but it is also possible to make one at home for internal use and reports as to its effectiveness are very favourable.

If it is desired to listen only to one range of frequencies (VHF air band for example) it will probably not be worth the time and expense to provide a multiple dipole type of antenna, since the range of frequencies is relatively short and reception is unlikely to be greatly improved by such a system. A straightforward dipole will almost certainly be adequate.

Directional Systems

All the systems discussed so far are types which operate on an 'omni-directional' principle. In other words, the signals detected by these antennas are received in more or less equal strength from every direction. This is usually ideal for the average air band listener.

Aircraft transmissions tend to come from all directions and it can be counterproductive to think of concentrating the signals into one direction because those from other areas may be lost or seriously impaired.

But there may be situations where there will be a benefit from 'aiming' the antenna towards a particular location, either a remote ATC transmitter or an airfield, so as to amplify the transmission which might otherwise go unheard.

These antennas are again based on a dipole design, but instead of being fixed vertically, they

Below left:
The ground plane design has always been popular. It consists of a dipole with four 'arms' projecting from the base.

Below:
'SLIM JIM' airband antenna, adjustable to match different frequencies. *Sandpiper*

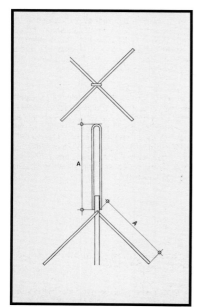

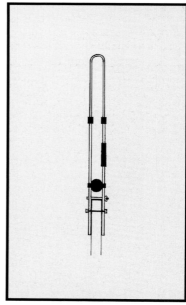

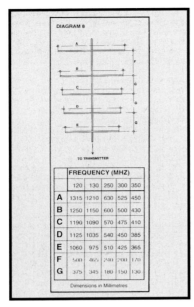

DIAGRAM 8

TO TRANSMITTER

FREQUENCY (MHZ)					
	120	130	250	300	350
A	1315	1210	630	525	450
B	1250	1150	600	500	430
C	1190	1090	570	475	410
D	1125	1035	540	450	385
E	1060	975	510	425	365
F	500	465	240	200	170
G	375	345	180	150	130

Dimensions in Millimetres

Above:
Reception from one particular source can be improved with a directional antenna manufactured to the dimensions indicated.

Opposite:
Automatic Dependent Surveillance enables aircraft to be tracked by satellite as they cross the oceans. The positions are displayed on the screen in real time. *Civil Aviation Authority*

are placed horizontally with the signals being concentrated by separate elements placed behind and in front of the main dipole.

This design of aerial is known as a 'Yagi'-type antenna.

The dimensions of the dipole part of the antenna are arrived at by the same calculation as for the more usual omni-directional types referred to earlier. The other elements and their distances apart are calculated in accordance with the diagrams. Although these may appear rather complex, they are actually quite easy to make from aluminium tube, but if your skills in the DIY line are limited one of the local television aerial companies might be persuaded to make up a design to suit your requirements.

Another way to manufacture a directional antenna for positioning in a loft is to attach copper wire or fine tubing to a lightweight flat

polystyrene sheet (obtainable from builders merchants) following the design measurements. This can be located in a convenient position and is easier to assemble than a traditional design.

Mobile Antennas
Most air band listeners will want to spend at least some of their time listening to aircraft at airports or in other areas away from their home base. Often the built-in aerial will be adequate, but performance will undoubtedly be improved with a separate external antenna. The most popular type is a single element aerial with a magnetic base which is attached to the roof of a vehicle, the metal roof acting as a ground screen.

Another type of portable aerial consists of a length of ribbon antenna with a cable connection for the receiver. This can be used in any location but is particularly useful since it can be folded away and easily carried.

It is impractical to attempt to manufacture such antennas as DIY projects; they are not too expensive and are readily available from the suppliers quoted at the end of the book.

Cables
The cable used with antennas suitable for UHF and VHF aeronautical transmissions is a co-axial type, very similar to television cable. It consists of a central core surrounded by insulation and covered by a woven wire screen which is again surrounded by a plastic outer cover.

Although television cable may provide acceptable results in some situations, it is more appropriate to use a cable of the 'low loss' type since these provide the best performance with the lowest degree of signal loss.

The best cables normally specified for air band use are URM67 or RG213U, both available from air band radio companies or the specialist cable suppliers such as Westlake.

Using these cables may not result in any significant advantage over standard cable, but it is probably worth using the best quality product for the relatively small extra outlay involved. If your receiver is in a poor location it is certainly good sense to use the very best low loss cable available.

Connections
Most modern receivers have antenna connections which are likely to be one of two types, known as PL259 or BNC.

In recent years the BNC connection seems to have become more popular; it is compact, easy to connect and efficient.

The PL259 is heavy and more cumbersome, although equally effective.

Whichever type is fitted to your receiver, there are adaptors which convert BNC to PL259 and vice versa, so there should be no problem with either fitting.

Some receivers, particularly in the low price range, may have one of several other kinds of antenna connection, but these are relatively unusual and it can be assumed that the majority of popular sets will be fitted with BNC or PL259 connections.

Low-priced receivers are generally fitted with simple extending aerials, often fixed to the receiver so that it is not possible to fit external antennas directly to the receiver. If it is intended to connect a separate aerial, the simplest method is to fully close the receiver's aerial and connect the external antenna to it by means of a small crocodile clip fed from the centre core of the co-axial cable.

Cable Feed

When deciding upon a suitable route for the antenna cable it is necessary to consider whether the cable will be placed close to anything which is likely to interfere with the quality of the reception.

The cable run should be as short as reasonably practical, but, more importantly, it should avoid any items of electrical equipment, especially television receivers and fluorescent light fittings. It also needs to be as vertical as possible for best results. The antenna itself can be hung in the loft (tape a piece of strong string

to the top of the antenna and hang it from the ridge timber in the roof space). For areas where reception is not particularly good the antenna should be fixed externally, probably to a chimney stack, but in any case out in the clear and as high as reasonably practical.

Antenna Manufacturers

There are several companies who are in the business of making antennas, and often these are advertised and promoted as exceptionally efficient pieces of equipment.

However, before spending a considerable amount of your hard-earned money on one of these aerials it might be well worth trying one of the DIY types described earlier in this chapter.

Experience has shown that the quality of reception from home-built antennas is as good as, if not better than, that derived from 'purpose-made' systems produced by commercial organisations.

Many of the systems on sale are not designed specifically for the air band listeners market — instead the antennas are suitable for wide coverage, not only for VHF and UHF aeronautical messages, but also for other kinds of transmissions, therefore the quality of reception is the result of a compromise in design. Wide band designs are not usually as efficient for air band listening as those

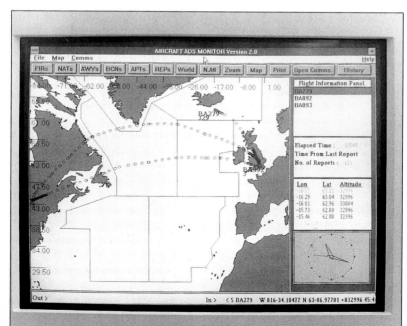

specifically designed for the purpose.

If your main interest is air band, then certainly try a simple home-made approach first — if this does not work, by all means experiment with more sophisticated commercial systems in an attempt to improve matters, but do not be surprised if the results are not what was expected.

Active Antennas

An active antenna is one which uses an electrical power supply for its operation. These are often much smaller than conventional antennas and can be used in smaller spaces and are less obtrusive. The power supply is provided via a battery or via a transformer from the mains supply. Active antennas are particularly useful in areas of poor reception and where the erection of an external antenna is not possible. Unfortunately, it is very difficult to assess the efficiency of such systems without actually having direct experience in your particular location. Sometimes the results will be very good but other times will be disappointing.

Summary: Whether you decide to choose a separate antenna to help your listening pleasure

or simply stay with the aerial provided with the receiver is a matter of choice. Many factors will influence your decision, the most important being related to the proximity of the various transmitting stations in your area.

If you do most of your listening near large busy airfields or close to en-route transmitter sites, the simple antenna system might well be sufficient for good quality listening. Most of us, though, are not in such a fortunate position. Living in relatively remote areas (in ATC terms) or surrounded by high ground and large buildings means that an efficient external antenna is essential.

In any case, no matter how good the quality without a sophisticated antenna there is little doubt that an external antenna will improve the range of messages received.

One final point to bear in mind is that many hand-held scanners can be overloaded by strong signals received through an external antenna. Base station sets are designed to operate with high gain aerials and there should be little difficulty in obtaining reasonable results. Depending on your location, an external system may be disappointing if it is connected to a lightweight hand-held receiver.

Right:
Locations of radio transmitter sites in the UK.

6 High Frequency Radio

Earlier in this book we dealt with VHF and UHF aeronautical radio, both of which are very effective when the transmitter and the receiver are fairly close to each other — in the region of 100 miles or so. The line-of-sight principle applies to aircraft communications in densely populated areas of the world. However, when flights are crossing large uninhabited regions or oceanic areas it is necessary to employ another more effective system of communication so that the aircraft are able to keep in touch with the land-based control centres.

The only system in worldwide operation at the moment is the high frequency (or Short Wave) radio coverage which operates over long distances, although it is true to say that it has certain disadvantages which will be discussed later. In spite of the drawbacks, it is the only suitable method at the present time of maintaining contact with flights which are crossing remote areas such as the Atlantic, the Pacific or the Sahara Desert.

The nearest area to the UK which has HF radio as its primary means of contact is the North Atlantic, with up to 1,000 flights being handled on a busy day in mid-summer.

Aircraft crossing the Atlantic, or any other large uninhabited area of the world, are first required to file a flight plan before the flight is due to leave. The plan will include the route across the land areas, together with the point of entry into the ocean region and the proposed route (or 'track') which will be specified in degrees of latitude and longitude, together with the aircraft's flight level and speed.

Once beyond the range of land-based radars and radio transmitters on VHF and UHF the flight conditions change from a radar control situation to one where the safety of the flight depends on reports passed by long-range radio back to the base station, perhaps 2,000 miles distant.

These 'Position Reports' are made in a predetermined format at set intervals to radio receiving stations where the operators pass the details of the aircraft's location to the appropriate control centre for comparison with the flight plan. This all takes place without the advantages of radar; separation of aircraft depends upon accurate radio reports from the flightcrews and the actual location of the flight depends in turn on the accuracy of the navigation process of the crews.

The kind of radio which is suitable for these long-range transmissions is known as 'High Frequency' or more usually 'HF'. Until a few years ago the term used was 'Short Wave' radio but this description has generally been superseded, although both terms ('HF' and 'Short Wave') have the same meaning.

High Frequency transmissions for aeronautical use are defined as those which take place between 2MHz and 23MHz, but only certain specific groups of frequencies within this range are allocated for aviation use.

The reason for such a wide selection of cover on the HF bands is due to the peculiar characteristics of the behaviour of transmissions across the range. Long-range radio is affected to a great extent by atmospheric conditions and by the effect of daylight and darkness on the quality of the signal.

Because of the curvature of the earth, it is not possible for one aircraft to receive transmission, from another aircraft or from a ground-based station on the VHF or UHF frequencies since the two stations will be out of sight of each other, although occasionally freak conditions exist which do make long-distance reception possible. Unfortunately, the times during which this is possible are so rare as to be impractical for regular use.

High Frequency transmissions, however, between 2 and 23MHz are able to reach distant areas because the signal from the transmitter travels upwards at an angle and is then reflected back down again at a similar angle, so that it is possible for the message to be detected by the ground receiver or by an aircraft in flight.

The atmospheric conditions which exist at the time of the transmission have a dramatic effect on the resulting quality of reception, and it is not always easy to predict how good the performance will be at any particular time.

For this reason, each agency operating on the HF bands will have been allocated a group of frequencies, normally referred to as a 'family', which are roughly spread across the aeronautical range between 2 and 23MHz. This enables the operator to choose any one of the frequencies in order to obtain the most effective result. As a general rule, frequencies at the lower end of the scale will be found to be more efficient during periods when both the transmitter and the receiver are in darkness, while frequencies at the higher end of the range will usually be best when both receiving and transmitting stations are in full daylight. Forecasts of the likely operating conditions (known as propagation) for HF transmissions are published by the aviation authorities covering the various times of the year and the hours of daylight and darkness.

At any one time, the frequency which has been found to give the best service in terms of loudness and clarity will be referred to as the primary frequency, with a second choice backup frequency, in another part of the range, known as the secondary frequency.

Listeners to HF radio will find that the

reception of transmissions can be predicted to a reasonably certain extent and experienced users will be able to judge quite accurately which of the frequencies to listen to at any particular time.

Unfortunately, one of the problems with HF radio is the fact that so many frequencies are available for use that the possibility of hearing traffic on any particular one is lower than with VHF or UHF radio.

The signals which travel upwards, and then downwards to earth, will to a greater or lesser degree continue to 'skip' across the surface of the earth until they reach right round the globe in favourable situations. On the other hand, interference on HF radio is often a problem, sometimes spoiling reception to such an extent that the messages are unreadable.

Many listeners to aeronautical radio are fascinated by HF radio. Whereas VHF or UHF messages are reasonably predictable and of fairly consistent quality, this cannot really be said of HF transmissions. There is also a wider variety of messages, especially of a 'company' nature, where pilots call their operating base with requests or reports on all kinds of matters.

Because the line-of-sight principle is not a matter of concern with HF, there is also a positive advantage for those people who are in areas of the country which are restricted in their ability to hear VHF or UHF transmissions due to the limitations of the surrounding terrain.

There are several parts of the UK where the number of transmissions on VHF or UHF are few and far between. Probably the only messages heard will be those from high-flying en-route traffic which is virtually overhead, so the satisfaction level for the enthusiast will be very low. With HF radio, the situation is completely different. Someone in the middle of the Lake District, for example, can listen to New York Oceanic Control Centre in contact with flights in their area of control with as much ease as anyone else.

Apart from the differences related to the kind of reception which can be expected, the messages on HF are quite different from those heard on VHF or UHF.

The main difference is that the aircraft on HF radio are not normally handled by Air Traffic Control, but by radio operators who relay their messages between pilots and the control centre. In the main, the messages are related to 'Position Reports' from pilots, or clearances to climb, descend, follow a particular route or change speed.

Other frequently heard messages are between pilots and their bases ('company' messages) often via agency stations which pass on details or alternatively connect the pilots with their company via the telephone network — a procedure known as 'patching'.

The agencies are often quite remote from the caller and the station being contacted. It is not unusual for a pilot on the ground in Geneva, for example, to contact Berne Radio (in Switzerland) and then to be patched through to Shannon, perhaps, with their message. The pilot in Geneva will then talk directly to his contact in Shannon and their discussion can normally be heard in the UK without very much difficulty.

This is part of the attraction of HF radio; the ability to receive so many different and interesting pieces of information on the airwaves throughout the 24 hours from all around the world does undoubtedly arouse curiosity. There are, of course, hundreds of messages unrelated to air traffic control which can be heard on HF; therefore it is a special hobby in its own right.

Below:
AOR AR8000 wide-range receiver, including the HF aeronautical bands. *AOR*

Provided the listener has the patience (and time) to scan through the large number of frequencies allocated to the air band side of HF radio, the rewards can be interesting and informative.

The Oceanic Area which creates the most interest in the UK and Europe is the North Atlantic Oceanic Region, known as 'NARTEL' — the North Atlantic Radio Telephony Network, which covers the regions of Shanwick, Gander, Santa Maria, New York and Iceland.

The Shanwick radio station is at Ballygirreen in Ireland, near Shannon, and it is from this location that messages are sent to aircraft over the North Atlantic in the Shanwick Oceanic Region.

As flights cross Europe and the United Kingdom, towards the North Atlantic and Canada, they reach the 'entry points' for the Atlantic crossing. As the aircraft enters the Atlantic area the crew will be instructed to contact the Shanwick Oceanic Control Centre at Prestwick (in Scotland) on the appropriate HF frequency, which in fact will be done via the radio station at Ballygirreen.

As the flight continues across the North Atlantic, position reports will be made at approximately hourly intervals on HF frequencies.

Each transmission will be made on the primary or secondary frequency which will be heard not only at Shanwick (Ballygirreen) but also by the other North Atlantic Stations at Gander, Santa Maria and New York.

All the radio stations in the NARTEL region are able to talk between themselves on the same frequencies that the flights use — in fact they can often be heard checking flight details of individual aircraft with each other.

Other areas of the world, of course, are covered by other control centres on different radio frequencies, details of which are given in the diagrams and the appendices.

If you wish to listen to aircraft messages on HF you need to obtain a radio receiver of a particular type, although you will find that they are more expensive than models suitable for VHF or UHF. If cost is a consideration, the air band listener will have to decide whether the extra expense is justified, especially when bearing in mind that during the next ten years or so HF aeronautical communications will be phased out in favour of satellite coverage of the main areas of the world.

None of the HF radio receivers are exclusively for air band use, so they will still be suitable for listening to the many other interesting transmissions which take place. Nevertheless, anyone who is unable to receive other transmissions on VHF or UHF is likely to be attracted by the idea of HF radio.

By comparison with VHF/UHF models there are far fewer HF radios available; it is also particularly important to appreciate the requirements necessary in an HF set which is to be used for aeronautical purposes. There is an increasing tendency for manufacturers to provide scanners which cover the entire aeronautical range of frequencies within the design of hand-held receivers. VHF and UHF are transmitted on AM whereas HF is transmitted on USB, part of the Single Side Band range. All of these facilities are now available in small portable receivers.

Aviation agencies transmit on the Single Side Band (SSB) system, which means that more channels can be accommodated within the same space and also that less interference occurs. Equipment with SSB is further divided into two alternatives: Upper Side Band or Lower Side Band. For our purposes, the receiver has to be suitable for operating on Upper Side Band, otherwise it will not be capable of resolving aircraft messages.

For air band use, an HF radio receiver must be capable of the following:

■ the frequencies are to be within the range of 2MHz to 23MHz without any breaks in the coverage;

■ Single Side Band must be provided; also the transmissions must be capable of operating on Upper Side Band;

■ digital readout of the precise frequency is desirable.

Some of the lower priced receivers have a tuning system whereby the main frequency is selected, and the precise frequency is found by a sensitive tuning dial known as a Beat Frequency Oscillator which must be used to finely tune the receiver. In fact, this is a relatively slow process and requires practice. For aeronautical purposes the signal is often finished before it can be tuned accurately.

As there are so many frequencies in use for aviation purposes, the ability to add them to the receiver's memory is a considerable advantage, but none of the currently available sets has a total of memories greater than a few dozen.

Antennas
It is normally quite easy to receive air band messages on VHF or UHF, since reception depends on line-of-sight between the transmitter and the receiver. Provided the signal is not interrupted by obstructions such as large buildings or hills, reception will probably be reasonably good at ranges up to 50 miles for ground transmitters or 200 miles for aircraft in flight.

With High Frequency radio the reception is far less predictable, even though the antenna system may be far less sophisticated. Often a simple length of wire connected to the receiver will give results which are as good as any more expensive system.

The quality of reception on HF depends so much on changing atmospheric conditions that the aerial system may not have a significant effect on the final result. However, it is perhaps worth trying some of the variations because one particular type might just work well in your circumstances. Unfortunately, no one particular type can be said to be better or worse than any other. It is very much a case of experimenting with the various options before a final decision is made, but even then it is quite possible that the simplest design is likely to be the most efficient.

HF Aerials

Most types of antenna suitable for use on HF are basically simple, consisting in the main of long lengths of wire stretched out in the open, in a roof space or around a room. If used out of doors a multi-strand pvc-covered wire specially made for such use is recommended because it can stand the strain of being pulled in tension between two points which are quite distant.

Below and opposite:
Various antenna systems for HF reception. Numerous other designs can be used, including 'passive' types.

Long lengths of wire are surprisingly heavy and a considerable load is required to pull the wire into the horizontal position.

There are a number of main kinds of HF antenna and these are described here.

Long Wire
This type of antenna is one of the simplest to install and yet still one of the most effective for HF listening. The wire should be not less than 30ft, stretched out in the open as high as reasonably possible, usually between the house and a pole or a tree, and insulated at each end by ceramic or plastic insulators which can be obtained from specialist suppliers.

The wire has to be strong enough to support itself and also it must be capable of resisting any corrosion. A long length of wire of perhaps 50ft needs a considerable load to stretch it to the horizontal position, therefore only the correct kind of wire is suitable.

Ideally, a 'north-south' installation will give the best results for traffic on the North Atlantic, although in practice this cannot be achieved in many cases. Other factors such as the proximity of buildings or hills may well affect the efficiency of the antenna.

The end of the wire closest to the receiver should be run down to the receiver, as near to the vertical as possible, and then to the external antenna socket on the receiver. If it is

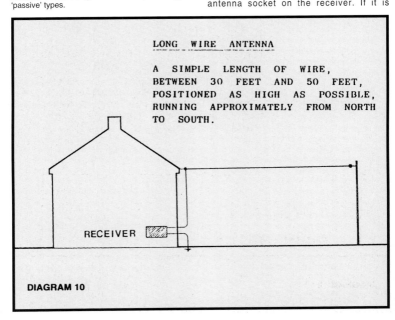

LONG WIRE ANTENNA

A SIMPLE LENGTH OF WIRE, BETWEEN 30 FEET AND 50 FEET, POSITIONED AS HIGH AS POSSIBLE, RUNNING APPROXIMATELY FROM NORTH TO SOUTH.

RECEIVER

DIAGRAM 10

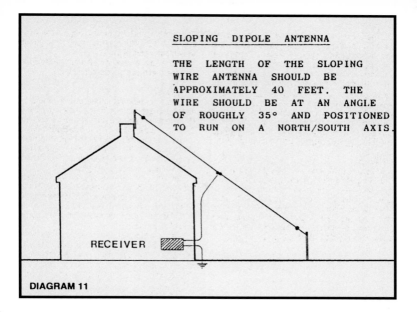

SLOPING DIPOLE ANTENNA

THE LENGTH OF THE SLOPING
WIRE ANTENNA SHOULD BE
APPROXIMATELY 40 FEET. THE
WIRE SHOULD BE AT AN ANGLE
OF ROUGHLY 35° AND POSITIONED
TO RUN ON A NORTH/SOUTH AXIS.

RECEIVER

DIAGRAM 11

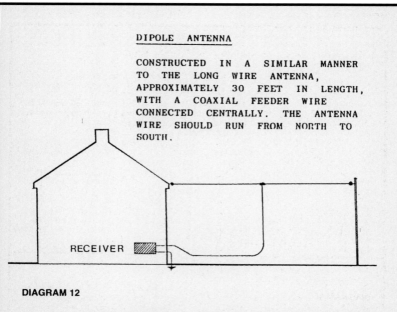

DIPOLE ANTENNA

CONSTRUCTED IN A SIMILAR MANNER
TO THE LONG WIRE ANTENNA,
APPROXIMATELY 30 FEET IN LENGTH,
WITH A COAXIAL FEEDER WIRE
CONNECTED CENTRALLY. THE ANTENNA
WIRE SHOULD RUN FROM NORTH TO
SOUTH.

RECEIVER

DIAGRAM 12

unavoidable to route the cable through the building, care must be taken to avoid any electrical circuits or television receivers.

Dipole Antenna

This is a variation on the simple long wire type of antenna. The wire is also stretched outside, in the clear, preferably at least 30ft in length and insulated at both ends in the same way as the long wire type. The difference is that the centre of the wire is cut and joined via a suitable weatherproof connection box to a co-axial down-lead (eg UR67) with the centre core being connected to one arm of the dipole and the outer braid to the other arm. The other end of the UR67 cable is connected to the receiver with the appropriate connector plug.

In order to ensure that the two arms of the dipole are matched, the junction at the point of the break in the main wire can be made by using a 'balun' transformer which balances the signal received so that (in theory at least) an improved signal will be picked up at the receiver. Again, it may well be necessary to experiment with such systems so that their suitability can be assessed.

Sloping Dipole Antenna

If space is a problem it might not be possible to erect a long wire type of antenna, therefore some kind of alternative system has to be considered.

In confined gardens the only suitable option could be to provide a system which achieves the required length but without taking up too much space.

In this design the wire is sloped at an angle so that the proportions are roughly equivalent to a 3:4:5 triangle, ie 30ft/40ft/50ft with the 50ft arm being the actual antenna.

To get the dimensions right it will be necessary to fit the highest end of the antenna wire to a mast on the chimney stack or to the highest point of a gable roof. Fixing the wire at the fascia level of the average two-storey house will not usually be high enough to achieve the correct proportions.

The connection to the receiver is made in the same way as for the previous dipole design, by splitting the wire at the centre and connecting a co-axial cable to the two elements.

Indoor Aerials

There will always be situations where it is not possible or convenient for an external antenna to be fitted, for example in flats.

In these cases the provision of an indoor antenna can often be quite acceptable and because the wire will not have to resist the weather or support its own weight it will be satisfactory to use thin wire which can be fitted around the room, under the carpet or even behind the wallpaper. The object in all cases is to provide at least 30ft of continuous wire stretched out as far as possible, although not necessarily in a straight line.

If possible, two independent antennas positioned at right angles to each other will be well worth trying, since each can be tested in different conditions in order to obtain the best results.

To avoid interference the antenna wires should be kept away from electrical circuits and television receivers.

Active Antennas

This term is used to describe a type of antenna which is electrically powered, the electronics being designed to match the signal at the receiver to the aerial. The antenna itself is 3 or

4ft in length, and is therefore suitable for fixing almost anywhere which is convenient. It is powered either by a mains transformer or by batteries, and although it may not be particularly better than a long wire design, it will give good results and is ideal where space is a problem or where a quick and simple system is desired.

Earthing

It is important that any HF aerial system should be isolated from the receiver to prevent damage in the event of a lightning strike. It is also recommended that a separate earth be taken from the set to a length of copper tube or rod driven into the soil to give improved reception.

Lightning Protection

It is advisable to provide a suitable means of isolating the antenna system from the receiver so that in the event of a lightning strike the receiver will not be damaged. An arrester provided between the antenna and the set will prevent lightning damage, although it is not very likely in this part of the world.

The necessary equipment can be purchased from radio equipment suppliers and fitted in accordance with the manufacturer's recommendations.

If for any reason you are using your receiver without such protection then it is advisable to disconnect the antenna lead from the equipment when not in use or whenever there is a possibility of an electrical storm.

Aerial Tuning Units (ATUs)

It is worth experimenting with an Aerial Tuning Unit (ATU) when using a long wire type of antenna. The ATU adjusts the signal on any particular frequency to match the length of the antenna wire so that the best results are obtained.

As the ATU is adjusted, the signal can be heard to improve as the background interference is reduced.

It is not necessary to spend a large sum on an ATU — simple inexpensive models usually give acceptable results.

Conclusion: The reception of transmissions on HF is not very predictable. Changes occur within a matter of a few hours, resulting in dramatic effects on the quality of reception. Sometimes the simplest of aerials, perhaps the in-built telescopic type, can give very good results; at other times reception is poor despite the most expensive and elaborate system. It is often a good idea to have two different systems in operation. Switching from one to the other so that the best results are achieved is usually worth while.

Although HF radio is still the main means of communication in remote areas, the use of datalinking is increasing, especially in the area of company messages. Datalink is more reliable and much faster than radio, and already North Atlantic track clearances are sent to many of the world's major airlines by this method. Within a few years flight plan clearances to aircraft at airports will also be using this system and as satellites become more reliable there is little doubt that the use of HF will diminish.

Opposite:
AOR AR7030 communications receiver. *AOR*

Below:
Heathrow. *Author*

7 Towards Better Listening

So far we have examined the equipment required for air band listening and the basic system operating in UK and European airspace. In this chapter, some of the mysteries contained within the process are explained and suggestions offered on how listening pleasure can be improved.

Simultaneous Transmissions
These almost always occur at times of the day when traffic levels are low and controller workload reduced; usually this is very early in the morning or late in the evening.

At these relatively quiet periods there is no need to keep the normal daytime number of controllers handling flights; the control centres will therefore close down some of their sector positions and transfer the control of aircraft in those sectors to adjacent controllers. In itself this is straightforward enough. The complication for the air band listener is that although there is one controller handling traffic in two sectors, the controller will often use two frequencies simultaneously. The listener will hear the controller talking to aircraft in both sectors but will hear replies only from aircraft in one of the sectors — the one to which the scanner is tuned.

Imagine two adjacent sectors — Sector A and Sector B. (Sectors are air traffic control areas for en-route flights). Sector A operates on VHF frequency 134.5, Sector B on 126.5. During normal operations, traffic in each sector would be handled by two separate control teams. As the traffic levels reduce, Sector B controller will hand over control of the traffic in the sector to the Sector A controller. Section A controller will then handle all the flights in both sectors. Flights in Sector A will transmit on 134.5; flights in Sector B will transmit on 126.5. The controller will talk to flights in both sectors, using both frequencies simultaneously. If your receiver is tuned to 134.5 you will hear all the controller's messages, on both frequencies, but only the replies from traffic in Sector A.

If the period of reduced traffic load is likely to be prolonged, the aircraft in both sectors will be transferred to one of the two frequencies. Both controllers and flights will then be on one frequency, until traffic increases and the requirement for two sector controllers becomes necessary.

Another occasional change from normal routine needs some explanation. In the example described earlier it sometimes happens that the aircraft appear to be transmitting on both sector frequencies, while the controller's messages are also heard on both frequencies.

In fact, the aircraft radio is not capable of being used on two frequencies simultaneously. Aircraft transmit on one frequency (the appropriate sector frequency). The message is picked up at one of the ATC radio receiving stations and this is then instantly retransmitted on a different frequency for the other sector.

If you have access to two receivers you can verify this by tuning them to the two sector frequencies — you will hear identical transmissions from aircraft on the two sets simultaneously. However, this does not happen very often, so it may never be heard in your area.

Aircraft messages being retransmitted in this way can mean a dramatic improvement in the quality of reception. An aircraft perhaps 250 miles away can transmit to a receiving station possibly only 50 miles away. The retransmitted message is then heard at full strength from a much closer location, giving the impression that the flight is much closer than it really is. There are other reasons for dramatic improvements in the range and quality of ATC transmissions, mainly due to the weather. These are discussed later.

Offset Frequencies
A number of VHF and UHF receivers are provided with the facility of selecting certain frequency steps.

The current steps between published frequencies in the air band range are 25kHz for VHF and UHF transmissions. Many receivers cannot be adjusted to receive frequencies other than those published.

Below:
Selective decoding of ACARS messages is now possible with the advent of new computer programmes and is much favoured by aircraft spotters. *Flightdeck*

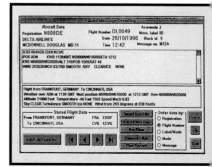

In practice, however, many en-route transmissions are made on frequencies which are in fact slightly higher or slightly lower than those published, and these are known as 'offsets'.

The reason for this is because of interference between two transmissions being made on the same frequency from separate transmitters.

In order to obtain maximum range on en-route frequencies, the ground transmissions are made simultaneously from two, three or four separate transmitters; to avoid interference between the transmitters the actual frequencies used are slightly higher or lower than those published.

Aircraft receivers are designed to cope with these variations in frequency; similarly anyone listening to a particular frequency with an air band receiver will have no reception difficulties provided one of the transmitters is nearby. The strength of the signal will not create any problem.

Where the receiver is located in an area on the fringe of the range of cover it is a different matter. The fact that the transmission is taking place on a slightly different frequency can result in the loss of the signal altogether; air band listeners can often be in a location where ground control transmissions are difficult or impossible to receive. If the receiver is tuned to the published frequency this may in fact result in failure to detect the actual transmission because the true frequency may be higher or lower than that selected on the set.

This is where an air band scanner with the facility of selecting small frequency steps can be a distinct advantage. Several of the more sophisticated receivers are tunable in 1kHz steps, so that the actual frequency chosen can be 1 or more kHz higher or lower than the one published. VHF frequency 128.400 can be changed, for example, to 128.395 or 128.405, and it is often the case that one of these frequencies will give better results than the original one. It is a fact that in situations where reception is difficult, one of the offset frequencies will enable the controller to be heard even though this may not be possible on the original frequency.

Offset frequencies are used only for en-route traffic where long range plus a large area of cover is essential. Aircraft radios transmit only on the published frequencies, ie in 25kHz steps. Offsets do not apply to airfield situations. The modern development of providing air band receivers with the ability to select steps as low as 1kHz gives the listener a complete range of frequencies to choose from.

Effect of Weather

Occasionally, usually during the spring or autumn, the weather system will provide conditions which give exceptional results in VHF

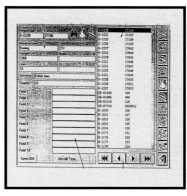

Above:
With the right equipment aircraft can be identified via the transmission of SELCALS on HF.
Flightdeck

and UHF reception. Such opportunities are quite rare — perhaps half a dozen times a year — but it is usually quite easy to predict when these conditions are likely to occur.

The reason for the unusual distances covered by ground transmissions is the effect of certain weather conditions causing the transmissions to be reflected back down to earth, so that signals not normally heard will be received with comparative ease.

The factors creating the opportunities for unusual reception are widespread, eg fog and a high pressure system covering the country, probably occurring during the early morning and lasting perhaps until lunchtime.

Reception of controllers from perhaps 200 miles away are likely to be received without difficulty, plus other broadcasts which might not usually be heard — for example, Volmet, Track Clearances, and even airport controllers over 100 miles away.

Almost invariably, a weather forecast of widespread fog on spring or autumn days will indicate that ATC transmissions will be dramatically improved.

As the fog lifts, and the weather gradually improves, the rarely heard transmission will slowly diminish in quality, with the background noise becoming worse until eventually the signal will be lost altogether.

Attenuators

According to the dictionary, the definition of 'attenuate' is to reduce in force or value.

This is precisely the effect of an attenuator fitted between a radio receiver and the antenna - the signal reaching the set is modified in such a

41

way as to lower its strength to a level which varies according to the value of the attenuator.

Attenuators are used to cancel out unwanted signals — naturally if the transmissions are being received loudly and clearly there will be no need to bother with an attenuator.

In practice, however, there are often occasions when the quality of reception is spoiled by interference or some other 'breakthrough' transmission which manages to interrupt the original message at a critical point.

A few air band receivers are provided with a built-in attenuator, perhaps with a value of 10 or 20 decibels, which is brought into the circuit simply by pressing the appropriate button or by using a slide switch on the receiver.

The attenuator, when switched in to the circuit, immediately reduces the signal strength. If part of the transmission is weak, it will probably be eliminated entirely when the attenuator is used.

For more flexibility, and for those receivers that do not contain a built-in attenuator, it is possible to purchase individual attenuators for several values, which can be fitted either singly or in tandem to provide a variety of optional degrees of attenuation.

These attenuators are approximately 20mm in length, of tubular shape, roughly the same diameter as the co-axial cable. They are plugged directly into the aerial socket on the receiver, either singly or in multiples, to give the required level of reduction. The aerial co-axial lead is then connected to the attenuator, so that any signals are reduced in value before they reach the receiver.

The attenuators can be used in any combination — if a 3db and two 6db attenuators are purchased, it is possible to use them in varying selections to give attenuations of 3, 6, 9, 12 and 15 decibels — usually more than enough for most situations.

Separate attenuators are supplied with BNC connections as standard, being appropriate for use with the majority of VHF/UHF antennas, although it is easy to fit adapters so that any kind of fitting can be accepted.

If interference or unwanted breakthrough signals are a problem, try fitting one or more attenuators to see if there is any improvement. It really is a question of experimentation until the right balance can be found.

Sometimes the use of an external antenna in conjunction with a hand-held portable receiver can cause the circuitry within the set to become overloaded by certain signals and the use of an attenuator in these situations can be a positive advantage.

Amplifiers

Alternatively (and surprisingly) it may be found that reception improvements can be made by amplifying the signal rather than trying to reduce

it. This feature of air band listening is covered next.

For those who are in areas of the country where reception on UHF or VHF is poor, it is sometimes possible to improve the signal by the use of a separate amplifier which is introduced into the system between the antenna and the receiver (usually close to the receiver).

The amplifier will have to be powered either from the mains or from a battery.

Unfortunately, they do not work in all situations. Experience has shown that, in some cases, they are actually detrimental and in fact produce results which are far worse than those experienced without amplification.

As with other ATC equipment, it is a case of trial and error. It might be that one particular unit will work well in one area but not in another; unfortunately, it is not possible to predict where the 'good' and 'bad' areas might be.

Amplifiers increase the intensity of the signal received via the antenna. Sometimes the effect is merely to increase interference to an unbearable level, where increasing the squelch to its maximum has no effect. In other cases, transmissions which might not otherwise be heard will be detected with quite reasonable results.

What is surprising is that normal reception, with various kinds of interference and breakthrough, can actually be improved by fitting an amplifier.

It would be reasonable to assume that a receiver suffering from breakthrough or other interference would in fact be made worse by the introduction of an amplifier, but this is not always the case. There is no way of telling how one particular situation will be affected. Only individual experiments with different pieces of equipment will provide the answer.

One further combination is possible - the use of an amplifier to boost the signal, while at the same time toning down its intensity by using an attenuator (different values can be used on an experimental basis).

Unfortunately, there are no hard and fast rules for using amplifiers or attenuators, except one (which has been given before): never assume that the most costly are the best! Often it is simply not so. It may be possible for an amplifier to be tested in your particular situation with an agreement from your supplier to accept the return of the unit if it does not perform as expected.

Using Tape Recorders

Most air band listeners will be able to expand their knowledge and have more enjoyment if air traffic control messages are recorded. Not only will this enable the listener to analyse particular situations by reviewing a particular message or group of messages, it will also permit a record of activity to be made during periods when it is inconvenient for the listener to spend time listening 'live' to the receiver.

Undoubtedly the beginner will benefit more than most by being able to listen carefully, sentence by sentence, to every message and phrase in order to learn more about what is going on. Most newcomers to air band listening find the rapid clipped speech used by controllers and pilots very difficult to follow. Add to this the wide use of standard phrases and abbreviations and the problem becomes even greater.

Many experienced listeners probably do not realise how much of a message they are actually missing until the same sentences are heard, one at a time, with an interval between each transmission which can be decided by pausing the recorder.

Another major advantage in using a tape recorder for air band messages is the ability to capture certain types of infrequent transmissions which the listener is very unlikely to hear during the normal periods of listening.

This point, however, leads on to a further consideration for the use of recorders. The normal apparatus allows the tape to run for a period of up to an hour, recording any sound which happens to occur during that period. Naturally, even if no sounds are heard the tape still runs to the end, so that the enthusiast then has to listen to the complete tape to find out if anything has been recorded.

The answer, of course, is to use a voice-operated-tape recorder or an ordinary tape recorder fitted with a sound-operated switch.

There are several of these units available and they are generally known as voice-activated recorders. The unit is set to record in the normal way, but if no sounds are detected the motor will be switched off after about three seconds and the tape will remain stationary.

When a sound is detected — the voice of a controller or a pilot for example — the motor is switched on and the tape starts to record. As long as the conversation continues the unit will record. At the end of a phrase or sentence the motor will continue to run for approximately three seconds. If no sound occurs during that period the motor will stop again.

The air band listener is able to return to the tape recorder after being away for several hours and listen to a tape which contains all the messages with virtually no break between them.

If no messages have been detected during that period the tape will still be in its original position.

Some tape recorders are provided with a built-in voice-activated system which can be brought into operation at the flick of a switch. One or two air band receivers have voice-operated switching actually provided within the receiver so that they can be connected directly to an ordinary recorder.

The alternative available to the air band listener is to introduce a separate and independent voice switching unit between the receiver and an ordinary tape recorder (for example the AUTO-VOX unit). The unit is connected to the wiring between the receiver and the tape recorder, with a separate connection to the cassette recorder motor which is activated whenever a sound is heard.

Normally, the switching of the cassette motor is achieved by connecting the switching unit to the remote on/off switch on the tape recorder.

However, it is quite possible that your particular recorder may not be provided with a built-in remote switch, in which case it will be necessary to open up the recorder and cut the lead to the motor so that the connection from the voice-operated unit can be made directly to the wiring to the cassette motor by the insertion of a 2.5mm socket.

The unit is operated by a standard PP3 battery. When a sound is detected, the relay within the unit closes and this completes the circuit and switches the recorder on enabling the recording to commence. When the sounds cease, the relay opens and the recording stops.

Tape Recorder Connections

A further problem often experienced with air band receivers concerns the type of tape recorder connection. Few scanners have tape recorder outlets. Many are provided with outlets for extension speakers or earphones but these are grossly overpowered for use with a tape recorder.

It is therefore essential to reduce the power from an extension speaker outlet to a level which is appropriate to the tape recorder if undistorted results are to be obtained.

This is in fact quite simple and inexpensive, and is achieved by inserting a resistor into the centre core of the lead between the receiver and the recorder, with the result that the recordings will be clear and undistorted. Resistors are very inexpensive items and two or three of different values can be purchased for less than a pound. As a suggestion, try a resistor with a value of 100K as a start. If the results are not to your liking, try one of a higher or lower value. They take only minutes to fit and are well worth the expense in terms of improved quality. They can be bought from most radio shops (eg Tandys) and are simply soldered to the centre core of the recorder cable.

Another problem with using a receiver which is not provided with a tape recorder socket is the loss of reception when a tape lead is plugged in. In other words, inserting the tape lead cuts out the signal to the receivers loudspeaker, so that it is not possible to hear what is being recorded. (This does not happen with tape recorder outlets which do allow the listener to hear what is being said.)

This problem can be overcome quite easily by using a 'splitter' which is plugged into the outlet on the radio receiver. This actually splits the signal so that one connection can be made to the tape recorder while the other connection is made to a separate loudspeaker. It is therefore possible to produce a tape recording while listening to the actual messages via the separate external loudspeaker.

It is well worth playing about with tape recorders and voice operated systems. Very good results can be obtained provided some thought is given to developing the end product and there is no doubt that many items of interest that would otherwise be missed can be captured and analysed.

Airborne Communication Addressing and Reporting System (ACARS)
Possession of an air band receiver enables the aviation enthusiast to become involved in a new and interesting aspect of the hobby.

Most of the world's large airlines now use a message transmission system to send information back to base, known as ACARS. Messages are sent by VHF datalink, in short bursts of digitally processed information, usually lasting no more than half a second. The European frequency is 131.725MHz.

Decoding equipment on the ground converts the signal back to its original format in a series of coded letters and numbers. Sometimes the message is sent by the crew; others are automatically prompted by predetermined events on the aircraft — for example, raising the undercarriage sends a departure message, releasing the brakes prompts an off-blocks message, and so on. Included are every time, of course, are the aircraft details — airline flight number and registration — and this information is particularly useful to the aircraft spotter.

Anyone can purchase the equipment to decode the messages. The VHF receiver is connected to the unit and the datalink messages can then be printed or alternatively viewed on a standard personal computer. Unfortunately, the messages can be extremely lengthy and they are further complicated by the fact that various airlines use different message formats.

The receiving equipment on the ground has sophisticated facilities for detecting errors in a message and, of course, it is possible that more than one transmission will be made at the same time. This means that the data can be sent several times in quick succession before being accepted, resulting in pages of useless information for the air band listener.

At least one programme is now available which analyses each message and selects only the vital information — airline, callsign, registration and

time. This can be stored and used as and when required or printed out as a report for each particular period of time. By this method the aircraft-spotter has a ready made listing for all flights heard and reports can be produced in numerous formats.

For full details of the system contact the suppliers listed in Appendix X.

Selective Calling (SELCAL) Analysis
Another area of possible interest is the ability to determine the identity of a flight by decoding its SELCAL. This is a four-digit number unique to each aircraft and is used by HF radio operators to make contact with the crew.

SELCALs consist of two pairs of letters which are transmitted to the aircraft. It is possible to purchase a decoder which receives the signal on HF and indicates on a panel readout the actual letters, enabling the enthusiast to identify the aircraft from a printed table.

Computer Control
A few scanners now have the facility for being managed through a personal computer. The receiver is connected to the PC via a special connecting lead and an interface unit.

Frequencies can be entered and sorted on the computer and downloaded to the receiver's memory. Various kinds of reports can also be produced.

It is doubtful if this arrangement is appropriate for the listener whose only interest is in air band since the need to manage and rearrange frequencies is relatively rare. Also, of course, access to a PC is required and the interface and software are not particularly cheap.

For further details contact one of the suppliers listed in Appendix X.

Below:
Reports can be generated in a variety of formats to produce aircraft lists. *Flightdeck*

Data for Flight Number: BA0178   Operator: BRITISH AIRWAYS
Flying from JFK, NEW YORK to LONDON HEATHROW
Between: 01/12/1995 and 22/12/1995

Reg	Selcal	Plane Type	Serial	Date	Tim
G-BDXP	AMGK	BOEING 747-200	24088	01/12/1995	19:5
G-AWNJ	BGDE	BOEING 747-100	20279	03/12/1995	20:0
G-BBPU	BDCH	BOEING 747-100	20953	04/12/1995	20:0
G-BNLF	BPAL	BOEING 747-400	24048	05/12/1995	19:4
G-BBPU	BDCH	BOEING 747-100	20953	06/12/1995	20:0
G-AWNA	BDAE	BOEING 747-100	19761	07/12/1995	20:0

8 VHF/UHF Receivers

This chapter provides details on most of the receivers available for air band listening. Several discontinued models have been included as these are available on the secondhand market and it is worth remembering that many of these will perform equally as well as new models currently on sale.

There is a growing tendency to produce receivers which are more and more sophisticated, covering a very wide range of frequencies as opposed to dedicated air band models. Generally speaking, the dedicated receiver will produce the best quality reception. Furthermore, high cost does not necessarily mean better results in the aeronautical range of frequencies.

Before deciding on a particular purchase consider the following points:

■ check the details with the supplier, since receivers with the same name and model number can have different specifications depending on when and where they were produced;
■ speak to one or more of the suppliers whose details are included in the appendices;
■ look out for special offers but check carefully that the features you require are covered;
■ try and persuade your supplier to let you have a receiver on trial — some do have a policy of accepting returns or exchanges.

The prices quoted are an approximate guide for 1997. However, variations do occur, particularly when models are at the end of their production or when special prices are on offer.

Below:
AOR AR3000A communications receiver. *AOR*

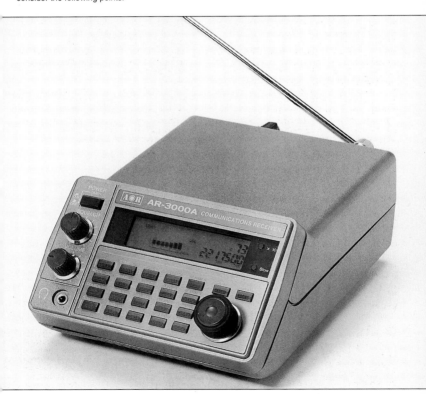

AOR AR - 1500
Hand-held wideband receiver covering civil, military and HF airbands; 1,000 memories in 10 banks (including automatic storage of all active channels if required). Frequency steps: programmable in steps of 5 or 12.5 kHz up to 995kHz.

Unable to receive the proposed 8.33kHz channels. Includes a built-in attenuator.
Price guide £195

✗ AOR AR - 2700
Hand-held wideband scanner covering civil and military air bands; 500 memories in 10 banks. Frequency steps (in Kilohertz): 5, 6.25, 9, 10, 12.5, 25, 50, 100.

A popular model produced by one of the most reputable companies in the business. The receiver has an optional facility for recording transmissions built into the set (c5sec duration).
Price guide: £175

AOR AR - 5000
Mains-operated base station with the ability to receive the full air band range — civilian VHF, military UHF and HF Short wave; 1,000 memories in 20 banks. Frequency steps: all modes have steps in multiples of 1 hertz.

This is a high-performance receiver capable of receiving all aeronautical transmissions, including the proposed 8.33kHz range. The set is fitted with a tape recorder facility and a built-in attenuator and also computer control if required. However, the cost is high for the air band listener.
Price guide: £1,750

AOR AR 8000
A sophisticated high-specification hand-held wideband scanner covering civilian VHF, military UFH and HF shortwave; 1,000 memories in 20 banks.

Frequency steps (in Kilohertz): 0.1 up to 995kHz in increments of 50Hz.

Another top-of-the-range receiver capable of receiving the proposed 8.33kHz transmissions and also airport repeaters. Provided with a programmable attenuator and the addition of text to indicate individual channels. Suitable for computer control if required. The only drawback is that it is probably too complex for the beginner.
Price guide: £350

COMMTEL 202
Hand-held civil air band scanner; 50 memories (no banks). Frequency steps (in Kilohertz): pre-set at 5, 12.5 and 25. A good value model for the beginner.
Price guide: £95

ICOM IC-R10
Hand-held wide band receiver covering civil, military and HF airbands; 1,000 memories in 10 banks. Frequency steps: multiples of 1kHz. A new model with the latest features including built-in 20db attenuator, and facilities for computer control.
Price guide £400

REALISTIC PRO-62
Hand-held scanner covering civil air band only; 200 memories in 10 banks. Frequency steps (in Kilohertz): 25.
Unable to receive proposed 8.33kHz channels.
Price guide £200

REALISTIC PRO-63
Hand-held scanner covering civil air band only; 200 memories in 10 banks. Frequency steps (in Kilohertz): 25.
Unable to receive proposed 8.33kHz channels.
Price guide £150

REALISTIC PRO - 60
A hand-held scanner suitable for civilian and military air band and airport repeaters; 200 memories in 10 banks. Frequency steps (in Kilohertz): pre-set at 5, 12.5 and 25. Receives in AM, narrow FM and wide FM modes. Unable to accept 8.33kHz channels.
Price range: £200

REALISTIC PRO - 26
Hand-held scanner covering civilian and military air band and airport repeaters; 200 memories in 10 banks. Frequency steps (in Kilohertz): pre-set at 5, 12.5 and 25.
Price range: £300

✗ REALISTIC PRO - 25
Hand-held scanner covering civilian and military air band; 100 memories in 10 banks. Frequency steps (in Kilohertz): 5, 25 (factory set).
Price range: £175

REALISTIC PRO - 2039
Base station scanner covering civilian and military air band; 200 memories in 10 banks. Frequency steps (in Kilohertz): pre-set at 5, 12.5 and 25.
Price range: £200

SKYVOICE
A basic model hand-held civil air band scanner. A simple to use beginner's model but lacking any sophisticated features.
Price guide: £95

SONY AIR 7 (MK II)
Hand-held scanner for civilian air band; 10 memories per band. Frequency steps (in Kilohertz): pre-set to suit band selected.

This model covers four wave bands including air band VHF with 25kHz steps limited to only 10 memories.
Price range: £295

SONY ICF PRO 80

Hand-held HF scanner. Note that civil air band requires the use of a separate conversion unit FRQ — 80; 40 memories in four banks. Frequency steps (in Kilohertz): 1 (factory set).
Price guide: £345

STEEPLETONE SAB 9, SAB 11, SAB 12

Steepletone produces three airband receivers eminently suitable for newcomers to the hobby. Each model covers medium wave and FM radio. Two models cover marine radio as well. The SAB 12 model is provided with a squelch facility. Because these receivers are of the continuous tuning type, they can handle the proposed 8.33kHz channels.
Price guide: SAB11 £18, SAB 9 £27, SAB 12 £33

TRIDENT TR-2400

Hand-held model with wide frequency range covering civilian and military air bands, HF (Short Wave) Upper Side Band and airport repeaters; 1,000 memories in 10 banks. Frequency steps (in Kilohertz): multiples of 1kHz.

An all-mode reception receiver with rotary or keypad frequency control and fast scan. Capable of receiving 8.33kHz channels.
Price range: £300

TRIDENT TR - 1200

Hand-held scanner with wide frequency range (not continuous) covering civilian and military air bands and airport repeaters; 1,000 memories in 10 banks. Frequency steps (in Kilohertz): from 5kHz upwards in multiples of 5 or 12.5 up to 995.

This model receives in AM, narrow FM and wide FM modes with rotary or keypad frequency control. However, it is not capable of receiving the proposed 8.33kHz channels.
Price range: £300

TRIDENT TR - 980

A hand-held scanner capable of receiving civilian and military air bands and airport repeaters; 125 memories in five banks. Frequency steps (in Kilohertz): 5, 10, 12.5, 25 and 30.

This model receives in AM, narrow FM and wide FM modes with rotary or keypad frequency control. However, not capable of receiving the proposed 8.33kHz channels.
Price range: £195

UNIDEN BEARCAT BC860XLT

Base station wideband scanner covering the civilian VHF air band; 100 memories in 10 banks. Frequency steps (in Kilohertz): 5, 12.5 (factory set).

A reasonably priced receiver with high-speed scan and search but it is unable to receive 8.33kHz channels.
Price guide: £145

UNIDEN BEARCAT BC9000XLT

Base station wideband scanner capable of receiving civilian VHF and military UHF air bands; 500 memories in 20 banks. Frequency steps (in Kilohertz): 5, 12.5, 25, 50.

Receives in AM, narrow FM and wide FM modes. Selectable attenuator, automatic tape recording feature and high-speed scan and search are among its features, but it is unable to receive 8.33kHz channels.
Price guide: £325

UNIDEN BEARCAT BC120XLT

Hand-held scanner capable of receiving civilian VHF air band; 100 memories in 10 banks. Frequency steps (in Kilohertz) 5, 12.5 (factory set).

Features high-speed scan and search with 10 priority channels, but it is unable to receive 8.33kHz channels. Requires a special rechargeable battery pack.
Price guide: £140

UNIDEN BEARCAT UBC220XLT

Hand-held scanner capable of receiving civilian VHF air band; 200 memories in 10 banks. Frequency steps (in Kilohertz): 5, 12.5 (factory set).

A reasonably priced scanner operating on batteries only, but unable to receive 8.33kHz channels. Requires a special rechargeable battery pack.
Price guide: £195

UNIDEN BEARCAT UBC3000XLT

Hand-held scanner capable of receiving civilian VHF and military UHF air band and airport repeaters; 400 memories in 10 banks. Frequency steps (in Kilohertz): 5, 12.5, 50.

Receives in AM, narrow FM and wide FM modes, and features high-speed search and scan, but it is unable to receive 8.33kHz channels.
Price guide: £250

WELZ WS - 1000

A miniature hand-held sophisticated scanner with many of the latest features, including the ability to receive the proposed 8.33kHz channels; 400 memories in 10 banks. Frequency steps (in Kilohertz): 1, 5, 6.25, 9, 10, 12.5, 15,

20, 25, 30, 50 and 100. Perhaps too complex for the beginner.
Price guide: £350

WIN 108
Hand-held dedicated scanner for civilian VHF air band, now available only on the secondhand market; 20 memories in two banks. Frequency steps (in Kilohertz): 25.

A basic inexpensive scanner, although early models did not extend beyond 136.0MHz. Unable to receive 8.33kHz channels.
Price guide: £100 (depending on condition)

YUPITERU VT125
A dedicated hand-held scanner from one of the best known companies in the air band business. Suitable for civilian VHF air band; 30 memories in one bank. Frequency steps (in Kilohertz): 25, 50, 100.

A very popular and efficient receiver, although unable to receive the 8.33kHz channels.
Price guide: £125 (secondhand)

YUPITERU VT225
A dedicated hand-held scanner covering civilian VHF and military UHF air bands and also marine frequencies; 100 memories in 10 banks. Frequency steps (in Kilohertz): 10, 12.5, 25, 50, 100.

Another popular choice and easy to use. Unable to receive the 8.33kHz channels.
Price guide: £200 (secondhand)

YUPITERU MVT6000
Mains-operated base station wide band scanner covering civilian VHF air band and military UHF air band and airport repeaters; 100 memories in 5 banks. Frequency steps (in Kilohertz): 5, 10, 12.5, 25. Unable to receive 8.33kHz channels.
Price guide: £150 (secondhand)

YUPITERU MVT7000
Hand-held wide range scanner capable of receiving civilian VHF and military UHF air bands and also airport repeaters; 200 memories in 10 banks. Frequency steps (in Kilohertz): 5, 10, 12.5, 25, 50 and 100.

Another popular choice, with the feature of rotary tuning, but unable to receive 8.33kHz channels.
Price guide: £200 (secondhand)

YUPITERU MVT7100
Hand-held wide range scanner capable of receiving civilian VHF, military UHF and HF Short Wave aeronautical bands. Note that this model is also known as the **MVT7100EX**; 1,000 memories in 10 banks. Frequency steps (in Kilohertz): 1, 5, 6.25, 10, 12.5, 20, 25, 50, 100 (for HF, steps are 50 or 100 hertz).

This receiver operates across the entire aeronautical range, including airport repeaters and the proposed 8.33kHz channels. However, Short Wave reception cannot be expected to match the performance of dedicated HF receivers.
Price guide: £300

YUPITERU MVT8000
Base or mobile scanning receiver covering civil and military air bands including airport repeaters, but not the proposed 8.33kHz channels; 200 memories in 10 banks. Frequency steps (in kilohertz): 5, 10, 12.5, 25, 50, 100.
Price guide £400

YUPITERU MVT9000
Hand-held wide band receiver covering civil, military and HF airbands; 1,000 memories in 20 banks with Alpha numeric 'labelling' of stations. Frequency steps (in kilohertz): 50, 100, 200Hz, 1, 5, 6.25, 8, 9, 10, 12.5, 15, 20, 25, 30, 50, 100, 125kHz.
A top of the range receiver with all the latest facilities, including tuning to 8.33kHz channels.

Note regarding the 8.33kHz channels
Reference to a receiver's ability to tune to the proposed new channel spacings are based on the provision of steps of 1kHz or less. In such cases it will be possible to select a frequency with an accuracy of at least 1kHz and then to store the channel in the memory. For example, the AR8000 can be tuned to 127.0083 and this can be stored. However, it will not be possible to search for channels since none of the receivers are provided with steps equal to the new channel spacings.

HF (Shortwave) receivers
Readers who may be contemplating the purchase of a receiver for HF listening are advised to discuss the matter with one of the suppliers listed in Appendix X, since the subject is rather specialised and can be somewhat complex.

Appendix I: Airfield Directory

Airfield	Service	VHF	UHF
Aberdeen/Dyce	App	120.4	353.55
	Tower	118.1	-
	Gnd	121.7	-
	ATIS	121.85	-
Aberporth	AFIS	122.15	259.0
Alderney	App	128.65	-
	Tower	125.35	-
Baldonnel/Casement	App	122.0	-
	Tower	123.5	-
	Gnd	123.1	-
Barkston Heath	App	-	340.47
	Tower	120.42	342.07
	Gnd	-	340.52
Belfast/Aldergrove	App	120.9	310.00
	Radar	120.9	310.00
	Tower	118.3	310.00
	Gnd	121.75	-
	Ops (RAF)	-	241.82
Belfast City	App	130.85	-
	Radar	134.8	-
	Tower	130.75	-
Benson	CAC (Brize)	134.3	257.1
	App	127.15	268.82
	SRE (Benson)	122.1	358.8
	Tower	130.25	279.35
	Gnd	-	340.32
Biggin Hill	App	129.4	-
	Tower	134.8	-
	ATIS	121.87	-
Birmingham	App	118.05	-
	Tower	118.3	-
	Gnd	121.8	-
	ATIS	126.27	-
Blackpool	Tower	118.4	-
	App	119.95	-
	Radar	135.95	-
	ATIS	121.75	-
Boscombe Down	App/SRE	126.7	291.65
	PAR	130.0	381.12
	Tower	130.75	370.1
	Gnd	130.75	299.4
	ATIS	-	263.5

Airfield	Service	VHF	UHF
Bournemouth	App	119.62	-
	Tower	125.6	-
	Radar	118.65	-
	Gnd	121.7	-
	ATIS	121.95	-
Bristol	App	128.55	-
	Radar	124.35	-
	Tower	133.85	-
	ATIS	126.02	-
Brize Norton (Brize Radar)	MAS/LARS/CAC	134.3	257.1
	App	133.75	342.45
	SRE (Director)	133.75	356.87
	SRE (Talkdown)	123.3	338.65
	Tower	126.5	381.2
	Gnd	126.5	370.3
	Ops	130.07	357.47
	ATIS	-	254.47
Cambridge	App	123.6	-
	Radar	130.75	372.42
	Tower	122.2	372.42
Campbeltown	Air/Gnd	125.9	-
Cardiff	App	125.85	277.22
	Tower	125.0	-
	ATIS	119.47	-
Church Fenton	App	126.5	254.52
	SRE	-	375.32
	SRE (Director)	-	344.0
	PAR (Talkdown)	123.3	386.72
	Tower	122.1	262.7
	Gnd	122.1	340.2
Colerne	App	122.1	277.27
	Tower	122.1	344.6
	Gnd	-	360.75
Coltishall	CAC (Eastern)	-	299.97
	App	122.1	379.27
	SRE (Director)	123.3	342.25
	SRE (Zone)	125.9	293.42
	PAR (Talkdown)	123.3	275.97
	Tower	122.1	339.95
	Gnd	-	296.72
	Ops	-	364.8
Coningsby	CAC	-	299.97
	App	120.8	312.22
	SRE	-	262.95
	PAR (Talkdown)	123.3	300.92
	Tower	122.1	275.87
	Gnd	122.1	358.55

Airfield	Service	VHF	UHF
Cork	App	119.9	-
	Radar	118.8	-
	Tower	119.3	-
	Gnd	121.8	-
	ATIS	120.92	-
Cosford	App	118.92	276.12
	Tower	118.92	357.12
	Gnd	121.95	-
Cottesmore	CAC	-	299.97
	App	130.2	312.07
	App (Wittering)	123.3	380.95
	SRE (Director)	123.3	312.07
	PAR (Talkdown)	123.3	262.9
	Tower	122.1	370.05
	Gnd	122.1	336.37
Coventry	App	119.25	-
	Radar	122.0	-
	Tower	119.25 (124.8)	-
	Gnd	121.7	-
Cranfield	App	122.85	-
	Tower	134.92	-
	ATIS	121.87	-
Cranwell	MAS	-	299.97
	App	119.37	340.47
	SRE (Radar)	-	250.05
	SRE (Director)	123.3	282.0
	PAR (Talkdown)	123.3	383.47
	Tower	122.1	379.52
	Gnd	-	297.9
Culdrose	App	134.05	241.95
	Radar	-	241.95
	PAR (Talkdown)	123.3	358.7
	Tower	122.1	380.22
	Gnd	-	299.4
	ATIS	-	372.3
Dishforth	App	125.0	357.37
	Tower	122.1	259.82
	Gnd	122.1	379.67
Dublin	App	121.1	-
	Radar	124.65	-
	SRE	119.55	-
	Tower	118.6	-
	Gnd	121.8	-
	ATIS	124.52	-
Dundee	App	122.9	-
	Tower	122.9	
Dunsfold	CAC (London)	-	275.47
	App	135.17	367.37
	SRE	135.17	367.37
	Tower	124.32	375.4

Airfield	Service	VHF	UHF
East Midlands	App	119.65	-
	Tower	124.0	-
	Gnd	121.9	-
Edinburgh	App	121.2	-
	Radar	121.2	362.3
	Tower	118.7	257.8
	Gnd	121.75	257.8
	ATIS	132.07	-
Exeter	App	128.15	-
	Tower	119.8	-
Fairford	CAC (Brize)	134.3	257.1
	App	122.1	342.45
	SRE (Brize)	119.0	376.62
	Tower	-	337.57
	Gnd	-	259.97
	Ops	-	379.47
Farnborough	App	134.35	336.27
	PAR	130.5	259.0
	Tower	122.5	357.4
	Ops	130.37	-
Filton	App	122.72	256.12
	SRE	122.72	256.12
	Tower	132.35	342.02
Glasgow	App	119.1	362.3
	Tower	118.8	-
	Gnd	121.7	-
	ATIS	132.17	-
Gloucestershire	App	125.65	-
	Tower	122.9	-
	Radar	120.97	-
	ATIS	127.47	-
Guernsey	App	128.65	-
	Radar	118.9	-
	Tower	119.95	-
	Gnd	121.8	-
	ATIS (GUR) VOR	109.4	-
Hawarden	App	123.35	-
	Radar	130.25	-
	Tower	124.95	336.32
Humberside	Radar	123.15	-
	App	124.67	-
	Tower	118.55	-
	ATIS	124.12	-
Inverness	App	122.6	362.3
	Tower	122.6	-
Ipswich	Air/Gnd	118.32	-
Isle of Man (Ronaldsway)	App	120.85	-
	Tower	118.9	-

Airfield	Service	VHF	UHF
Jersey	Zone	125.2	-
	Radar	118.55	-
	App	120.3	-
	Tower	119.45	-
	Gnd	121.9	-
	ATIS (JSY) VOR 112.2	-	
Kinloss	App (Lossiemouth) 119.35	-	376.65
	SRE	123.3	259.97
	PAR (Talkdown) 123.3	-	370.05
	Tower	122.1	336.35
	Ops	-	358.47
	Gnd	-	296.72
Kirkwall	App	118.3	-
	Tower	118.3	-
Lakenheath	CAC	-	299.97
	App (Honington) 128.9	-	
	App (Departures) 123.3	-	242.07
	SRE	123.3	309.07
	Tower	122.1	358.67
	Gnd	-	397.97
	Ops	-	300.82
	ATIS	-	249.7
Leeds-Bradford	App	123.75	-
	SRE	121.05	-
	Tower	120.3	-
	ATIS	118.02	-

Below:
RAF Tornado. *Rolls-Royce plc*

Airfield	Service	VHF	UHF
Leeming	App	127.75	337.82
	SRE (Zone)	127.75	292.7
	SRE (Director)	127.75	358.65
	PAR (Talkdown)	123.3	336.35
	Tower	122.1	344.57
	Gnd	-	338.85
	Ops	-	356.72
Leicester	Air/Gnd	122.12	-
Leuchars	App	126.5	255.4
	SRE (Director)	123.3	292.47
	PAR (Talkdown)	123.3	370.07
	Tower	122.1	258.92
	Gnd	122.1	259.85
	Ops	-	285.02
Linton-on-Ouse	App	129.15	362.67
	SRE (Radar)	129.15	292.8
	SRE (Director)	123.3	344.47
	SRE (Departures)	129.15	381.07
	PAR (Talkdown)	123.3	358.52
	Tower	122.1	300.42
	Gnd	122.1	340.02
	ATIS	-	241.65
Liverpool	App	119.85	-
	Radar	118.45	-
	Tower	118.1	-
Llanbedr	CAC (London)	-	292.52
	App	122.5	386.67
	PAR	122.5	370.3
	Tower	122.5	380.17
London/City	App (Thames Radar)	132.7	-
	Radar	128.02	-
	Tower	127.95 (118.07)	-
	ATIS	127.95	-
London/Gatwick	App	126.82 (118.95)	-
	Tower	124.22	-
	Clearances	121.95	-
	Gnd	121.8	-
	ATIS	128.47	-
London/Heathrow	App	119.72	-
		134.97	-
		120.4	-
		127.52	-
	Tower (Departures)	118.7	-
	Tower (Arrivals)	118.5	-
	Clearances	121.97	-
	Gnd	121.9 (121.7)	-
	ATIS	123.9	-
	ditto - Biggin VOR	115.1	-
	ditto - Bovingdon VOR	113.75	-

Airfield	Service	VHF	UHF
London/Luton	App	129.55	-
	Radar	128.75	-
	Tower	132.55	-
	Gnd	121.75	-
	ATIS	120.57	-
London/Stansted	App	120.62	-
	Tower	123.8	-
	Gnd	121.72	-
	ATIS	127.17	-
Lossiemouth	App	-	376.65
	SRE	123.3	259.97
	SRE (Departures)	119.35	258.85
	PAR (Talkdown)	123.3	250.05
	Tower	118.9	337.75
	Gnd	-	299.4
Lyneham	CAC (London)	-	275.47
	CAC (Brize)	134.3	257.1
	App	118.42	359.5
	SRE (Zone)	123.4	345.02
	SRE (Director)	123.4	300.47
	PAR (Talkdown)	123.3	375.2
	Tower	118.42	386.82
	Gnd	122.1	340.17
	Ops	-	254.65
	ATIS	-	381.0
Manchester	Area Control	124.2	-
	ditto	125.1	-
	ditto	133.05	-
	Pennine Radar	128.67	-
	App	119.4	-
	Arrivals	118.57	-
	Tower	118.62	-
	Clearances	121.7	-
	Gnd	121.7	-
	ATIS	128.17	-
Manston	CAC (London)	-	275.47
	App	126.35	379.02
	Radar	126.35	338.62
	PAR (Talkdown)	123.3	312.32
	Tower	119.27	344.35
Marham	CAC	-	299.97
	App	124.15	291.95
	SRE (Radar)	124.15	293.77
	PAR (Talkdown)	123.3	379.65
	Tower	122.1	337.9
	Gnd	-	336.35
	Ops	-	312.55
	ATIS	-	261.2
Merryfield	Tower	122.1	312.7
Middle Wallop	App	126.7	312.0
	SRE (Director)	-	312.67
	Tower	122.1	372.62

Airfield	Service	VHF	UHF
Mildenhall	CAC	-	299.97
	App	-	398.35
	Departures	-	242.07
	Tower	122.55	258.82
	Gnd	-	380.15
	Ops	-	365.1
	ATIS	-	277.07
Netheravon	App	-	362.22
	Tower	128.3	290.95
	A/G (Salisbury Plain)	122.75	282.25
Newcastle	App	124.37	284.6
	Tower	119.7	-
	ATIS	114.25	-
Newton	App	122.1	251.72
	Tower	119.12	375.42
	Gnd	-	258.97
Northolt	App	126.45	344.97
	SRE (Director)	130.35	379.42
	PAR (Talkdown)	125.87	375.5
	Tower	124.97	312.35
	Departures	120.32	-
	Ops	-	244.42
	ATIS	-	300.35
Norwich	App	119.35	-
	Tower	124.25	-
Nottingham	Air/Gnd	122.8	-
Odiham	App	125.25	386.77
	PAR (Talkdown)	123.3	300.45
	Tower	122.1	309.62
	ATIS	-	276.17

Airfield	Service	VHF	UHF
Oxford/Kidlington	CAC (Brize)	134.3	-
	App	125.32	-
	Tower	118.87	-
	Gnd	121.95	-
	ATIS	121.75	-
	Information	118.87	-
Plymouth	App	133.55	-
	Tower	122.6	-
Portland	App	124.15	300.17
	PAR (Talkdown)	-	312.4
	Tower	122.1	337.75
	ATIS	-	343.47
Prestwick	App	120.55	-
	Tower	118.15	-
	ATIS	127.12	-
St Athan	App (Cardiff)	125.85	277.22
	App (St Athan)	122.1	357.17
	SRE (Talkdown)	123.3	340.1
	Tower	122.1	336.52
	Gnd	-	386.5
	ATIS (Cardiff)	119.47	-
St Mawgan	CAC (London)	-	275.47
	App	126.5	357.2
	SRE (Director)	125.55	360.55
	PAR (Talkdown)	123.3	336.55
	Gnd	-	376.62
	Tower	123.4	241.82
	Ops	-	260.0
	ATIS	-	316.87
Isles of Scilly/St Marys	App	123.15	-
	Tower	123.15	-
Shannon	App	120.2	-
	Radar	121.4	-
	Tower	118.7	-
	Gnd	121.8	-
	ATIS	130.95	-
Shawbury	App	120.77	276.07
	SRE (Zone)	120.77	386.87
	SRE (Radar)	123.3	254.2
	PAR (Talkdown)	123.3	356.97
	Tower	122.1	269.1
	Gnd	-	337.9
	ATIS	-	340.7
Shoreham	App	123.15	-
	Tower	125.4	-
	ATIS	132.4	-

Opposite:
Qantas 747. *Qantas*

Airfield	Service	VHF	UHF
Southampton	App	128.85	-
	Zone (Solent)	120.22	-
	Radar	128.85	-
	Tower	118.2	-
	ATIS (SAM) VOR	113.35	-
	Ops	130.65	-
Southend	App	128.95	-
	Tower	127.72	-
	ATIS	121.8	-
Stornoway	App	123.5	362.3
	Tower	123.5	362.3
Sumburgh	App	123.15	-
	SRE	130.05	-
	Tower	118.25	-
	ATIS	125.85	-
Swansea	App	119.7	-
	Tower	119.7	-
Teesside	App	118.85	296.72
	Tower	119.8	379.8
Topcliffe	App	125.0	357.37
	SRE (Talkdown)	123.3	344.35
	SRE (Director)	125.0	255.6
	Tower	122.1	309.72
	Gnd	-	241.85
Unst	Air/Gnd	130.35	-
Valley	App	134.35	372.32
	SRE (Radar)	134.35	268.77
	SRE (Director)	123.3	337.72
	PAR (Talkdown)	123.3	358.67
	Tower	122.1	340.17
	Gnd	122.1	386.9
Waddington	CAC	-	299.97
	App	-	312.5
	SRE (Radar)	127.35	296.75
	SRE (Director)	123.3	300.57
	PAR (Talkdown)	-	309.67
	Departures	123.3	249.85
	Tower	123.3	285.05
	Gnd	-	342.12
	Ops	-	244.27
	ATIS	-	291.67
Warton	App	124.45	336.47
	SRE (Radar)	129.72	343.7
	Tower	130.8	311.3
Waterford	Tower	129.85	-

Airfield	Service	VHF	UHF
Wattisham	App	125.8	291.12
	Dir	123.3	283.57
	PAR	123.3	356.17
	Tower	122.1	343.42
West Freugh	App	130.05	383.52
	SRE (Radar)	130.72	259.0
	Tower	122.55	337.92
Wick	App	119.7	-
	Tower	119.7	-
Wittering	CAC (Easterly)	-	299.97
	CAC (Westerly)	-	275.47
	App	130.2	380.95
	SRE (Departures)	-	376.57
	PAR (Talkdown)	123.3	383.22
	Tower	122.1	357.15
	Gnd	-	311.95
Woodford	MAS	-	299.97
	App	130.75	269.12
	SRE	130.05	358.57
	Tower	126.92	358.57
Woodvale	App	121.0	312.8
	Tower	119.75	259.95
Yeovil	App	130.8	369.97
	Radar	130.8	300.67
	Tower	125.4	372.42
Yeovilton	App	127.35	369.87
	Radar	127.35	369.87
	SRE (Director)	123.3	338.87
	PAR (Talkdown)	123.3	339.97
	Tower	122.1	372.65
	Gnd	-	311.32
	ATIS	-	379.75

Key to Abbreviations

1. AFIS — Aerodrome Flight Information Service
2. App — Approach
3. ATIS — Automatic Traffic Information Service
4. CAC — Centralised Approach Control (Military)
5. Dep — Departures
6. Gnd — Gnd
7. LARS — Lower Airspace Radar Service
8. MAS — Middle Airspace Service
9. Ops — Operations
10. PAR — Precision Approach Radar
11. SRE — Surveillance Radar Element
12. VOR — Very High Frequency Omni Range (Navigation Beacon)

Military airfield frequencies are often referred to by 'stud' numbers, enabling the pilot to select changes of frequency easily and quickly. Stud numbers are given in specialist frequency publications.

Miscellaneous Frequencies

Emergency	121.500 (V) 243.000 (U)

Military pilots wishing
to carry out training fixes
in London airspace use
frequency 245.100

Shanwick North Atlantic Clearance Delivery

This frequency is used by airlines registered east of 30° west for obtaining clearance across the North Atlantic.	123.95
This frequency is for airlines registered west of 30° west for the same purpose.	127.65
This frequency is used at busy periods by various airlines, particularly British Airways, for clearance delivery.	135.525

These three frequencies can be heard in virtually all parts of the United Kingdom.

Fire Services	121.6
Unicom (Scene of Emergency)	130.42
Flight Information Services	127.275 Scottish (West)
	131.300 Scottish (North)
	119.875 Scottish (East)
	125.475 London (North)
	124.600 London (South East)
	124.750 London (South West)
Military Airspace Services	134.300, 249.475 Scottish
	127.450, 231.625 Midlands
	135.150, 275.475 South/South West
	135.275, 299.975 East Anglia/North East
UK Scene of Search and Rescue	244.600
NATO Search and Rescue Training	252.800
NATO International Combined Scene of Search and Rescue	123.100, 138.700, 282.800
London Joint Area Organisation	231.625 (North West)
	275.350 (Central)
	233.800 (Clacton)
	230.050 (Dover/Lydd)
	251.225 (Seaford/Hurn)
	235.050 (London above FL 300)

Appendix II: Airways and Upper Air Routes in UK Air Space

Below FL 245 (approximately 24,500ft) a system of airways provides a route structure for flights operating in controlled airspace. In upper airspace (above FL 245) the airways are replaced by a network of Air Traffic Service Routes. In the following listing, upper air routes are prefixed with the letter 'U'.

There are in fact several other routes which do not have specific letters of identification. These are known as 'direct tracks' (DT) and are allocated by Air Traffic Control on a tactical basis.

For full details of the routes refer to one of the radio navigation charts available from the suppliers whose addresses are given in Appendix X. The locations of the various naviation points can be found by reference to Appendix V.

A1/UA1	BAMES/VEULE/Midhurst/Honiley/Dean Cross/Glasgow
	A1 as above but Lichfield/Turnberry
A2/UA2	Boulogne/Lambourne/WELIN/Trent/Pole Hill/Dean Cross/Machrihanish
	A2 as above but Dean Cross/Talla
A20/UA20	Abbeville/NASDA/Biggin/Westcot/WELIN
A25/UA25	Dinard/SKESO/Berry Head/EXMOR/Brecon/Wallasey/Dean Cross/Talla
A30/UA30	Sandy/Biggin
UA29	BAKUR/MERLY/DAWLY/Berry Head/SALCO

Below:
Upper Airspace Control Area and Upper ATS Routes for the south-east. *CAA*

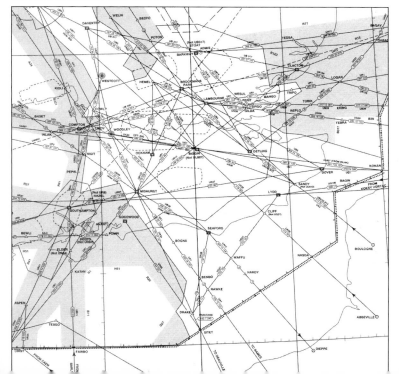

A34/UA34	Wallasey/TELBA/Midhurst/DRAKE/SITET/ETRAT/Deauville
A37/UA37	DANDI/ABSIL/SAMON/MULIT/BASAV/GABAD/LOGAN/Detling
A47/UA47	Daventry/Woodley/Seaford/Dieppe
B1/UB1	DEVOL/Dublin/Liffy/Wallasey/Ottringham/DOGGA/BLUFA
B2/UB2	Cork/Dublin/BESOP/Turnberry/Glasgow/FINDO/Perth/Aberdeen/FORTY/KLONN/Sola
B3/UB3	Belfast/Isle of Man/Wallasey/Honiley/Daventry/Brookmans Park/Dover
B4/UB4	FINDO/Talla/MARGO/SHAPP/RIBEL/Pole Hill/LESTA/Brookmans Park/Detling/Boulogne
B5/UB5	Glasgow/Talla/Newcastle/FAMBO/SILVA/DOGGA/ELDIN/Spijkeboor
B10/UB10	Cork/BANBA/Strumble
B11/UB11	FAWBO/Southampton
B29/UB29	Compton/Lambourne/TOBIX/ERING
B39/UB39	Dublin/TOLKA/BEGDA/RADNO/CHELT/BASET/Midhurst
UB40	BANLO/MERLY/SWANY/DIKAS
B53	NANTI/Lichfield/SAPCO
UB71	Honiley/Biggin
UB105	Pole Hill/GOLES/KIPPA/BLUFA
B226	Talla/ANGUS
UB295	Compton/Brookmans Park
B317/UB317	Daventry/Clacton
B321	Honiley/KIDLI/Compton
G1/UG1	Shannon/SLANY/Strumble/Compton/Dover/Koksy
UG4	DEVOL/Shannon/Cork/TIVLI/Land's End/LIZAD/Jersey/Caen
UG11	Sola/ORVIK/Sumburgh/SIDER
G27/UG27	DRAKE/HAWKE/WAFFU/Lydd
UG39	Lambourne/GILDA/REPLO/DENUT
UG45	BANLO/Land's End
UG106	Lydd/BAGIN/Koksy
H51	GIBSO/BEWLI/BEGTO/POMPI
UH70	Aberdeen/Wick/GONUT
UH71	Sumburgh/LIRKI
UL3	BANLO/PAVLO/DIDEL/TIVER/GIBSO/BEGTO/POMPI
UL7	Sumburgh/FORTY/TUBOT/SKATE/KOLEY/SAMON/Spijkerboor
UL74	TOPPA/MULIT/ROLLS/ANGEL/SKATE
UL607	Cork/EVRIN/INLAK/KONAN/Koksy
UL613	Boulogne/SANDY/Detling/HALIF/Talla
UL722	Berry Head/KORUL
UM14	WESUL/STOAT
UM16	Manchester/Wallasey
UN491	GUNSO/TAKAS/ODELO/ROSKO/Dinard
UN502	KENUK/RATKA/PHILI/UNROK/SUPAP/PIKOD/Jersey
UN512	RATKA/OMIMI/ODELO/Quimper
UN516	GIPER/Cork
UN517	Machrihanish/Belfast/DEGOS/Shannon/GIPER
UN522	DOLIP/BANLO
UN533	BURAK/Cork
UN535	BURAK/Shannon
UN536	BURAK/Dublin
UN537	Machrihanish/NIPIT/BURAK
UN545	Machrihanish/MOLAK/BABAN
UN546	Strumble/BAKUR/DEVOL
UN550	ERNAN/55N 10W
UN551	Belfast/TADEX/55N 10W
UN552	Talla/Machrihanish/55N 10W
UN559	MOLAK/55N 10W/Shannon
UN560	ERNAN/TADEX/56N 10W
UN561	Belfast/56N 10W
UN562	Machrihanish/56N 10W
UN563	Glasgow/56N 10W
UN569	MOLAK/56N 10W
UN570	Belfast/57N 10W
UN571	Machrihanish/57N 10W
UN572	Tiree/57N 10W

UN580	Glasgow/Tiree/58N 10W
UN581	Aberdeen/Benbecula/58N 10W
UN583	Stornoway/58N 10W
UN584	Sumburgh/RONVI/58N 10W
UN585	FINDO/NEVIS/Benbecula
UN590	HALIF/MARGO/Glasgow/Benbecula/59N 10W
UN591	SKATE/Aberdeen/Stornoway/59N 10W
UN593	RONVI/59N 10W
UN601	Talla/NEVIS/Stornoway/60N 10W
UN603	Sumburgh/BILLY/60N 10W
UN610	Stornoway/BILLY/61N 10W
UN612	Sumburgh/61N 10W
UN614	Stornoway/OLKER
UN615	Glasgow/Stornoway/MATIK
UN862	Dinard/SKESO/Berry Head/TUTON/CUMRI/MADLI/ELGAR/MYNDA/KARNO/NOKIN/Wallasey
N863/UN863	Berry Head/SALCO/BALOT/Monts D'Aree
UN865	Berry Head/SALCO/BALOT/Monts D'Aree
UP2	Strumble/NUMPO/NIGIT
UP4	DIKAS/EVRIN
UP6	MOGLI/LESTA/Trent/Manchester/REMSI/BESOP/DUNLO/56N 10W
R1/UR1	ORTAC/KATHY/Midhurst
UR12	Lambourne/Clacton/REDFA/TULIP/Spijkerboor
R3	ROBIN/Trent/Wallasey
UR4	Isle of Man/REMSI/Pole Hill/Ottringham/SOTOL/DANDI
R8/UR8	GAPLI/Land's End/GIBSO/Southampton/Midhurst
R12/R123	Brookmans Park/Clacton
R14/UR14	Dublin/VATRY/Strumble/SWANY/EXMOR/GIBSO
UR23	Glasgow/St Abbs/TUBOT/GORDO/GARNA
UR24	ORIST/ASPEN
R25/UR25	SITET/Goodwood
R37/UR37	Cork/NORLA/MERLY/EXMOR/Southampton/Midhurst/Dover
UR38	Newcastle/Stornoway
UR40	GAPLI/LIZAD/BALOT/Dinard
R41/UR41	ORTAC/Southampton/Westcott
UR72	Dublin/BANBA/Land's End/KORUL
UR77	ADMIS/TEDSA/BASAV
R84/UR84	ORTAC/HAZEL/Midhurst
R101	STAFA/Pole Hill
UR116	GAPLI/NAKID/ANNET/Guernsey/Caen
R126	LOGAN/BLUSY/SASKI
UR168	Land's End/CAVAL/ROSKO/Monts D'Aree
R803	Midhurst/Seaford
SL1	Supersonic Eastbound OMOKO/BISKI/Guernsey/Caen (for Paris)
SL2	Supersonic Westbound MALBY/MERLY/BANLO/Sierra Mike
SL3	Supersonic Eastbound Sierra November/BARIX/MATIM/MALBY (for London)
SL4	Supersonic Westbound EVX/TESGO/AKELO/RILKA/RATKA/Sierra Mike
SL5	Supersonic Eastbound OMOKO/BARIX/MATIM/MALBY (for London)
SL7	Supersonic Eastbound Sierra Oscar/OMOKO/TAKAS/Guernsey/Caen (for Paris)
UT7	Land's End/UNROK/ASKIL/KORUL
V14	Shannon/Dublin
W12	Shannon/Killiney
W13	Shannon/RANAR
W15	Galway/KORAK
W70/UW70	COWLY/Biggin
UW501	GAPLI//Compton/REDFA

UW502	Berry Head/BRYNA/Turnberry
UW532	TOPPA/FINDO
UW534	TOPPA/Stornoway
UW536	TOPPA/SNIPE/Aberdeen
UW538	LONAM/ROLLS/SINGA/Aberdeen
UW550	Southampton/ROYCE/ROLLS/DANDI
UW701	Machrihanish/Glasgow
Y98/UY98	NITON/NOKIN/BARTN/Pole Hill
Y99/UY99	NOKIN/CROFT/RIBEL

Advisory Routes (All in Lower Airspace)

A1D	Glasgow/Stornoway/60N 10W
B2D	Aberdeen/KLONN
G4D	Land's End/TIVLI/Cork
N552D	Turnberry/Machrihanish/55.20N 06.55W
N553D	Machrihanish/TABIT/FYNER
N562D	Turnberry/Machrihanish/56N 10W
N573D	Glasgow/Tiree/57N 10W
W2D	Isle of Man/MORBY/Pole Hill/Leeds-Bradford
W3D	Glasgow/Inverness/Wick/Kirkwall/Sumburgh
W4D	Aberdeen/Wick
W5D	Aberdeen/Sumburgh
W6D	Inverness/Stornoway
W911D	Newcastle/Dean Cross/Isle of Man/Dublin
W928D	Isle of Man/BLACA
W958D	Turnberry/TABIT/BRUCE/Benbecula

Military TACAN Routes in Upper Airspace

TB1	VLN/WDI/VYL/QQ1/BEZ
TB2	CNO/SAM/BZN/WD2/VYL/LUK/KSS
TB4	WD4/CGY/QM8
TB5	WTM/MLD/CGY/WD8/QQ1/KSS
TB6	SPT/MAY/WD6/WTM/MC6
TB7	QN9/LUK/QM8/CSL/WD7/DVR/EPT
TL4	WTM/WD7/NPT/KOK
TL6	WD6/MLD/MC6
TR1	LND/VLN/BZN/WD4/MLD/CSL/MCI
TR3	VYL/CGY/CSL/MC6

Appendix III: Aeronautical En-Route Frequencies

The majority of aeronautical radio frequencies for the United Kingdom and Ireland are listed, divided into various geographical regions, together with their operating agencies.

Frequencies are given in six figures. However, note that the sixth digit is not spoken — for example, 126.075 is spoken 'one two six decimal zero seven'. Also, where the fifth digit is zero it is not spoken - for example, 129.600 is spoken 'one two nine decimal six'.

For airport frequencies refer to a separate appendix.

Station	Frequencies	
Area 1 — Scotland/North Sea		
123.775	Scottish Control	Primary Frequency
129.225	Scottish Control	Hebrides Upper Control
124.500	Scottish Control	
125.675	Scottish Control	Hebrides Upper Control
133.675	Scottish Control	Hebrides Upper Control
134.775	Scottish Control	
126.300	Scottish Control	TMA via Talla
124.825	Scottish Control	TMA via Galloway
134.300	Scottish Military	
249.475	Scottish Military	
119.875	Scottish Information	Eastern
127.275	Scottish Information	Western
126.250	Scottish Information	Northern
133.875	Scottish Information	Southern
122.100	Watchdog	Fisheries Protection
123.650	Watchdog	Fisheries Protection
118.150	Sumburgh Radar	
123.150	Sumburgh Radar	
121.250	Aberdeen Radar	
134.100	Aberdeen Radar	
353.550	Aberdeen Radar	
135.175	Aberdeen Information	
129.950	Viking Approach	East Shetlands Helicopters
122.000	Forties Charlie	Helicopter Routes
122.050	Thistle Alpha	Helicopter Routes
122.450	Claymore Alpha	Helicopter Routes
129.700	Montrose Alpha	Helicopter Routes
129.750	Frigg	Helicopter Routes
Area 2 — Ireland/Isle of Man		
131.050	London Control	Primary Frequency
135.575	London Control	Primary Frequency
125.675	Scottish Control	Primary Frequency
129.225	Scottish Control	Primary Frequency
121.700	Oceanic Clearances	Aircraft on the ground
124.700	Shannon Control	Shannon Sector
127.500	Shannon Control	Cork Sector
131.150	Shannon Control	Cork Sector
132.150	Shannon Control	DEVOL/BABAN Sectors
134.275	Shannon Control	Shannon Sector
135.225	Shannon Control	Shannon Oceanic Transition Area
135.600	Shannon Control	Shannon Oceanic Transition Area
129.175	Dublin Control	Northern Sector
124.650	Dublin Control	Southern Sector
231.625	Scottish Military	

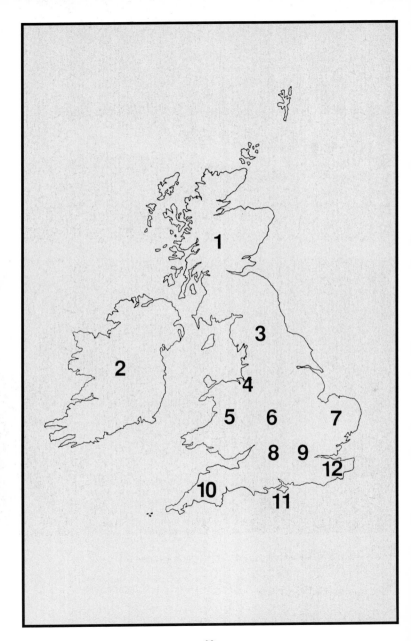

Opposite:
The aeronautical radio frequencies in Appendix III are set out in accordance
with the areas on this map.

Top:
Cathay Pacific B747-300. *Cathay Pacific*

Above:
Approach Control, Aberdeen airport *Civil Aviation Authority*

| 249.475 | Scottish Military |
| 127.450 | Scottish Military |

Area 3 — Northern England

118.775	London Control	Primary Frequency
126.775	London Control	Primary Frequency
131.050	London Control	Primary Frequency
121.325	London Control	
128.125	London Control	
133.525	London Control	
136.275	London Control	
123.700	Amsterdam Control	
126.650	Manchester Control	FL 195 and below
128.675	Pennine Radar	
125.475	London Information	
127.450	London Military	
135.275	London Military	
231.625	London Military	
299.975	London Military	

Area 4 — North Wales/Manchester

118.775	London Control	Primary Frequency
131.050	London Control	Primary Frequency
135.575	London Control	Primary Frequency
124.200	Manchester Control	FL 195 and below
125.100	Manchester Control	FL 195 and below
126.650	Manchester Control	FL 195 and below
125.475	London Information	
127.450	London Military	
231.625	London Military	

Area 5 — South and Mid Wales

133.600	London Control	Primary Frequency
129.375	London Control	
136.400	London Control	
135.150	London Military	
275.475	London Military	
124.750	London Information	
135.600	Shannon Control	

Area 6 — Midlands/Birmingham

127.100	London Control	Primary Frequency
130.925	London Control	Primary Frequency
131.125	London Control	Primary Frequency
132.450	London Control	Primary Frequency
118.475	London Control	
127.875	London Control	
128.475	London Control	
129.200	London Control	
132.600	London Control	
133.975	London Control	
124.600	London Information	
127.450	London Military	
135.275	London Military	
231.625	London Military	
275.475	London Military	
299.975	London Military	

Opposite:
Oceanic entry points to the North Atlantic. *Aerad*

OCEANIC ENTRY/EXIT POINTS

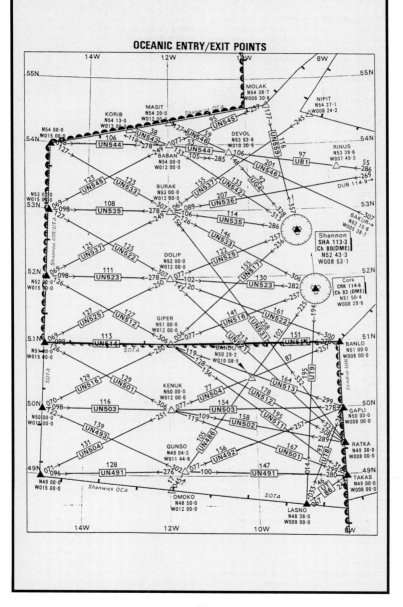

Area 7 — East Anglia

129.600	London Control	Primary Frequency
118.475	London Control	Primary Frequency
132.450	London Control	Primary Frequency
133.450	London Control	Primary Frequency
133.525	London Control	
125.275	Anglia Radar	
128.925	Anglia Radar	
264.575	Anglia Radar	
283.475	Anglia Radar	
125.750	Amsterdam Control	
124.600	London Information	
135.275	London Military	
233.800	London Military	
299.975	London Military	

Area 8 — Thames Valley

134.750	London Control	Primary Frequency
133.600	London Control	
136.400	London Control	
126.075	London Control	
135.150	London Military	
275.475	London Military	
124.750	London Information	

Area 9 — Greater London

127.425	London Control	High Level Overflights
135.425	London Control	High Level Overflights
128.425	London Control	
131.125	London Control	
132.450	London Control	
132.600	London Control	
135.325	London Control	
132.700	Thames Radar	
118.825	London Control	Departures via Brookmans Pakr
119.775	London Control	Departures via Bovingdon
120.175	London Control	Inbounds via LUMBA and TIMBA
120.475	London Control	Inbounds via WILLO and Departures via Midhurst and Worthing
120.525	London Control	Departures via Detling
121.225	London Control	Inbounds via Lambourne
121.275 } 129.275 }	London Control	Inbounds via Bovingdon
129.075	London Control	Inbounds via Ockham and Departures via Compton & Southampton
235.050	London Military	
275.350	London Military	
124.600	London Information	

Area 10 — South West England

126.075	London Control	Primary Frequency
132.950	London Control	
135.250	London Control	
135.150	London Military	
124.750	London Information	
129.500	Brest Control	
131.175	Brest Control	
133.475	Brest Control	
136.350	Brest Control	
131.150	Shannon Control	
135.600	Shannon Control	
123.650	Watchdog	Fisheries Protection

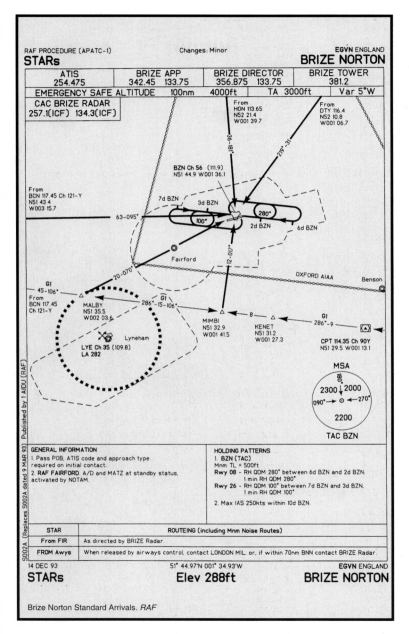

ATIS	BRIZE APP	BRIZE DIRECTOR	BRIZE TOWER
254.475	342.45 133.75	356.875 133.75	381.2

EMERGENCY SAFE ALTITUDE	100nm	4000ft	TA 3000ft	Var 5°W

CAC BRIZE RADAR
257.1(ICF) 134.3(ICF)

From
HON 113.65
N52 21.4
W001 39.7

From
DTY 116.4
N52 10.8
W001 06.7

181°-36°

219°-31°

BZN Ch 56 (111.9)
N51 44.9 W001 36.1

From
BCN 117.45 Ch 121-Y
N51 43.4
W003 15.7

7d BZN   3d BZN

63-095°   100°   280°

2d BZN   6d BZN

12-017°

⊙ Fairford

20-070°

OXFORD AIAA   Benson ⊙

G1
45-106°
From
BCN 117.45
Ch 121-Y

286°-15-106°
G1

MALBY
N51 35.5
W002 03.6

✕ Lyneham

LYE Ch 35 (109.8)
LA 2B2

MIMBI
N51 32.9
W001 41.5

8   △
KENET
N51 31.2
W001 27.3

G1
286°-9

CPT 114.35 Ch 90Y
N51 29.5 W001 13.1

MSA

180°
2300 ↓ 2000
090° → ⊙ ← 270°
2200

TAC BZN

Published by 1 AIDU (RAF) S002A dated 9 MAR 93 (Replaces S002A

GENERAL INFORMATION
1. Pass POB, ATIS code and approach type required on initial contact.
2. RAF FAIRFORD. A/D and MATZ at standby status, activated by NOTAM.

HOLDING PATTERNS
1. BZN (TAC)
Mnm TL + 500ft
Rwy 08 – RH QDM 280° between 6d BZN and 2d BZN.
1 min RH QDM 280°
Rwy 26 – RH QDM 100° between 7d BZN and 3d BZN.
1 min RH QDM 100°

2. Max IAS 250kts within 10d BZN.

STAR	ROUTEING (including Mnm Noise Routes)
From FIR	As directed by BRIZE Radar.
FROM Awys	When released by airways control, contact LONDON MIL. or, if within 70nm BNN contact BRIZE Radar.

Brize Norton Standard Arrivals. *RAF*

Area 11 — Southern England/Isle of Wight

129.425	London Control	Primary Frequency
135.050	London Control	Primary Frequency
135.325	London Control	
120.225	Solent Radar	
125.500	Brest Control	
133.000	Brest Control	
133.475	Brest Control	
134.825	Brest Control	
136.075	Paris Control	
132.000	Paris Control	
132.825	Paris Control	
120.450	Jersey Approach	
125.200	Jersey Approach	
124.750	London Information	
135.150	London Military	
251.225	London Military	
275.350	London Military	
275.475	London Military	

Area 12 — South East England

128.425	London Control	Primary Frequency
134.900	London Control	Primary Frequency
132.325	London Control	
132.450	London Control	
135.325	London Control	
135.425	London Control	
136.600	London Control	
132.200	Maastricht Control	
132.750	Maastricht Control	
127.625	Maastricht Control	
127.300	Paris Control	
128.275	Paris Control	
131.350	Paris Control	
136.075	Paris Control	
124.750	London Information	
135.150	London Military	
230.050	London Military	
251.225	London Military	

Below:
British Aerospace BAe 1000. *British Aerospace*

Appendix IV: ICAO Airfield Decode

Four-letter airport decodes in the United Kingdom with a selection of principal airfields
in Europe and America.

EG	**United Kingdom**
EGAA	Belfast/Aldergrove
EGAB	Enniskillen/St Angelo
EGAC	Belfast/City
EGAE	Londonderry/Eglinton
EGBB	Birmingham
EGBD	Derby
EGBE	Coventry
EGBG	Leicester
EGBJ	Gloucestershire
EGBK	Northampton/Sywell
EGBM	Tatenhill
EGBN	Nottingham
EGBO	Halfpenny Green
EGBP	Pailton
EGBS	Shobdon
EGBW	Wellesbourne Mountford
EGCB	Manchester/Barton
EGCC	Manchester
EGCD	Woodford
EGCF	Sandtoft
EGCG	Strubby (Heliport)
EGCH	Holyhead (Heliport)
EGCI	Doncaster
EGCJ	Sherburn in Elmet
EGCK	Caernarfon
EGCL	Fenland
EGCS	Sturgate
EGDA	Brawdy
EGDC	Chivenor
EGDG	St Mawgan
EGDJ	Upavon
EGDL	Lyneham
EGDM	Boscombe Down
EGDN	Netheravon
EGDP	Portland
EGDR	Culdrose
EGDT	Wroughton
EGDX	St Athan
EGDY	Yeovilton
EGFC	Cardiff (Heliport)
EGFE	Haverfordwest
EGFF	Cardiff
EGFH	Swansea
EGGD	Bristol
EGGP	Liverpool
EGGW	Luton
EGHA	Compton Abbas
EGHC	Land's End/St Just
EGHD	Plymouth
EGHE	Scilly Isles/St Marys
EGHG	Yeovil
EGHH	Bournemouth
EGHI	Southampton/Eastleigh
EGHJ	Bembridge (Isle of Wight)
EGHK	Penzance (Heliport)
EGHN	Sandown (Isle of Wight)

EGHO	Thruxton
EGHR	Chichester/Goodwood
EGJA	Alderney
EGJB	Guernsey
EGJJ	Jersey
EGKA	Shoreham
EGKB	Biggin Hill
EGKH	Lashenden/Headcorn
EGKK	London/Gatwick
EGKR	Redhill
EGLA	Bodmin
EGLC	London/City
EGLD	Denham
EGLF	Farnborough (Civ)
EGLK	Blackbushe
EGLL	London/Heathrow
EGLM	White Waltham
EGLS	Old Sarum
EGLW	London (Westland Heliport)
EGMC	Southend
EGMD	Lydd
EGMH	Manston (Civ)
EGNB	Brough
EGNC	Carlisle
EGNF	Nether Thorpe
EGNH	Blackpool
EGNI	Skegness/Ingoldmells
EGNJ	Humberside
EGNL	Barrow/Walney Island
EGNM	Leeds/Bradford
EGNO	Warton
EGNR	Hawarden
EGNS	Isle of Man/Ronaldsway
EGNT	Newcastle
EGNV	Teesside
EGNW	Wickenby
EGNX	East Midlands
EGOD	Llanbedr
EGOE	Ternhill
EGOQ	Mona
EGOS	Shawbury
EGOV	Valley
EGOW	Woodvale
EGOY	West Freugh
EGPA	Kirkwall
EGPB	Sumburgh
EGPC	Wick
EGPD	Aberdeen/Dyce
EGPE	Inverness
EGPF	Glasgow
EGPG	Cumbernauld
EGPH	Edinburgh
EGPI	Islay
EGPJ	Fife/Glenrothes
EGPK	Prestwick (Civ)
EGPL	Benbecula
EGPM	Scatsta

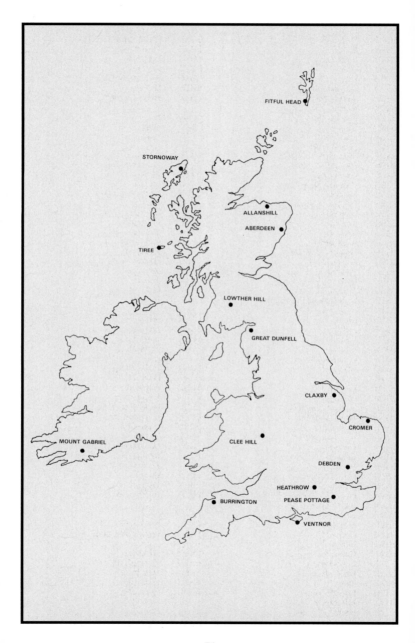

EGPN	Dundee	EGXU	Linton-on-Ouse
EGPO	Stornoway	EGXW	Waddington
EGPR	Barra	EGXZ	Topcliffe
EGPT	Perth/Scone	EGYC	Coltishall
EGPU	Tiree	EGYD	Cranwell
EGPW	Unst	EGYE	Barkston Heath
EGPY	Dounreay/Thurso	EGYM	Marham
EGQJ	Machrihanish	EGYP	Mount Pleasant
EGQK	Kinloss		
EGQL	Leuchars	**BI ICELAND**	
EGQM	Boulmer	BIKF	Keflavik
EGQR	Saxa Vord	BIRK	Reykjavik
EGQS	Lossiemouth		
EGQT	Edinburgh/Turnhouse (Mil)	**CY**	**CANADA**
EGSB	Bedford (Castle Mill)	CYAY	St Anthony
EGSC	Cambridge	CYEG	Edmonton
EGSD	Great Yarmouth (North Denes)	CYHZ	Halifax
EGSE	Ipswich	CYMX	Montreal/Mirabel
EGSF	Peterborough/Conington	CYOW	Ottawa
EGSG	Stapleford	CYQB	Quebec
EGSH	Norwich	CYQM	Moncton
EGSJ	Seething	CYQX	Gander
EGSL	Andrewsfield	CYVR	Vancouver
EGSM	Beccles (Heliport)	CYWG	Winnipeg
EGSO	Crowfield	CYXD	Edmonton
EGSP	Peterborough/Sibson	CYYC	Calgary
EGSS	London/Stansted	CYYR	Goose
EGSU	Duxford	CYYT	St Johns
EGTB	Wycombe Air Park/Booker	CYYZ	Toronto
EGTC	Cranfield		
EGTD	Dunsfold	**EB BELGIUM**	
EGTE	Exeter	EBAW	Antwerp
EGTF	Fairoaks	EBBR	Brussels
EGTG	Filton	EBOS	Ostend
EGTK	Oxford/Kidlington		
EGTO	Rochester	**ED GERMANY (CIVIL)**	
EGTR	Elstree	EDAF	Rhein Main
EGUB	Benson	EDDF	Frankfurt Main
EGUC	Aberporth	EDDH	Hamburg
EGUF	Farnborough (Mil)	EDDI	Berlin (Tempelhof)
EGUH	High Wycombe	EDDK	Cologne-Bonn
EGUL	Lakenheath	EDDL	Dusseldorf
EGUM	Manston (Mil)	EDDM	Munich
EGUN	Mildenhall	EDDN	Nuremberg
EGUO	Colerne	EDDS	Stuttgart
EGUP	Sculthorpe	EDDT	Berlin (Tegel)
EGUS	Lee-on-Solent	EDDV	Hannover
EGUY	Wyton	EDDW	Bremen
EGVA	Fairford	EDLE	Essen/Mulheim
EGVN	Brize Norton		
EGVO	Odiham	**EF FINLAND**	
EGVP	Middle Wallop	EFHF	Helsinki (Malmi)
EGWC	Cosford	EFHK	Helsinki (Vantaa)
EGWN	Halton		
EGWU	Northolt	**EH NETHERLANDS**	
EGXC	Coningsby	EHAM	Amsterdam/Schiphol
EGXD	Dishforth	EHBK	Maastricht
EGXE	Leeming	EHEH	Eindhoven
EGXG	Church Fenton	EHRD	Rotterdam
EGXJ	Cottesmore		
EGXN	Newton		
EGXT	Wittering		

Opposite:
Locations of radar stations in the UK.

EI IRELAND
EICK	Cork
EIDW	Dublin
EIKN	Connaught
EIKY	Kerry/Farranfore
EIME	Baldonnel/Casement
EINN	Shannon
EISG	Sligo
EIWF	Waterford

EK DENMARK
EKCH	Copenhagen/Kastrup
EKEB	Esbjerg
EKRK	Copenhagen/Roskilde

EL LUXEMBOURG
ELLX	Luxembourg

EN NORWAY
ENBO	Bodo
ENBR	Bergen/Flesland
ENCN	Kristiansand/Kjevik
ENFB	Oslo/Fornebu
ENGM	Oslo/Gardermoen
ENKB	Kristiansund/Kvernberget
ENVA	Trondheim/Vaernes
ENZV	Stavanger/Sola

EP POLAND
EPGD	Gdansk/Rebiechowo
EPWA	Warsaw/Okecie

ES SWEDEN
ESCN	Stockholm/Tullinge
ESKN	Stockholm/Skavsta
ESMS	Malmo/Sturup
ESSA	Stockholm/Arlanda
ESSB	Stockholm/Bromma

ET GERMANY (MILITARY)
ETAR	Ramstein
ETUL	Laarbruch
ETUO	Gutersloh
ETUR	Bruggen

EV LATVIA
EVRA	Riga

GC CANARY ISLANDS
GCLP	Las Palmas De Gran Canaria
GCRR	Lanzarote
GCTS	Tenerife Sur/Reina Sofia
GCXO	Tenerife/Santa Cruz

KAKW UNITED STATES
KABQ	Albuquerque Intl, NM
KADW	Andrews AFB, Md
KAEX	England AFB, La
KATL	Atlanta Intl, FA
KBFI	Seattle (Boeing Field), Wa
KBGR	Bangor Intl, Me
KBOS	Boston Logan, Ma
KBWI	Baltimore-Washington Intl, Md
KCHS	Charleston AFB, SC
KCVS	Cannon AFB, NM
KDOV	Dover AFB, De
KEDW	Edwards AFB, Ca
KELP	El Paso Intl, Tx
KEWR	Newark Intl, NJ
KEYW	Key West Intl, Fl
KFLL	Fort Lauderdale, Fl
KFMH	Otis AFB, Ma
KFOE	Forbes AFB, Ks
KFWH	Carswell AFB, Tx
KGFA	Malmstrom AFB, Mont
KGFK	Grand Forks Intl, ND
KGTF	Great Falls Intl, Mt
KGUS	Grissom AFB, In
KGVW	Richards-Gebaur AFB, Mt
KHMN	Holloman AFB, NM
KHOU	Houston, Tx
KHST	Homestead AFB, Fl
KIAB	McConnell AFB, Ks
KIAD	Washington/Dulles
KIAG	Niagara Falls Intl, NY
KIAH	Houston International, Tx
KIND	Indianapolis Intl, Id
KJAX	Jacksonville Intl, Fl
KJFK	John F Kennedy Intl, NY
KLAX	Los Angeles Intl, Ca
KLFI	Langley AFB, Va
KLGA	La Guardia, NY
KLRF	Little Rock AFB, Ar
KLVS	Las Vegas, Nv
KMCI	Kansas City Intl, Mo
KMEM	Memphis Intl, Tn
KMIA	Miami Intl, Fl
KMSP	Minneapolis-St Paul Intl, Mn
KMSY	New Orleans, La
KNBG	New Orleans NAS, La
KNIP	Jacksonville NAS, Fl
KNSF	Andrews AFB/NAF Washington, Md
KONT	Ontario Intl, Ca
KORD	Chicago O'Hare, Il
KPDX	Portland Intl, Or
KPHL	Philadelphia Intl, Pa
KPIT	Pittsburgh, Pa
KPOB	Pope AFB, NC
KPSM	Pease AFB, NH
KRCA	Ellsworth AFB, SD
KRIC	Richmond International, Va
KRNO	Reno Intl, Nv
KSAN	San Diego Intl, Ca
KSAT	San Antonio Intl, Tx
KSEA	Seattle, Wa
KSFO	San Francisco Intl, Ca
KSKF	Kelly AFB, Wash
KSLC	Salt Lake City Intl, Ut
KSTL	St Louis Intl, Mo
KTPA	Tampa Intl, Fl
KTUL	Tulsa Intl, Ok
KVAD	Moody AFB, Ga

KWRI	McGuire AFB, NJ
KYIP	Detroit, Mi

LB BULGARIA
LBBG	Burgas
LBSF	Sofia
LBWN	Varna

LC CYPRUS
LCLK	Larnaca
LCPH	Paphos Intl
LCRA	Akrotiri
LCRR	Nicosia (Mil)

LD CROATIA
LDDU	Dubrovnik
LDSP	Split
LDZA	Zagreb

LE SPAIN
LEAL	Alicante
LEAS	Asturias
LEBB	Bilbao
LEBL	Barcelona
LEGE	Gerona
LEGR	Granada
LEIB	Ibiza
LEMD	Madrid/Barajas
LEMG	Malaga
LEMH	Isla De Menorca/Menorca
LEPA	Palma De Mallorca
LESO	San Sebastian
LEST	Santiago
LETO	Madrid/Torrejon De Ardoz
LEVC	Valencia
LEXJ	Santander
LEZL	Seville

LF FRANCE
LFAT	Le Touquet/Paris Plage
LFBD	Bordeaux/Merignac
LFBF	Toulouse/Francazal
LFLF	Orleans
LFMN	Nice/Cote D'Azur
LFMP	Perpignan/Rivesaltes
LFMT	Montpellier/Frejorques
LFPB	Paris/Le Bourget
LFPG	Paris/Charles De Gaulle
LFPO	Paris/Orly
LFSB	Basle/Mulhouse
LFSD	Dijon/Longvic
LFST	Strasbourg/Entzheim

LG GREECE
LGAT	Athens Intl
LGEL	Athens/Elefsis
LGZA	Zakinthos

LH HUNGARY
LHBP	Budapest/Ferihegy

LI ITALY
LIMC	Milan/Malpensa
LIMF	Turin/Caselle
LIML	Milan/Linate
LIPX	Verona/Villafranca
LIPZ	Venice/Tessera
LIRA	Rome/Ciampino
LIRF	Rome/Fiumicino
LIRN	Naples/Capodichino
LIRP	Pisa/San Giusto
LIRQ	Florence

LJ SLOVENIA
LJLJ	Ljubljana
LJMB	Maribor
LJPZ	Potoroz

LK CZECH REPUBLIC
LKPR	Prague/Ruzyne

LL ISRAEL
LLBG	Tel Aviv/Ben Gurion
LLJR	Jerusalem

LM MALTA
LMML	Luqa

LO AUSTRIA
LOWI	Innsbruck
LOWK	Klagenfurt
LOWS	Salzburg
LOWW	Vienna/Schwechat

LP PORTUGAL (MADEIRA & AZORES)
LPAZ	Santa Maria
LPFL	Flores
LPFU	Funchal
LPLA	Lajes
LPPD	Ponta Delgada
LPPR	Porto
LPPT	Lisbon

Right:
Scottish Air Traffic Control Centre, Prestwick. *Civil Aviation Authority*

LQ BOSNIA AND HERZEGOVINA
LQSA   Sarajevo

LR ROMANIA
LRBS   Bucharest/Baneasa
LROP   Bucharest/Otopeni

LS SWITZERLAND
LSGG   Geneva/Cointrin
LSGL   Lausanne
LSGZ   Zermatt
LSMB   Berne
LSXM   St Moritz
LSZB   Berne/Belp
LSZH   Zurich

LT TURKEY
LTAC   Ankara/Esenboga
LTAD   Ankara/Etimesgut
LTAE   Ankara/Akinci
LTBA   Istanbul/Ataturk
LTBU   Corfu
LTBJ   Izmir/Adnan Menderes Intl
LTBL   Izmir/Cigli

LW MACEDONIA
LWSK   Skopje

LX GIBRALTAR
LXGB   Gibraltar

LY YUGOSLAVIA
LYBE   Belgrade

LZ SLOVAK REPUBLIC
LZIB   Bratislava

OA AFGANISTAN
OAKB   Kabul

OB BAHRAIN
OBBI   Bahrain Intl

OE SAUDI ARABIA
OEDR   Dhahran Intl
OEJN   Jeddah/King Abdul Aziz Intl
OERK   Riyadh/King Khalid Intl
OERY   Riyadh

OI IRAN
OIID   Tehran/Doshan Tappeh
OIIG   Tehran/Ghale Morghi
OIII   Tehran/Mehrabad Intl
OISS   Shiraz Intl
OIZH   Zahedan Intl

OJ JORDAN
OJAI   Amman/Queen Alia Intl
OJJO   Jericho

OK KUWAIT
OKAF   Kuwait Military
OKBK   Kuwait Intl

OL LEBANON
OLBA   Beirut Intl

OM UNITED ARAB EMIRATES
OMAA   Abu Dhabi Intl
OMDB   Dubai Intl
OMFJ   Fujairah Intl
OMSJ   Sharjah Intl

OO OMAN
OOMS   Muscat/Seeb Intl

OP PAKISTAN
OPKC   Karachi Intl
OPKD   Hyderabad
OPLA   Lahore
OPRN   Islamabad/Chaklala
OPSF   Karachi/Sharea Faisal

OR IRAQ
ORBS   Baghdad/Saddam Intl
ORMM   Basrah
ORNW   Baghdad/Muthenne

OS SYRIA
OSDI   Damascus Intl

OT QATAR
OTBD   Doha Intl

OY YEMEN REPUBLIC
OYAA   Aden Acc/Aden Intl

PA ALASKA
PANC   Anchorage Intl
PAFA   Fairbanks Intl

SF FALKLAND ISLANDS
SFAL   Stanley

TX BERMUDA
TXKF   Bermuda

UL/UU RUSSIA
ULLI   St Petersburg/Pulkovo
UUEE   Moscow/Sheremetyevo
UUMM   Murmansk
UUWW   Moscow/Vnukovo

UK UKRAINE/MOLDAVIA
UKBB   Kiev
UKOO   Odessa

UL ESTONIA
ULTT   Tallinn

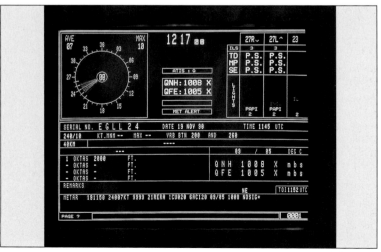

Top:
RAF Victor tanker and Tornado GR1. *Ministry of Defence*

Above:
Runway information as displayed to controllers at Heathrow. *Civil Aviation Authority*

Appendix V: ATC Reporting Points

Modern navigation relies on a combination of radio beacons and reporting points at airway intersections and airspace boundaries. Aircraft positions are determined by on-board inertial navigation systems as well as radio signals from VHF beacons.

The following lists cover UK five-letter reporting points, followed by radio navigation facilities, with a selection from adjoining regions.

The first list covers five-letter reporting points. These are navigation positions, none of which has a radio transmitter on the ground. They are invariably at airway or upper air route intersections or on national airspace boundaries.

The name of the facility is followed by the co-ordinates and the third column indicates its purpose.

Name	Co-ordinates	Location
ABDAL	N5127 W0150	Arrivals to Bristol/Cardiff
ABSIL	N5438 E0420	UA37
ACORN	N5114 E0011	LTMA — Gatwick SIDs
ADMIS	N5160 E0011	UB317 and UR77
ADSON	N5103 W0215	R37
AGANO	N4939 W0200	Channel Islands CTR — Alderney Arrivals
AKELO	N4946 W0353	SL1 — SL4 — SL7
ALICE	N5817 W0250	Aberdeen/Atlantic Rim
ALKIN	N5123 E0011	LTMA — London/City and Biggin Hill STARs
ALLOY	N6121 E0147	East Shetland
ALVIN	N5139 W0240	G1
ALWYN	N6048 E0144	East Shetland
AMLET	N5316 W0150	Manchester TMA
AMMAN	N5150 W0359	G1
ANGEL	N5447 E0308	UL74 — UR4
ANGLA	N4942 W0201	Channel Islands CTR
ANGLO	N4956 W0027	Jersey/Guernsey Arrivals
ANGUS	N5641 W0303	B2 — B226
ANNET	N4939 W0400	UL722 — UR116
APPLE	N5430 W0231	UN590
ARTHA	N5347 W0217	Manchester/Liverpool Arrivals
ASKEY/LOREL	N5200 W0003	Stansted and Luton STARs
ASKIL	N4903 W0700	UT7 Brest Boundary
ASPEN	N5017 W0148	UR24 — UR41
ASTRA	N5051 W0008	LTMA — Gatwick STARs
AVANT	N5049 W0056	Gatwick Arrivals
BAGIN	N5102 E0135	UG106 — Gatwick STARs
BAKER	N5129 E0018	B4 — LTMA
BAKUR	N5215 W0538	UA29 — UN546
BALIS	N5714 W0203	Aberdeen ATSU
BAMES	N4858 E0129	UA1 (near Paris CDG)
BANBA	N5157 W0614	UB10 — UR72 Shannon Boundary
BANDU	N5029 W1008	Shannon Oceanic Transition
BANLO	N5100 W0800	Shannon Oceanic Transition
BARIX	N5025 W0800	Shannon Oceanic Transition
BARLU	N4941 W0118	UB11 Brest Control
BARTN	N5328 W0225	Manchester TMA
BASAV	N5206 E0206	UA37 — UR77
BASET	N5133 W0142	UB39 — UG1
BATEL	N5053 E0033	LTMA
BEDFO	N5213 W0033	B4 — UB4
BEECH	N5028 E0012	G27 — London/City and Biggin Hill STARs
BEENO	N5312 E0302	B5 — UA37 — UB5
BEGAS	N4500 W0900	Shannon Oceanic Transition
BEGDA	N5236 W0402	UB39 — UW502
BEGTO	N5046 W0114	H51 — R84 — Heathrow Arrivals

Name	Co-ordinates	Location
BEKET	N5853 W0131	W5D
BENBO	N5027 E0000	A1 — A56 — UA1
BENDY	N5017 W0148	Southampton CTA
BENIX	N4932 W0129	Channel Islands CTR
BENTY	N5946 W0108	Sumburgh Heli Routes
BEREK	N5139 W0105	A1 — LTMA — Gatwick STARs
BESOP	N5433 W0527	UB2 — UP6
BEVAV	N4904 W0141	Channel Islands Arrivals
BEWLI	N5046 W0148	H51 — Heathrow/Gatwick Arrivals
BEXIL	N5042 E0044	En-Route Hold — Gatwick STARs
BILLY	N6001 W0083	UN603 — UN610 — Hebrides UTA
BIRCH	N5224 W0155	Birmingham CTR and CTA
BISKI	N4906 W0800	Shannon Oceanic Transition
BLACA	N5453 W0509	B2 — Edinburgh — Glasgow STARs
BLUFA	N5256 E0309	B1 — UB1 — UB105
BLUSY	N5137 E0209	R126 — Heathrow STARs — UR126
BODAM	N5955 W0116	Sumburgh Heli Routes
BOGNA	N5042 W0015	A1 — Heathrow/Gatwick SIDs
BONBY	N5753 W0420	W3D — Inverness
BONDY	N5107 E0045	LTMA — London/City and Biggin Hill STARs
BORVE	N5748 W0228	Aberdeen/Atlantic Rim
BOVVA	N5143 W0032	LTMA — Heathrow STARs
BOWES	N5431 W0206	Northern Radar Advisory Area
BOYNE	N5346 W0530	W911D
BOYSI	N5159 E0032	Luton and Stansted Arrivals
BRAIN	N5148 E0039	R123 — London/City and Biggin Hill STARs
BRASO	N5141 E0041	R1 — LTMA — Heathrow — Stansted — Luton STARs
BREKI	N6232 W1932	Iceland UIR
BRILL	N4942 W0223	Channel Islands CTR
BRIPO	N5042 W0245	R8
BRUCE	N5614 W0550	N573D — W958D
BRYNA	N5151 W0351	UW502
BUKEN	N5420 W0206	Manchester and Liverpool SIDs
BURAK	N5300 W1200	Shannon UIR
BURNI	N5344 W0231	Manchester/Liverpool Arrivals
BUSTA	N5205 E0004	LTMA — Stansted and Luton STARs
BUZAD	N5156 W0033	A20 — B3 — Heathrow/Northolt/Stansted SIDs
CALDA	N5346 W0238	A1— UA1 — Manchester TMA
CAMBO	N4917 W0551	UR72 Brest Boundary
CASEL	N5349 W0410	B3 — Isle of Man Arrivals
CAVAL	N4929 W0452	UR168
CEDAR	N5231 W0149	Birmingham CTA
CELLO	N6214 W2028	Iceland UIR
CHANL	N5027 E0010	Gatwick Hold
CHASE	N5236 W0154	Birmingham Arrivals
CHELT	N5152 W0222	B39 — UA251 — UB39
CHINN	N5757 W0411	W3D
CHUBB	N4925 W0248	Jersey Arrivals and SIDs
CLIFF	N5052 E0043	A20 — Heathrow STARs — UA20
CLIPY	N5200 W0105	Luton and Stansted Arrivals
CLYDE	N5557 W0447	Glasgow STARs and SIDs — Scottish TMA — W910D
CODEY	N5119 W0132	Farnborough Arrivals
COLRE	N5507 W0644	Londonderry/Eglinton
CONGA	N5308 W0211	A1 — R101 — Manchester TMA — Manchester SIDs
COWLY	N5137 W0103	A1 — R41 — UA1 — UR41
CREWE	N5249 W0218U	A251
CROFT	N5336 W0231	Manchester TMA
CUMBO	N5556 W0357	Edinburgh SIDs — Scottish TMA
CUMRI	N5143 W0260	UN862

Name	Co-ordinates	Location
DALEY/ROSUN	N5340 W0221	Manchester/Liverpool Arrivals
DALKY	N5359 W0554	B2 — UB2 — Belfast TMA
DANDI	N5520 E0500	UA37 — UR4
DAVOT	N5720 W0405	En-Route Hold (Advisory Routes) — W3D
DAWLY	N5034 W0327	R8 — UA25 — UA29
DAYNE	N5314 W0202	Manchester Arrivals
DEGOS	N5411 W0654	UN517
DELBO	N5153 W0116	Gatwick Arrivals — Holding Fix
DENBY	N5331 W0157	Manchester CTR
DEPSO	N6055 E0152	East Shetland Basin
DIDEL	N5051 W0400	UA29 — UL3
DIKAS	N5146 W0315	UA25 — UB40 — UG1
DOGGA	N5323 E0155	B1 — B5 — UB1 — UB5
DOLIP	N5200 W1200	Shannon UIR
DONNA	N5142 W0044	Heathrow Arrivals
DOWNI	N5704 W0206	Aberdeen Holding Fix
DRAKE	N5012 W0004	A34 — A56 — R25 — UA34
DUFFY	N5430 W0551	Belfast TMA
DUMBA	N5556 W0433	Glasgow SIDs — Scottish TMA
DUNLO	N5458 W0642	UN570 — UP6
EAGLE	N5124 E0005	Biggin Hill
EASIN	N5339 E0007	Southern North Sea Area
EBONY	N5220 W0203	Birmingham CTR and CTA
EIDER	N6121 E0109	East Shetland Basin
ELDER	N5039 W0120	Heathrow/Gatwick STARs
ELDIN	N5309 E0321	B5 — UB5
ELGAR	N5223 W0256	UN862
EMJEE	N5423 E0153	UW534
ERING	N5135 E0136	B29 — UB29
ERMIN	N5020 W0355	Plymouth
ERNAN	N5416 W0723	UN550 — UN560
ERWAN	N4556 W0512	UR107 Brest Control
ESKDO	N5517 W0312	B4 — Edinburgh STARs
ESTRY	N5340 W0316	Manchester/Warton/Blackpool
ETIKI	N4800 W0845	Brest Oceanic Transition
ETRAT	N4941 E0009	A34 France Control
EVRIN	N5146 W0634	UL607 Shannon Boundary
EXMOR	N5110 W0321	UA25 — UA251 — UR14 — UR37
FAMBO	N5430 W0027	UB5
FAWBO	N5000 W0119	B11 — UB11
FENIK	N5543 W0417	UA1 — UB2 Scottish TMA
FERAS	N5138 E0038	London TMA
FERIT	N5138 E0032	UB29 — UM14
FINCH	N5133 W0010	A20
FINDO	N5622 W0327	UB2 — UB4 — UR38
FINMA	N5160 W0103	A47 — B71
FIWUD	N5352 W0304	Leeds/Bradford Departures
FLAME	N6102 E0155	East Shetland Basin
FORTY	N5757 E0035	UB2 — UL7
FOYLE	N5608 W0422	Glasgow STARs and SIDs
FRANK	N5142 W0041	LTMA — Northolt SIDs
FULMA	N5530 W0500	Scottish TMA — W958D
FYNER	N5602 W0506	Glasgow Arrivals
GABAD	N5201 E0203	Stansted/Luton Arrivals
GAPLI	N5000 W0800	Shannon Oceanic Transition
GARVA	N5741 W0430	W6D
GATER	N5440 W0206	Northern Radar Advisory
GAVEL	N5923 W0124	W5D

Name	Co-ordinates	Location
GELKI	N5360 W0554	Belfast Terminal Area
GERPA	N5417 W0150	Northern Radar Advisory
GIBSO	N5045 W0230	R8 — UR8 — UR14
GILDA	N5136 E0035	UG39 — UR12
GIPER	N5100 W1200	Shannon Oceanic Transition
GIRVA	N5511 W0453	Edinburgh/Glasgow STARs
GLESK	N5654 W0247	B2
GODAL	N5116 W0044	Gatwick Arrivals
GOLES	N5336 W0104	UB1 — UB105
GONUT	N6100 W0435	UH70
GORDO	N5550 E0500	UR23
GORSE	N5710 W0153	Aberdeen Heli Routes
GRICE	N5611 W0341	Edinburgh STARs and SIDs — Glasgow STARs
GULDA	N4923 W0155	Jersey Departures
GUNPA	N6100 0000	UP19 — UP610
GUNSO	N4904 W1144	Shannon Oceanic Transition
HALIF	N5344 W0135	UL613 — UN590 — UR4
HANKY	N5107 W0108	London Terminal Area/PEPIS
HARDY	N5028 E0029	A47 — Heathrow SIDs — UA47 — Gatwick SIDs
HASTY	N5043 E0032	G27
HAWKE	N5022 E0006	A1 — G27 — UA1 — UG27
HAYDO	N5328 W0233	UP6 Radar Vectoring Point
HAZEL	N5100 W0058	Heathrow/Stansted/Luton STARs
HEIDI	N5206 W0037	A2 — B317
HELEN	N5114 E0352	UB29 Brussels
HEMEL	N5148 W0025	UA20 — UH52 — UH53 — UH54
HERON	N5520 W0500	Scottish TMA — N552D — N562D
HILLY	N5120 E0015	Heathrow Arrivals
HOLLY	N5053 W0005	Gatwick Arrivals
INLAK	N5128 W0131	UB29 — UB39 — UL607
IZACK	N5953 W0101	Sumburgh Heli Routes
JACKO	N5144 E0125	B317 — R1
KARIL	N4919 W0152	Channel Islands CTR — Jersey Arrivals and SIDs
KARNO	N5253 W0254	N862 — UN862
KATHY	N5031 W0119	B11 — UB11 — Gatwick STARs
KELLY	N5354 W0421	B3 — Isle of Man Arrivals
KENET	N5131 W0127	G1 — Heathrow/Gatwick/Stansted/Luton STARs
KENUK	N5000 W1200	Shannon Oceanic Transition
KETIK	N4919 W0152	Jersey Departures
KIDLI	N5146 W0122	A34 — B321 — UA34 — UB321
KINDR	N5323 W0156	Woodford Arrivals
KIPPA	N5310 E0143	UB105
KIRBY	N5328 W0252	Manchester TMA
KISTA	N5930 W0156	En Route Hold W3D
KLONN	N5823 E0249	UB2 — B2D
KOKAL	N5857 W0253	W3D
KOLEY	N5448 E0313	UL7 — UR4
KOMIK	N5259 E0251	UA37 — UB105
KONAN	N5107 E0200	UG1 — UL1
KORAK	N5323 W0746	Shannon UIR
KORIB	N5413 W1300	North Atlantic Entry Point
KORUL	N4450 W0655	Brest/Madrid Boundary
KULOK	N5641 E0330	UN582
LAGER	N5336 W0008	Southern North Sea HMR 9
LAKEY	N5414 W0009	Manchester/Liverpool Arrivals
LAMMA	N5551 W0245	UR38

Name	Co-ordinates	Location
LANAK	N5542 W0355	Glasgow STARs — Scottish TMA
LAPEX	N4700 W0080	Brest Oceanic Transition
LARCK	N5054 E0027	Gatwick STARs
LASNO	N4835 W0900	Shannon Oceanic Transition
LERAK	N4902 W0225	Channel Islands CTR
LESTA	N5244 W0104	B4 — UB4 — UP6
LIBBA	N5543 W0345	Edinburgh/Glasgow Arrivals
LIFFY	N5328 W0530	B1 — UB1
LINDY	N5128 W0102	UA34 — UG1
LIRKI	N6100 W0151	UH71
LISBO	N5431 W0605	Belfast TMA
LIZAD	N4935 W0420	Jersey SIDs — UG4 — UR40 — G4D
LOGAN	N5144 E0136	A37 — R1 — R126 — Heathrow/London City/Biggin Hill/ Stansted and Luton STARs
LOMON	N5603 W0434	Scottish TMA — Glasgow STARs and SIDs
LONAM	N5350 E0356	UL7
LOREL/ASKEY	N5200 W0003	LTMA — Stansted and Luton STARs
LOTEE	N4439 W0550	Brest/Madrid Boundary
LOVEL	N5315 W0216	A1 — UA1 — UA251
LUCCO	N5041 W0106	Gatwick Arrivals/PONPI Holds
LUMBA	N5056 E0015	LTMA — Gatwick STARs
LUSIT	N4913 W0147	Channel Islands CTR
LYNAS	N5326 W0419	Manchester/Liverpool Arrivals
MADLI	N5208 W0258	UN862
MAGEE	N5447 W0536	Belfast TMA
MALBY	N5135 W0203	B39 — G1
MANGO	N5141 E0047	UR1 — UR12
MANTA	N4942 W0235	Channel Islands CTR
MAPLE	N5223 W0140	Birmingham CTA — Birmingham STARs and SIDs
MARGO	N5442 W0246	B4 — UB4 — UN571 — UN590 — Edinburgh/Glasgow STARs
MASIT	N5420 W1200	North Atlantic Entry Point
MATCH	N5146 E0015	R123 — LTMA — Stansted SIDs
MATIK	N6100 W0804	UN615
MATIM	N5110 W0403	SL3 — SL5
MAYLA	N5137 E0043	LTMA — London/City and Biggin Hill STARs
MELEE	N4825 E0222	UG32 (near Paris CDG)
MERLY	N5120 W0500	En-Route Hold — UA29 — UB40 — UR37 — SL2
MIKEL	N5417 W0452	W928D
MILDE	N5335 W0015	Southern North Sea HMR 9
MIMBI	N5132 W0141	G1 — Farnborough Arrivals (Via CODEY)
MINQI	N4902 W0203	Channel Islands CTR — Jersey Arrivals
MIRSI	N5332 W0243	Manchester/Liverpool Arrivals
MOCHA	N5932 W0121	W5D — Aberdeen ATSU
MOGLI	N5218 W0016	UL613 — UP6
MOLAK	N5436 W0930	UN545 — UN559 — UN569
MONTY	N5253 W0310	A25 — Manchester TMA — Manchester SIDs
MOODY	N5020 W0354	Plymouth Instrument Approach Procedures
MORAY	N5805 W0249	W4D
MORBY	N5355 W0328	W2D
MULIT	N5341 E0328	UA37 — UL74
MULLA	N5411 W0544	B2 — Belfast TMA
MYNDA	N5243 W0255	N862 — UN862
NADIR	N5749 0000	B2D
NAKID	N4942 W0437	UG4 — UR116
NANTI	N5308 W0233	B3 — B53 — Manchester TMA — Liverpool SIDs
NASDA	N5034 E0112	A20 — UA20 — London/City STARs Stansted and Luton STARs

Name	Co-ordinates	Location
NEDUL	N5039 W0133	Solent Control Area Arrivals
NELSA	N5352 W0211	Leeds/Bradford Departures
NEPTU	N5231 E0250	London/Amsterdam Boundary
NEVIL	N5000 W0021	G27
NEVIS	N5642 W0433	UN585 — UN601
NIGIT	N5118 W0110	UB39 — UP2
NIPIT	N5427 W0824	UN537
NITON	N5233 W0311	A25 — UA25 — Y98 — UY98
NOBAL	N5715 W0203	Aberdeen ATSU
NOKIN	N5305 W0253	N862 — Y98 — Y99 — UN862 — UY98 — UT99 — Manchester and Liverpool Arrivals
NORBO	N5535 W0445	Glasgow SIDs — Scottish TMA
NORDA	N4947 W0105	Channel Islands CTR
NORLA	N5137 W0651	UR37
NORRY	N5128 W0107	G1 — R41 — UG1 — UR41
NORSE	N6049 E0135	East Shetland Basin Route Structure
NOTRO	N4913 W0646	UT7 — SOTA
NUMPO	N5136 W0316	UA25 — UP2
OLGUD	N5048 W0121	Heathrow/Gatwick Arrivals BEWLI Holds
OLIVE	N5224 W0156	Birmingham CTR and CTA — Birmingham STARs
OLKER	N6100 W0630	UN614
OLNEY	N5207 W0043	A20 — B317 — Heathrow SIDs
OMIMI	N4916 W0713	UN512 — SOTA
OMOKO	N4850 W1200	SL1 — SL5 — SOTA
ORIST	N5000 W0150	UR24
ORMER	N4936 W0251	Channel Islands CTR — Guernsey SIDs
ORTAC	N5000 W0200	UR41 — UR84 — UR1 Jersey and Guernsey Arrivals/Departures
ORVIK	N5938 E0039	UG11
OSPOL	N5009 W0011	G27
OYSTA	N4906 W0231	Channel Islands CTR
PAVLO	N5056 W0554	UL3 — UR72
PELIK	N4844 W0410	Brest Control
PEPIS	N5111 W0114	B321 — R41 — UR41
PERCH	N4907 W0157	Channel Islands CTR
PHILI	N4929 W0701	UN502
PIKEY	N4929 W0213	Guernsey Departures
PIKOD	N4925 W0516	UN502
PIRNO	N4948 W0122	B11 Brest Control
PLYMO	N5021 W0438	UR8 En-Route Hold
POMPI	N5046 W0057	H51 — UL3 Gatwick Arrivals
POTON	N5205 W0025	B4 — B317 — UB4 — UB317
RADNO	N5214 W0313	A25 — B39 — UA25 — UB39
RANAR	N5340 W0719	Shannon UIR
RANOK	N5642 W0414	W3D
RATKA	N4930 W0800	UN512 — SOTA
REBKA	N4912 W0300	Channel Islands CTR
REDFA	N5206 E0229	R12 — UR12
REGHI	N4800 W0800	Brest Oceanic Transition
REMSA	N5358 W0350	UP6 — UR4
REPLO	N5133 E0108	UA37 — UG39
REXAM	N5304 W0309	A25 — Manchester TMA
RIBEL	N5400 W0217	B4 — Northern Radar Area
RILKA	N4925 W0620	SL1 — SL4 — SL7
RINGA	N5423 W0534	B2 — B3 — Belfast TMA
RIVAK	N4600 W0800	Brest Oceanic Transition
ROBBO	N5553 W0454	Glasgow SIDs — Scottish TMA
ROBIN	N5257 W0117	B4 — R3 — UB4 — UR3

Name	Co-ordinates	Location
ROLLS	N5414 E0318	UW538 — UW550
RONAR	N5731 W0539	A1D
RONVI	N5917 W0430	UN584 — UN593 — Hebrides UTA
ROSUN/DALEY	N5340 W0221	Manchester/Liverpool Arrivals
ROWAN	N5145 E0015	LTMA — Stansted SIDs
ROYCE	N5352 E0246	UW534 — UW550
RUPAS	N4930 W0200	Channel Islands CTR — Guernsey SIDs
RUSEL	N5900 W0234	Aberdeen Atlantic Rim (HMR Victor)
SABER	N5142 E0057	Heathrow/Stansted/Luton Arrivals
SADAL	N5136 E0048	London/City STARs
SALCO	N4944 W0331	UA29 — UN863 — UN865
SAMON	N5403 E0347	UA37 — UL7
SANDY	N5103 E0104	A2 — R803 — Heathrow/Stansted/Luton STARs
SAPCO	N5232 W0121	A2 — B53 — East Midlands CTA
SAPOT	N5915 W0222	W3D
SASKI	N5132 E0230	UB29 Amsterdam UIR
SEPAL	N4700 W0845	Brest Oceanic Transition
SETEL	N5400 W0226	A2 — UA2 — Manchester CTR — Manchester/Liverpool STARs
SHAPP	N5430 W0237	B4 — UB4
SHARK	N4911 W0225	Channel Islands CTR — Jersey Arrivals
SHRUB	N5718 W0149	Aberdeen Air Traffic Service
SIDER	N6100 W0508	UG11
SILOK	N5946 W0129	Sumburgh Heli Routes
SILVA	N5358 E0041	UB5 — UR4
SINGA	N5438 E0240	UW538
SIRGO	N5137 E0038	B29 — UB29 — UR12
SITET	N5006 0000	A34 — A56 — R25 — UA34 — UR25
SITKO	N5302 E0253	B1 — UA37 — UB1
SIVIR	N4600 W0845	Brest Oceanic Transition
SKATE	N5500 E0304	UL7 — UL74 — UN591
SKERY	N5000 W0310	A25 — Channel Islands CTR
SKESO	N4949 W0302	UA25 — UN862
SLANY	N5209 W0550	G1 — UG1
SLYDA	N5412 W0505	B3
SMOKI	N5746 W0235	En-Route Hold W4D
SNIPE	N5556 W0002	UW536
SOTOL	N5502 E0400	UR4
SPEAR	N5134 E0042	LTMA — London/City and Biggin Hill STARs
SPIKE	N5732 W0139	Aberdeen ATSU
SPRAT	N5225 E0222	UA37
STAFA	N5251 W0214	B3 — R101 — Birmingham STARs
STIRA	N5608 W0349	Edinburgh/Glasgow Arrivals
STOAT	N5202 W0001	UL613 — UM14
STOCK	N5332 W0149	B1 — Manchester TMA — Manchester/Liverpool SIDs
SUDBY	N5200 E0039	London Terminal Area
SUPAP	N4926 W0549	UN502 — UR72
SWANY	N5133 W0407	UB40 — UR14
TABIT	N5548 W0520	N553D — W958D
TADEX	N5451 W0814	UN551 — UN560
TAKAS	N4900 W0800U	N490 — UN551 — UN508 — SOTA
TANET	N5126 E0055	A37 — Gatwick STARs
TARAN	N5050 W0201	Heathrow/Gatwick Arrivals BEWLI Holds
TARTN	N5542 W0308	Edinburgh STARs — Scottish TMA
TAWNY	N5138 E0009	LTMA — Heathrow STARs — Stansted/Luton Arrivals
TEBRA	N5129 E0136	UG39
TEDSA	N5203 E0108	R77 — UR77
TELBA	N5239 W0219	UA34 — UA251
TESGO	N5011 W0130	SL4 — SL7

Name	Co-ordinates	Location
THRED	N5030 W0140	Solent Control Arrivals
TIGER	N5104 E0027	Heathrow/Gatwick Arrivals and Departures
TILBY	N5126 E0021	LTMA — London/City and Biggin Hill STARs
TIMBA	N5056 E0015	LTMA — Gatwick Arrivals
TINAC	N5615 E0500	UN581
TIRIK	N5932 W0112	Aberdeen Air Traffic Service
TIVER	N5049 W0325	UA25 — UL3
TIVLI	N5116 W0729	UG4 — G4D
TOBIX	N5136 E0117	Gatwick Arrivals
TOLKA	N5311 W0530	B39 — UB39
TOMIN	N6000 W0400	Aberdeen Atlantic Rim (HMR Victor)
TOMPO	N5043 W0333	Exeter Approaches
TOPPA	N5324 E0333	UL74
TOVRI	N4859 W0731	UN491
TRIPO	N5142 E0104	Heathrow/Stansted/Luton/London City/Biggin Hill Arrivals
TROUT	N5730 W0124	En-Route Hold — B2D
TUBOT	N5554 E0221	UL7 — UR23
TULIP	N5222 E0351	R12 Amsterdam FIR
TULTA	N4935 W0800	Shannon Oceanic Transition
TUNBY	N5110 E0019	LTMA — Gatwick SIDs
TUNEL	N5126 E0014	LTMA — Biggin Hill Missed Approach Procedures
TUNIT	N4922 W0300	Channel Islands CTR — Jersey Arrivals and SIDs
TUTON	N5109 W0306	UN862
TWEED	N5540 W0316	Edinburgh STARs — Scottish TMA
TYSTI	N5922 W0114	Aberdeen ATSU
ULLAP	N5754 W0510	W6D — Inverness Arrivals
UNROK	N4927 W0630	UN502 — UT7
UPTON	N5335 W0118	B1
VALOG	N4936 W0105	Jersey/Guernsey Arrivals
VANIN	N5359 W0402	Isle of Man Arrivals — W2D
VATRY	N5233 W0530	R14 — UR14
VEULE	N4951 E0037	A1 France Control
WAFFU	N5035 E0021	A47 — G27 — UA47 — UG27
WEALD	N5119 E0002	Heathrow Arrivals
WELIN	N5214 W0051	A2 — A20 — UA2
WESUL	N5140 E0029	UM14 — UR1
WILLO	N5059 W0011	Gatwick Arrivals
WIZAD	N5106 E0057	R8 — Gatwick Departures
WOBUN	N5201 W0044	B3 — Heathrow Departures
WOTAN	N5137 W0220	G1

Below:
BAe 146 of Virgin. *Civil Aviation Authority*

RADIO NAVIGATIONAL AIDS BY IDENTIFICATION

Navigational aids are covered in the following list. The identification is given first, followed by the name, then the type of facility and finally its position.

The ident letters are transmitted in Morse on a specific frequency for each beacon. These can be found on navigation charts. The third column indicates the purpose. VOR indicates a Very High Frequency Omni—Directional Range. NDBs are more simple non—directional aids, and locaters serve a similar purpose.

Callsign	Station	Facility	Position
ABB	Abbeville	VOR	N5008 E0151
AC	Glasgow	Locator	N5548 W0432
ADN	Aberdeen/Dyce	VOR/DME	N5718 W0215
ADR	Belfast/Aldergrove	NDB	N5437 W0617
ALD	Alderney	Locator	N4942 W0211
AMB	Amboise	VOR	N4725 E0104
AQ	Aberdeen	NDB	N5708 W0224
ARE	Monts D'Arree	VOR	N4820 W0336
ATF	Aberdeen	NDB	N5704 W0206
BAL	Baldonnel/Casement	DVOR	N5318 W0627
BCN	Brecon	VOR	N5144 W0316
BEL	Belfast	VOR	N5440 W0614
BEN	Benbecula	VOR	N5729 W0722
BHD	Berry Head	VOR	N5024 W0330
BIG	Biggin	VOR	N5120 E0002
BKY	Barkway	VOR	N5160 E0004
BMH	Bournemouth	NDB	N5046 W0157
BNE	Boulogne	VOR	N5037 E0154
BNN	Bovingdon	VOR	N5143 W0033
BPK	Brookmans Park	VOR	N5145 W0006
BPL	Blackpool	Locator	N5346 W0302
BRI	Bristol	Locator	N5122 W0243
BRY	Bray	VOR	N4824 E0317
BUR	Burnham	NDB	N5131 W0040
BZ	Brize Norton	Locator	N5145 W0136
CAM	Cambridge	Locator	N5213 E0011
CAN	Caen	VOR	N4910 W0027
CDF	Cardiff	Locator	N5124 W0320
CFD	Cranfield	VOR	N5204 W0036
CHT	Chiltern	NDB	N5137 W0031
CHW	Chartres	VOR	N4829 E0059
CIT	Cranfield	Locator	N5208 W0033
CL	Carlisle	Locator	N5456 W0248
CLN	Clacton	VOR	N5151 E0109
COA	Costa	VOR	N5121 E0324
CON	Connaught	DVOR	N5354 W0849
CPT	Compton	VOR	N5129 W0113
CRK	Cork	DVOR	N5150 W0829
CT	Coventry	Locator	N5225 W0124
DCS	Dean Cross	VOR	N5443 W0320
DET	Detling	VOR	N5118 E0036
DH	Norwich	Locator	N5240 E0110
DIK	Diekirch	VOR	N4952 E0608
DIN	Dinard	VOR	N4835 W0205
DND	Dundee	Locator	N5627 W0307
DO	Dounreay/Thurso	NDB	N5835 W0344
DPE	Dieppe	VOR	N4955 E0110
DTY	Daventry	VOR	N5211 W0107

Callsign	Station	Facility	Position
DUB	Dublin	DVOR	N5330 W0618
DVL	Deauville	VOR	N4918 E0018
DVR	Dover	VOR/DME	N5109 E0121
EAS	Southampton/Eastleigh	Locator	N5057 W0121
EDN	Edinburgh	Locator	N5559 W0317
EME	East Midlands	Locator	N5250 W0112
EMW	East Midlands	Locator	N5250 W0127
ENS	Ennis	NDB	N5254 W0855
EPN	Epsom	NDB	N5119 W0022
EX	Exeter	Locator	N5045 W0318
FOY	Foynes	NDB	N5234 W0911
FY	Finningley	NDB	N5329 W0100
GAM	Gamston	VOR	N5317 W0057
GAR	Dublin	NDB	N5332 W0627
GE	Gatwick	NDB	N5110 W0004
GLG	Glasgow	Locator	N5555 W0420
GM	Birmingham	Locator	N5224 W0141
GOW	Glasgow	VOR	N5552 W0427
GRB	Guernsey	Locator	N4926 W0238
GST	Gloucestershire	Locator	N5153 W0210
GUR	Guernsey	VOR	N4926 W0236
GWC	Goodwood	VOR	N5051 W0045
GX	Birmingham	Locator	N5231 W0149
GY	Gatwick	NDB	N5108 W0019
HAV	Haverfordwest	NDB	N5150 W0458
HAW	Hawarden	Locator	N5311 W0257
HB	Belfast/City	Locator	N5437 W0553
HBR	Humberside	Locator	N5339 W0018
HG	Halfpenny Green	NDB	N5231 W0215
HON	Honiley	VOR	N5221 W0140
HRN	Bournemouth	NDB	N5048 W0144
INS	Inverness	VOR	N5733 W0402
IOM	Isle of Man	VOR	N5404 W0445
JSY	Jersey	VOR	N4913 W0203
JW	Jersey	Locator	N4912 W0213
KER	Kerry/Farranfore	NDB	N5210 W0931
KIM	Humberside	Locator	N5334 W0021
KLY	Killiney	NDB	N5316 W0606
KNK	Connaught	NDB	N5354 W0856
KOK	Koksy	VOR	N5105 E0239
KS	Kinloss	NDB	N5739 W0335
KW	Kirkwall	Locator	N5857 W0254
KWL	Kirkwall	VOR	N5857 W0253
LA	Lyneham	NDB	N5130 W0200
LAM	Lambourne	VOR	N5139 E0009
LAY	Islay	Locator	N5541 W0615
LBA	Leeds/Bradford	Locator	N5352 W0139
LE	Leicester	NDB	N5236 W0102
LIC	Lichfield	NDB	N5245 W0143
LND	Land's End	VOR	N5008 W0538
LON	London	VOR	N5129 W0028
LPL	Liverpool	NDB	N5320 W0243
LUT	Luton	Locator	N5153 W0015

Callsign	Station	Facility	Position
LUX	Luxembourg	VOR	N4937 E0612
LYX	Lydd	Locator	N5058 E0057
MAC	Machrihanish	DVOR	N5526 W0539
MAY	Mayfield	VOR	N5101 E0007
MCR	Manchester	Locator	N5318 W0222
MCT	Manchester	VOR	N5321 W0216
ME	Manchester	NDB	N5324 W0211
MID	Midhurst	VOR	N5103 W0037
MW	Middle Wallop	NDB	N5109 W0133
ND	Great Yarmouth	Locator	N5238 E0143
NEW	Newcastle	VOR	N5502 W0142
NGY	New Galloway	NDB	N5511 W0410
NH	Norwich	Locator	N5241 E0123
NOT	Nottingham	NDB	N5255 W0105
NTM	Nattenheim	VOR	N5000 E0632
OB	Cork	Locator	N5145 W0826
OC	Cork	Locator	N5154 W0832
OCK	Ockham	VOR	N5118 W0027
OE	Heathrow	NDB	N5128 W0020
OF	Filton	Locator	N5131 W0235
OK	Connaught	NDB	N5355 W0842
OL	Shannon	Locator	N5245 W0849
OLD	Oldham	NDB	N5333 W0203
OTR	Ottringham	VOR	N5342 W0006
OW	Heathrow	NDB	N5128 W0035
OX	Oxford/Kidlington	Locator	N5150 W0119
OY	Belfast/Aldergrove	Locator	N5441 W0605
PE	Prestwick	Locator	N5528 W0428
POL	Pole Hill	VOR	N5344 W0206
PSW	Ipswich	NDB	N5202 E0112
PTH	Perth/Scone	VOR	N5626 W0322
PW	Prestwick	Locator	N5533 W0441
PY	Plymouth	Locator	N5025 W0407
REM	Reims	VOR	N4918 E0402
RNR	Radnor	NDB	N5214 W0315
ROU	Rouen	VOR	N4928 E0117
RSH	Rush (Dublin)	NDB	N5331 W0607
RWY	Ronaldsway	Locator	N5405 W0436
S	Shannon	Locator	N5243 W0854
SAB	St Abbs	VOR	N5554 W0212
SAM	Southampton	VOR	N5057 W0121
SAN	Stansted	Locator	N5156 E0019
SAY	Stornoway	NDB	N5813 W0619
SBH	Sumburgh	Locator	N5953 W0118
SFD	Seaford	VOR	N5045 E0007
SHA	Shannon	DVOR	N5243 W0854
SHM	Shoreham	Locator	N5050 W0018
SHD	Scotstownhead	NDB	N5734 W0149
SLG	Sligo	NDB	N5417 W0836
SM	St Mawgan	NDB	N5026 W0459
SND	Southend	NDB	N5134 E0042
SPI	Sprimont	VOR	N5030 E0537
STM	Isles of Scilly	Locator	N4955 W0617
STN	Stornoway	VOR	N5812 W0611
STU	Strumble	VOR	N5160 W0502

Above:
Fokker 100 flightdeck. *Rockwell International/ Collins*

Callsign	Station	Facility	Position
SUM	Sumburgh	VOR	N5953 W0117
SWN	Swansea	Locator	N5136 W0404
TD	Teesside	Locator	N5434 W0120
TIR	Tiree	VOR	N5630 W0652
TLA	Talla	VOR	N5530 W0321
TNT	Trent	VOR	N5303 W0140
TRN	Turnberry	VOR	N5519 W0447
UT	Unst	Locator	N6044 W0049
UW	Edinburgh	Locator	N5554 W0330
WAL	Wallasey	VOR	N5323 W0308
WCO	Westcott	NDB	N5151 W0058
WFD	Woodford	NDB	N5320 W0209
WHI	Whitegate	NDB	N5311 W0237
WIK	Wick	VOR	N5827 W0306
WL	Barrow/Walney Island	NDB	N5408 W0316
WOD	Woodley	NDB	N5127 W0053
WTD	Waterford	NDB	N5211 W0705
WTN	Warton	Locator	N5345 W0251
WZ	Newcastle	Locator	N5500 W0148
YVL	Yeovil	Locator	N5056 W0240

Appendix VI: Airline Callsigns

This appendix lists most of the airlines which operate in UK airspace. In most cases the callsign will incorporate the name of the operator but there are quite a number of exceptions, the best known being British Airways which uses the callsigns 'Speedbird' or 'Shuttle'. Flights are normally identified by a two, three or four-character number after the callsign name and usually this number relates to the airline timetable. However, there is a growing tendency for some airlines to use numbers which have no relationship to their timetable; therefore the airband listener will find it difficult to identify some flights. Publications are available which are invaluable in providing a decode for flight numbers and some of these listings include UK overflights.

The callsigns listed are current at the time of publication, but unfortunately they are subject to change.

(I am indebted to Aviation Data Research and Javiation of Bradford for their assistance in keeping the list up to date.)

Call Sign	Airline	Call Sign	Airline
Abbas	Abbas Air	American	American
Abex	Airborne Express	Amiri	Qatar Government/Royal Flight
Adria	Adria Airways		
Advent	ATS/Vulcan	AmTran	American Trans Air
Aerocharter	Aero Charter Midlands Limited	Army Air	Army Air Corps
		Ascot	Royal Air Force Transport
Aero Croat	Aero Croatia	Asia	Japan Asia Airlines
Aeroflot	Aeroflot	Aspro	Intereuropean Airways
Aeronaut	Cranfield Institute of Technology	Atlantic	Air Atlantique
		Austrian	Austrian
Air Algeria	Air Algeria	Aviaco	Aviaco
Air Atlantique	Air Atlantique	Avro	British Aerospace Woodford
Air Bahama	Air Bahama		
Air Berlin	Air Berlin	Ayline	Aurigny Air Services
Air Bridge	Hunting Cargo	Aztec Air	Air Bristol
Air Canada	Air Canada	Backer	British Charter
Air Chester	City Air	Bafair	Belgian Air Force
Aircom	Air Commuter	Bafjet	British Air Ferries Business Jets
Air Discovery	Discovery Airways		
Air Ecosse	Air Ecosse	Bahrain One	The Amiri Royal Flight
Air Espana	Air Espana	Balair	Balair
Air Europe	Air Europe	Balkan	Balkan
Air Express	Air Express	Bangladesh	Bangladesh
Air Ferry	British World Airlines	Bea Tours	Caledonian Airways
Air Force 1	USAF (President)	Beech Air	Beecham Group
Air Force 2	USAF (Vice-President)	Bee-Wee	British West Indian Airways
Air France	Air France		
Air India	Air India	Beeline	Biggin Hill Executive Aviation
Air Jamaica	Air Jamaica		
Air Lanka	Air Lanka	Belgian Air Force	Belgian Air Force
Airlift	Airlift	Big A	Arrow Air
Air London	Air London	Biggles	Express Air Charter
Air Malta	Air Malta	Blue Eagle	Eagle Air
Air Maroc	Royal Air Maroc	Bristow	Bristow Helicopter Group
Air Mauritius	Air Mauritius	Britannia	Britannia
Air Mexico	Aeromexico	British Island	British Island Airways
Air Mike	Continental Micronesia	Caledonian	Caledonian Airways Ltd
Air New Zealand	Air New Zealand	Calibrator	CAA Calibration Flight
Air Portugal	Air Portugal (TAP)	Caljet	Calair
Airtax	Birmingham Aviation	Camair	Cameroon Airlines
Airwork	Airwork Services Training	Canadian	Canadian Airlines
Air Zaire	Air Zaire	Canadian Military	Canadian Military
Alidair	Alidair	Capital	Capital
Alitalia	Alitalia	Cargolux	Cargolux

Call Sign	Airline	Call Sign	Airline
Caribbean	Caribbean	Iberia	Iberia
Cathay	Cathay Pacific	Iceair	Icelandair
Celtic	Celtic Airways	Indonesia	Garuda
Centreline	Centreline Air Services	Intercity	Intercity
Channel	Channel	Iranair	Iranair
Channex	Channel Express	Iraqi	Iraqi
China	China Airlines	Irish Air Corps	Irish Air Corps
CIL	Cecil Aviation	Israeli Air Force	Israeli Air Force
City	KLM Cityhopper	Italian Air Force	Italian Air Force
City Flite	City Airways	Itavia	Itavia
Clansman	Airwork	Jan	Janus Airways
Clanspeed Airways	Scottish European	Japanair	Japan Airlines
		Jersey	Jersey European
Clifton	Bristol Flying Centre	Jetset	Air 2000
Compass	Compass Aviation	Jetstar	Jetstar
Compass	Compass Helicopters, Bristol	Jordanian	Alia Royal Jordanian
		Juliett Juliett	Avio Genex
Condor	Condor	Juliett Papa	Inex Adria Avio Promet
Continental	Continental	Kenya	Kenya
Crossair	Crossair	Kestrel	Airtours International
CSA/Czechoslovakian	CSA	Kilro	Air Kilroe
Cubana	Cubanair	Kite	Kite
Cyprus	Cyprus	Kitty/Kittyhawk	Queen's Flight
Delta	Delta	Kiwi	Royal New Zealand Air Force
Directflight	Directflight		
Dynasty	China Air Lines	KLM	KLM Royal Dutch Airlines
Eagle	Eagle Flying Services	Korean	Korean
Eastern	Eastern	Kuwait	Kuwait
Echo Jet	Berlin European	Libyan	Libyan
Egyptair	Egyptair	Logan	Loganair
El Al	El Al	Lot	Lot
Ethiopian	Ethiopian	Lufthansa	Lufthansa
Euroair	Euroair	Luxair	Luxair
Euroflite	Euroflite	Lyddair	World Executive Airways
Euromanx	Manx Airlines [Europe]	MAC	Military Airlift Command USA
Europa	Air Europa		
European	London European	Macline	McAlpine Limited
Evergreen	Evergreen	Maersk	Maersk Air
Evergreen Airlines	Evergreen International	Malaysian	Malaysian
		Malev	Malev
Exam	CAA Flight Examiners	Manx	Manx Airlines
Express	Federal Express	Martinair	Martinair
Expressair	Expressair Services	Medivac	London Helicopter Emergency Service
Fairflight	Fairflight		
Fanum	Automobile Association	Merlin	Rolls-Royce
Federal Express	Federal Express	Merrix	Eagle European Airways/Merrix Air Ltd
Finnair	Finnair		
Fordair	Ford Motor Company	Metropolitan	Metropolitan
Genair	Genair	Middle East	Middle East
German Air Force	German Air Force	Midland	British Midland
Ghana	Ghana	Minair	CAA Flying Unit
Gibair	GB Airways	Monarch	Monarch
Global	Global	Montana	Montana
Granite	Business Air	Nationair	Nation Air
Guernsey	Guernsey Airlines	National	National Airways
Gulf Air	Gulf Air	Navy	Royal Navy
Gulf Stream	Gulf Stream	Nigerian	Nigerian
Hapaglloyd	Hapaglloyd	Nitro	TNT
Hawaiian	Hawaiian	Northwest	Northwest
Heavy Lift	Heavy Lift	Ocean	Atlantic Aviation
Hotair	Baltic Airlines	Olympia	Olympia

Call Sign	Airline	Call Sign	Airline
Orange	Air Holland	UK Leisure	Air UK Leisure
Orion	Orion	United	United
Pacific Western	Pacific Western	UPS	United Parcel Service
Pakistan	Pakistan	UTA	UTA
Parachute	UK Parachute Centre	Varig	Varig
Paramount	Paramount	Vernair	Vernons Pools
Piedmont	Piedmont	Viasa	Viasa
Qantas	Qantas	Vickers	Vickers
Quebecair	Quebecair	Viking	Scanair
Rafair	Royal Air Force	Virgin	Virgin
Rainbow	Royal Air Force (Duke of Edinburgh)	Viva	Viva Air
		Watchdog	Min of Agriculture, Fisheries & Food
Romanian	Romanian		
Rosie	Rosenbalm/Emery	Western	Western
Ryanair	Ryanair	West Indian	West Indian
Sabena	Sabena	World	World
Sam	Sam	Worldways	Worldways
Sapphire	British Aerospace (Filton)	Yemen	Yemen
Saudi	Saudi	Yugair	Air Yugoslavia/JAT
Scandinavian	Scandinavian	Zaire	Zaire
Scotair	Air Charter (Scotland)	Zambia	Zambia
Scottish Express	Scottish Express	Zimbabwe	Air Zimbabwe
Shamrock	Air Lingus		
Short	Short Brothers		
Shuttle 2	BA Shuttle LHR-Manchester		
Shuttle 3	BA Shuttle Manchester-LHR		
Shuttle 4	BA Shuttle LHR-Belfast		
Shuttle 5	BA Shuttle Belfast-LHR		
Shuttle 6	BA Shuttle LHR-Glasgow		
Shuttle 7	BA Shuttle Glasgow-LHR		
Shuttle 8	BA Shuttle LHR-Edinburgh		
Shuttle 9	BA Shuttle Edinburgh-LHR		
Sierra Leone	Sierra Leone		
Singapore	Singapore		
Skyship	Airship Industries		
Spacegrand	Spacegrand Aviation		
Special Support	Metropolitan Police Air		
Speedbird	British Airways		
Speedwing	Deutsche BA		
Springbok	South African		
Starjet	Novair International		
Stol	London City Airways		
Sudan	Sudan		
Swissair	Swissair		
Syrian	Syrian Air		
Tarom	Tarom		
Teastar	TEA		
Tester	Empire Test Pilots School, Boscombe Down		
Thai	Thai		
Tradewinds	Tradewinds		
Transamerica	Transamerica		
Tunis	Tunis		
TWA	Transworld Airlines		
Uganda	Uganda		
Ukay	Air UK		

Top:
The new control centre at Swanwick, near Fareham in Hampshire, is due to become operational early in 1998. *Author*

Above:
Approach Control, London Gatwick. *Civil Aviation Authority*

Appendix VII: Voice Weather Broadcasts

A - ACTUAL WEATHER REPORT
F - LANDING FORECAST
S - SIGMET
T - FORECAST TREND TYPE

Location	Broadcast time	Infor	Airports covered
CROUGHTON 6750 H24 11176 H24 13214 08-2100	H+25 & +55	T	LAJES, MILDENHALL, RAMSTEIN, RHEIN MAIN
DUBLIN 127.0 H24	Continuous	AFT	DUBLIN, SHANNON, CORK, BELFAST, GLASGOW, PRESTWICK, MANCHESTER, LONDON/HEATHROW, LONDON/GATWICK
GANDER 3485 H24 6604 H24	H+20/25	F A	MONTREAL/MIRABEL, TORONTO MONTREAL/MIRABEL, TORONTO GANDER, OTTAWA, GOOSE
10051 H24	H+25/30	A	WINNIPEG, EDMONTON, CALGARY, CHURCHILL
13270 H24			
			KUUJJUAQ, WINNIPEG, CHURCHILL
	H+50/55	F A	GANDER, ST JOHNS, HALIFAX MONTREAL/MIRABEL, GANDER STEPHENVILLE, HALIFAX,ST JOHNS
	H+55/60	FS A	GOOSE, IQALUIT, SONDRESTROM GOOSE, IQALUIT, SONDRESTROM, KUUJJUAQ
LAJES 6750 H24 8967 H24 13244 10-2100	H+00 & +30	T	LAJES, MILDENHALL, RAMSTEIN, RHEIN MAIN

Left:
Japan Air 747. *Japan Air Lines*

Location	Broadcast time	Infor	Airports covered
LONDON (MAIN) 135.375 H24	Continuous	AT	AMSTERDAM, BRUSSELS, DUBLIN, GLASGOW, LONDON/GATWICK, LONDON/HEATHROW, LONDON/STANSTED, MANCHESTER, PARIS/CHARLES DE GAULLE
LONDON (SOUTH) 128.6 H24	Continuous	AT	BIRMINGHAM, BOURNEMOUTH, BRISTOL, CARDIFF, JERSEY, LUTON, NORWICH, SOUTHAMPTON, SOUTHEND
LONDON (NORTH) 126.6 H24	Continuous	AT	BLACKPOOL, EAST MIDLANDS, LEEDS BRADFORD, LIVERPOOL, LONDON/GATWICK, MANCHESTER, NEWCASTLE, ISLE OF MAN/RONALDSWAY, TEESSIDE
NEW YORK 3485 H24 6604 H24 10051 H24 13270 H24	H+00	F A	DETROIT, CHICAGO, CLEVELAND DETROIT, CHICAGO, CLEVELAND, NIAGARA FALLS, MILWAUKEE, INDIANAPOLIS
	H+05	FS AS	BANGOR, PITTSBURGH, CHARLOTTE BANGOR, PITTSBURGH, WINDSOR LOCKS, ST LOUIS, CHARLOTTE, MINNEAPOLIS
	H+10	F A	NEW YORK, NEWARK, BOSTON NEW YORK, NEWARK, BOSTON, BALTIMORE, PHILADELPHIA, WASHINGTON
	H+15	FS AS	BERMUDA NAS, MIAMI, ATLANTA BERMUDA NAS, MIAMI, NASSAU, FREEPORT, TAMPA, WEST PALM BEACH, ATLANTA

Location	Broadcast time	Infor	Airports covered
	H+30	F	NIAGARA FALLS, MILWAUKEE, INDIANAPOLIS
		A	DETROIT, CHICAGO, CLEVELAND, NIAGARA FALLS, MILWAUKEE, INDIANAPOLIS
	H+35	FS	WINDSOR LOCKS, ST LOUIS
		AS	BANGOR, PITTSBURGH, WINDSOR LOCKS, ST LOUIS, CHARLOTTE, MINNEAPOLIS
	H+40	F	BALTIMORE, PHILADELPHIA, WASHINGTON
		A	NEW YORK, NEWARK, BOSTON, BALTIMORE, PHILADELPHIA, WASHINGTON
	H+45	FS	NASSAU, FREEPORT
		AS	BERMUDA NAS, MIAMI, NASSAU, FREEPORT, TAMPA, WEST PALM BEACH, ATLANTA
SCOTTISH 125.725 H24	Continuous	AT	ABERDEEN, BELFAST/ALDERGROVE, EDINBURGH, GLASGOW, INVERNESS, LONDON/HEATHROW, PRESTWICK, STORNOWAY, SUMBURGH
SHANNON 3413 HN 5505 H24 8957 H24 13264 HJ	H+00	FS	BRUSSELS NTL, HAMBURG
		AS	BRUSSELS NTL, HAMBURG, FRANKFURT (MAIN), COLOGNE BONN, DUSSELDORF, MUNICH
	H+05	F	SHANNON, PRESTWICK, LONDON/HEATHROW
		A	SHANNON, PRESTWICK, LONDON/HEATHROW, AMSTERDAM/SCHIPOL, MANCHESTER, LONDON/GATWICK
	H+10	AS	COPENHAGEN/KASTRUP, STOCKHOLM/ARLANDA, GOTHENBURG/LANDVETTA, BERGEN/FLESLAND, OSLO/GARDEMOEN, HELSINKI/VANTAA, DUBLIN, BARCELONA
	H+15	F	MADRID/BARAJAS, LISBON, PARIS/ORLY
		A	MADRID/BARAJAS, LISBON, SANTA MARIA, PARIS/ORLY, PARIS/CHARLES DE GAULLE, LYON/SATOLAS

Opposite left:
One of the UK's VHF/UHF transmitters. *Author*

Opposite right:
Oceanic Control, Prestwick. *Civil Aviation Authority*

Location	Broadcast time	Infor	Airports covered
	H+20/25	FS	ROME/FIUMICINO, MILAN/MALPENSA
		AS	ROME/FIUMICINO, MILAN/MALPENSA, ZURICH, GENEVA/COINTRIN, TURIN/CASELLE, KEFLAVIK
	H+30	FS	FRANKFURT (MAIN), COLOGNE-BONN
		AS	BRUSSELS NATIONAL, HAMBURG, FRANKFURT (MAIN), COLOGNE-BONN, DUSSELDORF, MUNICH
	H+35	F	AMSTERDAM/SCHIPHOL, MANCHESTER, LONDON/GATWICK
		A	SHANNON, PRESTWICK, LONDON/HEATHROW, AMSTERDAM/SCHIPHOL, MANCHESTER, LONDON/GATWICK
	H+40	AS	COPENHAGEN/KASTRUP, STOCKHOLM/ARLANDA, GOTHENBURG/LANDVETTER, BERGEN/FLESLAND, OSLO/GARDEMOEN, HELSINKI/VANTAA, DUBLIN, BARCELONA
	H+45	F	SANTA MARIA, ATHENS, PARIS/CHARLES DE GAULLE
		A	MADRID/BARAJAS, LISBON, SANTA MARIA, PARIS/ORLY, PARIS/CHARLES DE GAULLE, LYON/SATOLAS
	H+50/55	FS	ZURICH, GENEVA/COINTRIN
		AS	ROME/FIUMICINO, MILAN/MALPENSA, ZURICH, GENEVA/COINTRIN, TURIN/CASELLE, KEFLAVIK

TRENTON (MILITARY)

15034 1000-0000 6754 2300-1100	H+30	AT*	TRENTON, OTTAWA, TORONTO/L.B. PEARSON INTL,
		* T	- IF TIME PERMITS QUEBEC CITY, BAGOTVILLE, NORTH BAY

ROYAL AIR FORCE

4715 H24 11253 H24	Continuous Continuous	A	BELFAST/ALDERGROVE, BENSON, BRIZE NORTON, FINNINGLEY, KINLOSS, LEUCHARS, LONDON/HEATHROW, LYNEHAM, MANCHESTER, NORTHOLT, ODIHAM, PRESTWICK, ST MAWGAN, WADDINGTON,WYTON, DUSSELDORF, LAARBRUCH, KEFLAVIK, ASCENSION

Note:

H24 indicates that the broadcast is continuous.

H+ minutes indicates the time at which the broadcast commences, eg H25 means that the broadcast takes place at 25min past each hour.

Appendix VIII: Worldwide High Frequency Coverage

A - ACTUAL WEATHER REPORT
F - LANDING FORECAST
S - SIGMET
T - FORECAST TREND TYPE

The following listings cover HF aeronautical channels for different regions of the world. Each region is followed by the radio stations within the network and the various allocated frequencies. Note, however, that the full range of frequencies will not normally be covered by every station within the group.

North Atlantic 'A'
NAT-A
CANARIES, GANDER, NEW YORK, PARAMARIBO, PIARCO, SANTA MARIA, SHANWICK
2962, 3016, 5598, 6533, 6628, 8825, 8906, 13306, 17946

North Atlantic 'B'
NAT-B
GANDER, REYKJAVIK, SHANWICK
2899, 5616, 8864, 11279, 13291, 17946

North Atlantic 'C'
NAT-C
GANDER, REYKJAVIK, SHANWICK
2872, 5649, 8879, 11336, 13306, 17946

North Atlantic 'D'
NAT-D
BODO, BAFFIN, CHURCHILL, IQALUIT, KANGERLUSSUAQ, REYKJAVIK, SHANWICK
2971, 2983, 4666, 4675, 6544, 8840, 8891, 11279, 13291, 17946

North Atlantic 'E'
NAT-E
NEW YORK, SANTA MARIA
2962, 6628, 8825, 11309, 13354, 17946

North Atlantic 'F'
NAT-F
GANDER, SHANWICK
3476, 6622, 8831, 13291, 17946

Europe
EUR
MALTA, TUNIS
5661, 10084

Middle East
MID-1
ADEN, AMMAN, BAGHDAD, BAHRAIN, BASRAH, JEDDAH, KUWAIT, RIYAN, SANAA, TEHRAN
2992, 3404, 5603, 5667, 8918, 13312

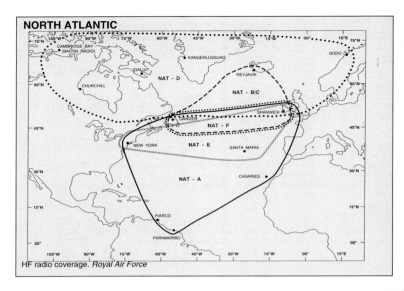

NORTH ATLANTIC

HF radio coverage. *Royal Air Force*

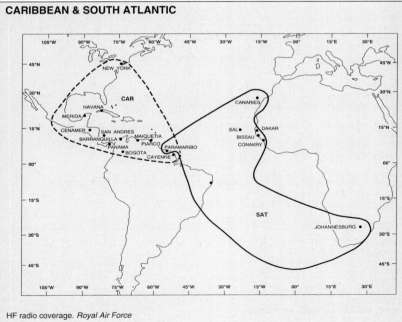

CARIBBEAN & SOUTH ATLANTIC

HF radio coverage. *Royal Air Force*

Middle East 2

MID-2

BAHRAIN, DELHI, ISLAMABAD, KABUL, KARACHI, KATHMANDU, KUWAIT, LAHORE, MALE, MUSCAT, PESHAWAR, SEYCHELLES, SHIRAZ, TEHRAN
2923, 3467, 5601, 5658, 7595, 10018, 13288

African 1

AFI-1

ABIDJAN, BAMAKO, BISSAU, BOBO, CANARIES, CASABLANCA, CONAKRY, DAKAR, FREETOWN, KORHOGO, MONROVIA/ROBERTS, NOUADHIBOU, NOUAKCHOTT, OUAGADOUGOU, SAL
3452, 6535, 6573, 6589, 8861, 13357, 17955

African 2

AFI-2

ALGIERS, GAO, GHARDAIA, KANO, MAIDUGURI, N'DJAMENA, NIAMEY, TAMANRASSET, TRIPOLI, TUNIS
3419, 5652, 5680, 8873, 8894, 13273, 17961

African 3

AFI-3

ADDIS ABABA, ADEN, ASMARA, BENGHAZI, BUJUMBURA, CAIRO, COMORES, DAR ES SALAAM, DJIBOUTI, ENTEBBE, HARGEYSA, JEDDAH, KHARTOUM, KIGALI, MOGADISHU, MUMBAI, NAIROBI, RIYAN, SANAA, SEYCHELLES, TRIPOLI
3467, 5505, 5517, 5540, 5658, 6574, 7595, 8854, 8870, 8959, 10025, 11300, 13288, 17961

African 4

AFI-4

ABIDJAN, ACCRA, BANGUI, BATA, BRAZZAVILLE, BUJUMBURA, DOUALA, ENTEBBE, GABORONE, GBADOLITE, HARARE, JOHANNESBURG, KANO, KINSHASA, KUMASI, LAGOS, LIBREVILLE, LILONGWE, LOME, LUANDA, LUSAKA, MAIDUGURI, MALABO, NAIROBI, N'DJAMENA, NIAMEY, OUAGADOUGOU, SAO TOME, TAKORADI, TAMALE, WINDHOEK
2851, 2878, 5493, 6559, 6586, 6879, 8861, 8873, 8888, 8903, 9495, 13294

African 5/Indian Ocean 1

AFI-5/INO-1

ANTANANARIVO, BUJUMBURA, COCOS, COLOMBO, COMORES, DAR ES SALAAM, HARARE, JOHANNESBURG, LUSAKA, MAHAJANGA, MAURITIUS, MUMBAI, NAIROBI, PERTH, ST DENIS, SEYCHELLES, TOAMASINA
2376, 3425, 3476, 3682, 4657, 5634, 6915, 7595, 8849, 8861, 8879, 10018, 11300, 13306, 17961, 21926

South East Asia 1

SEA-1

CALCUTTA, COCOS, COLOMBO, DHAKA, JAKARTA, KATHMANDU, KUALA LUMPUR, MADRAS, MALE, SINGAPORE, TRIVANDRUM, YANGON (RANGOON)
2947, 3470, 3491, 5670, 6556, 10066, 11285, 13318, 17907

South East Asia 2

SEA-2

BANGKOK, HO CHI MINH CITY, HONG KONG, KINABALU, KUALA LUMPUR, MANILA, SINGAPORE, VIENTIANE
3485, 5655, 8942, 11396, 13309

South Asia 3

SEA-3

BALI, CALCUTTA, COCOS, DARWIN, JAKARTA, MALE, PERTH, SINGAPORE, TRIVANDRUM, UJUNG PANDANG
3470, 6556, 11285, 11396, 13318, 17907

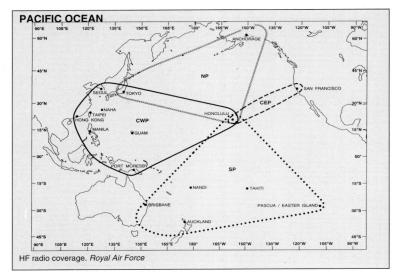

PACIFIC OCEAN

HF radio coverage. *Royal Air Force*

Central West Pacific
CWP
GUAM, HONG KONG, HONOLULU, MANILA, NAHA, PORT MORESBY, SEOUL, TAIPEI, TOKYO
2998, 3455, 4666, 6532, 8903, 11384, 13300, 17904

North Pacific
NP
ANCHORAGE, HONOLULU, TOKYO
2932, 5628, 6655, 8915, 8951, 10048, 11330, 13273, 13294, 21925

Central Pacific
CEP
HONOLULU, SAN FRANCISCO
2869, 3413, 5547, 5574, 6673, 8843, 10057, 11282, 13288, 13354, 17904

South Pacific
SP
AUCKLAND, BRISBANE, HONOLULU, NANDI, PASCUA/EASTER ISLAND, TAHITI
3467, 5643, 8867, 13261, 13300, 17904

South America 1
SAM-1
ANTOFAGASTA, ASUNCION, BOGOTA, CORDOBA, EZEIZA/BUENOS AIRES, GUAYAQUIL, LA PAZ, LIMA, MENDOZA, PANAMA, PASCUA/EASTER ISLAND, PUERTO MONTT, PUNTA ARENAS, RESISTENCIA, SALTA, SANTA CRUZ, SANTIAGO
2944, 4669, 5454, 5583, 5595, 5604, 6649, 6535, 10024, 10066, 11360, 17907

South America 2
SAM-2 .
ASUNCION, BELEM, BOGOTA, BRASILIA, CAMPO GRANDE, CAYENNE, CURITIBA, EZEIZA/BUENOS AIRES, GEORGETOWN, LA PAZ, LETICIA, MAIQUETIA, MANAUS, MONTEVIDEO, PARAMARIBO, PIARCO, PORTO ALEGRE, PORTO VELHO, RECIFE, SANTA CRUZ
3479, 3488, 5526, 6533, 8855, 8894, 10096, 13297, 17907

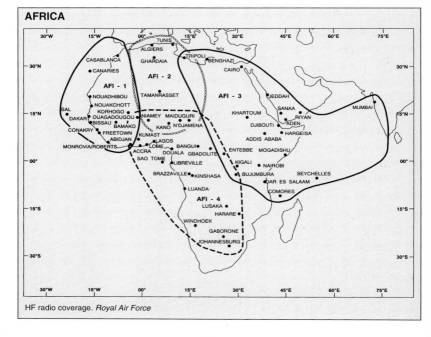

INDIAN OCEAN & SOUTH EAST ASIA

30°N · 30°E · 45°E · 60°E · 75°E · 90°E · 105°E · 120°E · 135°E

KATHMANDU · DHAKA · HONG KONG
CALCUTTA
MUMBAI · YANGON · VIENTIANE · MANILA
MADRAS · BANGKOK · SEA - 2
TRIVANDRUM · COLOMBO · HO CHI MINH
SEA - 1 · KINABALU
MALE · KUALA LUMPUR
SINGAPORE
NAIROBI
BUJUMBURA · SEYCHELLES · JAKARTA · UJUNG PANDANG
DAR ES SALAAM · BALI · DARWIN
COMORES · COCOS
AFI - 5/INO - 1 · SEA - 3
MAHAJANGA
HARARE · ANTANANARIVO · MAURITIUS
BEIRA · ST DENIS GILLOT
JOHANNESBURG · PERTH

HF radio coverage. *Royal Air Force*

AFRICA

30°W · 15°W · 00° · 15°E · 30°E · 45°E · 60°E · 75°E

TUNIS
ALGIERS · TRIPOLI
CASABLANCA · GHARDAIA · BENGHAZI
CANARIES · CAIRO
AFI - 2
NOUADHIBOU · TAMANRASSET · AFI - 3 · JEDDAH
NOUAKCHOTT · SANAA · MUMBAI
SAL · KORHOGO · KHARTOUM · RIYAN
DAKAR · OUAGADOUGOU · NIAMEY MAIDUGURI · DJIBOUTI · ADEN
BISSAU · BAMAKO · KANO N'DJAMENA · HARGEISA
CONAKRY · FREETOWN · KUMASI · ADDIS ABABA
ABIDJAN · LAGOS
MONROVIA/ROBERTS · LOME · BANGUI · ENTEBBE · MOGADISHU
ACCRA · DOUALA · GBADOLITE
SAO TOME · LIBREVILLE · KIGALI · NAIROBI
BRAZZAVILLE · KINSHASA · BUJUMBURA · SEYCHELLES
DAR ES SALAAM
LUANDA · COMORES
AFI - 4
LUSAKA
HARARE
WINDHOEK
GABORONE
JOHANNESBURG
AFI - 1

HF radio coverage. *Royal Air Force*

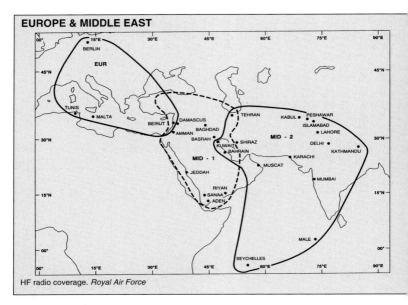

HF radio coverage. *Royal Air Force*

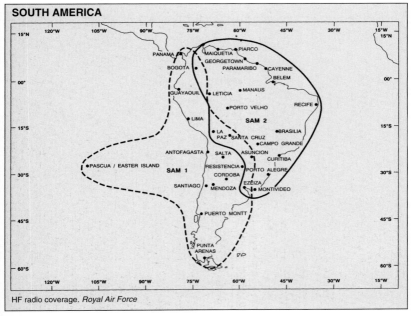

HF radio coverage. *Royal Air Force*

Caribbean
CAR
BARRANQUILLA, BOGOTA, CAYENNE, CENAMER, HAVANA, MAIQUETIA, MERIDA, NEW YORK, PANAMA, PARAMARIBO, PIARCO, SAN ANDRES
2887, 5520, 5550, 6532, 6577, 6728, 8918, 10017, 11387, 11396, 13297, 13339, 17907

South Atlantic
SAT
ABIDJAN, BISSAU, CANARIES, CONAKRY, DAKAR, JOHANNESBURG, PARAMARIBO, RECIFE, SAL, SAO TOME
2854, 3432, 3452, 5565, 6535, 8861, 11291, 13315, 13357, 17955, 21926

Miscellaneous HF Frequencies

RAF FLIGHT WATCH CENTRES

RAF KINLOSS AND RAF BAMPTON CASTLE (CALLSIGN 'ARCHITECT')
2591, 4540, 4742, 5714, 6739, 8190, 9031, 11205, 11247, 13257, 15031, 18018

ASCENSION (CALLSIGN 'HAVEN')
4742, 9031, 11247

CYPRUS (CALLSIGN 'CYPRUS')
4730, 9031, 11247

GIBRALTAR (CALLSIGN 'GIBRALTAR')
4742, 11247

Below:
The London Area and Terminal Control Centre at West Drayton currently handles flights in the London FIR. It will eventually be replaced by the new centre at Swanwick in Hampshire. *Author*

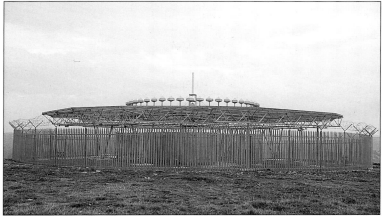

Top:
747-400 flightdeck. *Rockwell International/ Collins*

Above:
Long-range navigation beacon 'BRECON' (BCN). *Author*

Appendix IX: Company Frequencies

All flights need to speak to their operational base from time to time on matters not related to air traffic control.

Specific frequencies are set aside for this purpose, both on VHF and HF. Those on VHF are almost all between 130MHz and 132MHz, with a small number in the 136MHz range, while those on HF are spread throughout the band.

Many companies who do not have their own radio-equipped bases are able to keep in contact by using message-handling agencies (eg Servisair), sometimes being connected to their bases by land-line.

On HF there are many kinds of messages being transmitted on the company frequencies, often via handling agencies such as Stockholm Radio, Berne Radio and Portishead Radio.

VHF Company Frequencies

Handling Organisations

130.600	Servisair
130.650	Gatwick Handling
130.650	Manchester Handling
131.625	Portishead

Airline

131.425	Air New Zealand (LHR)
	British Midland (LHR)
	Virgin (LHR)
131.450	Air Canada (LHR)
	Alitalia (LHR)
	Pakistan (LHR)
131.475	Sabena (LHR)
	Speedbird North (LGW)
131.500	Air France (LHR)
131.525	American (LHR)
131.550	Speedbird (LHR)
131.600	TWA (LGW)
131.625	Speedbird South (LGW)
131.650	Japan Air (LHR)
	KLM (LHR)
131.675	Britannia (LGW)
131.700	Scandinavian (LHR)
	Swissair (LHR)
131.750	Shamrock (Aer Lingus) (LHR)
	Air UK (LHR)
	Continental (LHR)
131.800	Speedbird (LHR)
131.875	Qantas (LHR)
131.900	Speedbird Long Haul (LHR)
131.925	Air India (LHR)
	Lufthansa (LHR)

HF Company Frequencies

Berne (Switzerland)	4654, 6643, 8936, 10069, 13205, 15046, 18023, 21988, 23285
Portishead (England)	4810, 5607, 6634, 8185, 8960, 10291, 11306, 12133, 14890, 15964, 16273, 18210, 19510, 20065, 23142, 25109
Stockholm (Sweden)	3494, 5541, 8930, 11345, 13342, 17916, 23210
British Airways (London)	5535, 8921, 10072, 13333, 17922, 21948
Rainbow (Canada)	3458, 5604, 8819, 10264, 13285, 13339, 13420, 17910

Note: Many more frequencies are obtainable from specialist books, available from several of the companies listed at the end of the book. Amateur radio magazines also carry advertisements for frequency publications.

Appendix X: Useful Addresses

Most of the following companies supply receivers and other equipment related to airband listening. Contact them for comprehensive catalogues and price lists. Many of the suppliers can also offer second-hand items.

Air Supply,
97 High Street,
Yeadon,
LEEDS LS19 7TA
Tel: (0113) 250 9581
Fax: (0113) 250 0119

Amateur Radio Communications Limited,
38 Bridge Street,
Earlestown,
NEWTOWN-LE-WILLOWS,
Merseyside WA12 9BA
Tel: (01925) 229881
Fax: (01925) 229882

AOR UK Limited,
4E East Mill,
Bridgefoot,
BELPER,
Derbyshire DE56 2UA
Tel: (01773) 880788
Fax: (01773) 880780

ARE Communications,
6 Royal Parade,
Hanger Lane,
Ealing,
LONDON W5A 1ET
Tel: (0181) 997 4476

ASK Electronics Limited,
248 Tottenham Court Road,
LONDON W1P 9AD
Tel: (0171) 637 0353
Fax: (0171) 637 2690

The Aviation Hobby Centre,
Visitors Centre,
Main Terminal,
Birmingham International Airport,
BIRMINGHAM B26 3QJ
Tel: (0121) 782 2112
Fax: (0121) 782 6423

The Aviation Hobby Shop,
4 Horton Parade,
Horton Road,
WEST DRAYTON,
Middlesex UB7 8EA
Tel: (01895) 442123

Communication Centre,
(Photo Acoustics Limited),
58 High Street,
NEWPORT PAGNELL,
Bucks MK16 8AQ
Tel: (01908) 610625
Fax: (01908) 216373

Flightdeck,
The Airband Shop,
192 Wilmslow Road,
Heald Green,
CHEADLE,
Cheshire SK8 3BH
Tel: (0161) 499 9350
Fax: (0161) 499 9349

Garex Electronics,
Unit 8,
Sandpiper Court,
Harrington Lane,
EXETER EX4 8NS
Tel: (01392) 466899
Fax: (01392) 466887

Haydon Communications,
132 High Street,
EDGWARE,
Middlesex HA8 7EL
Tel: (0181) 951 5781
Fax: (0181) 951 5782

Below:
Scottish ATC and Oceanic Control Centre, Prestwick. *Author*

Opposite:
Visual Control Room, London Heathrow. *Civil Aviation Authority*

West Midlands Branch
Haydon Communications,
Unit 1,
Canal View Industrial Estate,
Brettel Lane,
BRIERLEY HILL,
West Midlands DY5 3LO
Tel: (01384) 481681

C. M. Howes Communications,
Eydon,
DAVENTRY,
Northants NN11 3PT
Tel: (01327) 260178

Javiation,
Carlton Works,
Carlton Street,
BRADFORD,
West Yorkshire BD7 1DA
Tel: (01274) 732146
Fax: (01274) 722627

Link Electronics,
216 Lincoln Road,
Millfield,
PETERBOROUGH PE1 2NE
Tel: (01733) 345731
Fax: (01733) 346770

Lowe Electronics Limited,
Chesterfield Road,
MATLOCK,
Derbyshire DE4 5LE
Tel: (01629) 580800
Fax: (01629) 580020

Branch Offices:
East Anglia — 152 High Street, Chesterton,
CAMBRIDGE CB4 1NL
Tel: (01223) 311230

North East — Unit 18B, Airport Ind. Estate,
NEWCASTLE NE3 2EF
Tel: (0191) 214 5424

South East — High Street, HANDCROSS,
West Sussex RH17 6BW
Tel: (01444) 400786

South West — 117 Beaumont Road, St
Judes, PLYMOUTH PL4 9EF
Tel: (01752) 257224

West — 79 Gloucester Road, Patchway,
BRISTOL BS12 5QJ
Tel: (0117) 931 5263

Yorkshire — 12 Station Road, Crossgates,
LEEDS LS15 7JX
Tel: (0113) 232 8400

Martin Lynch & Son,
140/142 Northfield Avenue,
Ealing,
LONDON W13 9SB
Tel: (0181) 566 1120
Fax: (0181) 566 1207

Multicomm,
Unit 3,
86 Cambridge Street,
ST NEOTS,
Cambridgeshire PE19 1PJ
Tel: (01480) 406770
Fax: (01480) 406770

Nevada Communications,
189 London Road,
PORTSMOUTH PO2 9AE
Tel: (01705) 662145
Fax: (01705) 690626

Showroom:
Nevada Communications,
1A Munster Road,
PORTSMOUTH PO2 9BS

Photavia Press,
Sunrise Break,
Chiseldon Farm,
South Down Hill,
BRIXHAM,
Devon TQ5 0AE
Tel: (01803) 855599

SRP Radio Centre,
1686 Bristol Road South,
Rednall,
BIRMINGHAM B45 9TZ
Tel: (0121) 461581
Fax: (0121) 459009

Sandpiper Communications,
Pentwyn House,
Penyard,
Llwydcoed,
ABERDARE,
Mid Glamorgan CF44 0TU
Tel: (01685) 870425

Solid State Electronics (UK),
6 The Orchard,
Bassett Green Village,
SOUTHAMPTON SO16 3NA
Tel: (01703) 769598

South Midlands Communications,
S M House,
School Close,
Chandlers Ford Industrial Estate,
EASTLEIGH,
Hants SO53 4BY
Tel: (01703) 255111
Fax: (01703) 263507

Steepletone Products Ltd
Park End Works
Croughton
BRACKLEY
Northants NN13 5BR
Tel: (01869) 810081
Fax: (01869) 810784

Tandy Corporation
Shops in all principal towns throughout
the UK
(See telephone directory for local
information)

Waters and Stanton,
22 Main Road,
HOCKLEY,
Essex SS5 4QS
Tel: (01702) 206835
Fax: (01702) 205843

W. H. Westlake Electronics,
West Park
CLAWTON HOLSWORTHY,
Devon EX22 6QN
Tel: (01409) 253758
Fax: (01409) 253458

The following organisations should be
contacted for aeronautical navigation charts
for the UK and most other areas of the
world:

Civil Aviation Authority,
Chart Room,
CAA House,
45-49 Kingsway,
LONDON WC2B 6TE
Tel: (0171) 379 7311

British Airways (AERAD),
Customer Services,
Aerad House,
PO Box 10,
Heathrow Airport,
HOUNSLOW,
Middlesex TW6 2JA
Tel: (0181) 562 0795

Royal Air Force,
No 1 AIDU,
RAF Northolt,
West End Road,
RUISLIP,
Middlesex HA4 6NG
Tel: (0181) 845 2300

Below:
Boeing 767 of Britannia Airways. *Britannia*